Faraday Redisco

Plate 1 Faraday's Laboratory. Harriet Moore. Royal Institution. Watercolour.

FARADAY REDISCOVERED

Essays on the Life and Work of Michael Faraday,
1791–1867

Edited and Introduced by

David Gooding
Frank A. J. L. James

MACMILLAN PRESS

First edition 1985
Reprinted (with corrections) 1989

Published by
THE MACMILLAN PRESS LTD
Brunel Road, Houndmills, Basingstoke, Hants RG21 2XS, England

British Library Cataloguing in Publication Data
Faraday rediscovered: essays on the life and
work of Michael Faraday, 1791–1867.
1. Faraday, Michael   2. Physicists——Great
Britain——Biography
I. Gooding, David   II. James, Frank A. J. L.
530'.092'   QC16.F2
ISBN 0–333–51122–0

Printed in Hong Kong

Contents

List of Plates

Notes on Contributors

Brian Bowers is Curator of Lighting and Electric Power in the Science Museum, London. He was educated at King's College, London where he became interested in Charles Wheatstone, the subject of his doctoral thesis. His publications include *A History of Electric Light and Power* and *A Children's Biography of Faraday*.

Address: Department of Electrical Engineering, Science Museum, Exhibition Road, London, SW7 2DD, England.

Geoffrey N. Cantor lectures in the history and philosophy of science at the University of Leeds. He is the author of *Optics after Newton* and co-editor of *Conceptions of Ether*. Following on from the paper published in this volume he intends to make a more extensive study of Faraday and the London Sandemanians.

Address: Department of Philosophy, University of Leeds, Leeds, LS2 9JT, England.

Elspeth Crawford graduated in mathematics from Queen's University, Belfast, taught young children for some years, then returned to academic work studying history and philosophy of science at Chelsea College, University of London. She completed her doctoral thesis in 1985 on 'The ideas of particle and field in Michael Faraday's work 1831–1845'. She has also been a tutor in scientific education at the University of London Institute of Education and currently teaches physics at North London Collegiate School.

Address: 105 Broadhurst Gardens, London, NW6 3BJ, England.

Sophie Forgan was educated at London University where she completed her doctoral thesis on the Royal Institution in 1977. She lectures in history of design at Teesside Polytechnic. Her research interests include the history of learned societies, and the relations between architecture, science and society.

Address: Department of Design, Teesside Polytechnic, Middlesbrough, Cleveland, TS1 3BA, England.

David Gooding is Senior Lecturer in History and Philosophy of Science at the University of Bath and is a Visiting Research Fellow of the Royal Institution Centre for the History of Science and Technology. He has published several articles on Faraday, is writing a biography of Faraday and is studying the influence of the practical experimental contexts of nineteenth-century science on the ways that scientists describe nature.

Address: School of Humanities and Social Science, University of Bath, Claverton Down, Bath, Avon, BA2 7AY, England.

Frank A. J. L. James is Secretary of the Royal Institution Centre for the History of Science and Technology, London, he is also Lecturer in History of Science. His main research interest is in nineteenth-century physical science and its cultural context. He has recently completed an edition of the diary of Herbert McLeod from 1860 to 1870.

Address: Royal Institution Centre for the History of Science and Technology, The Royal Institution, 21 Albemarle Street, London, W1X 4BS, England.

David M. Knight teaches history and philosophy of science in the Philosophy Department of the University of Durham. He is the editor of the *British Journal for the History of Science*. He has written and edited several books including *The Nature of Science, Natural Science Books in English* and *The Transcendental Part of Chemistry*.

Address: Department of Philosophy, University of Durham, 50 Old Elvet, Durham, DH1 3HN, England.

Nancy J. Nersessian was formerly Associate Professor of the History and Philosophy of Science at the Technical University of Twente, and a Research Fellow at the Centre for Philosophy of Science at the University of Pittsburgh. She has been a Fulbright Research Scholar at the University of Leiden, a Fellow of the Netherlands Institute for Advanced Study, and is editor of the *Science and Philosophy* series published by Martinus Nijhoff.

Address: Program in History of Science, Princeton University, 220 Palmer Hall, Princeton, NJ 08544, USA.

Gertrude M. Prescott is Assistant Curator, Iconography Collections, Wellcome Institute for the History of Medicine. She was educated at Princeton

University and the University of Texas at Austin where she is currently completing her doctoral thesis on portrait publications in nineteenth-century Britain. She was a Fulbright Scholar and is a Visiting Research Scholar at the Royal Institution Centre for the History of Science and Technology.

Address: Wellcome Institute for the History of Medicine, 183 Euston Road, London, NW1 2BP, England.

Ryan D. Tweney is Professor of Psychology at Bowling Green State University. He co-edited (with M.E. Doherty and C.R. Mynatt) *On Scientific Thinking* and (with W. Bringmann) *Wundt Studies*. He is currently conducting research on the cognitive psychology of science with a special focus on the inferential heuristics of Michael Faraday.

Address: Department of Psychology, Bowling Green State University, Bowling Green, Ohio 43403, USA.

L. Pearce Williams is the John Stambaugh Professor of the History of Science at Cornell University and the author of *Michael Faraday, A Biography, Album of Science: The Nineteenth Century* and *The Origins of Field Theory*. He is working on a biography of André-Marie Ampère.

Address: Department of History, McGraw Hall, Cornell University, Ithaca, New York 14853, USA.

Foreword

Those of us who are fortunate enough to work here in Faraday's laboratory and even, in my case, to live in his home, feel his influence all around us. Never have a great scientist and a building been so closely linked. This happy association, coupled with the meticulous way in which he recorded all his work and the fact that his successors were wise enough to keep carefully the great quantity of experimental apparatus he left behind, has resulted in the happy circumstance that we have, for our greatest experimentalist, the most complete historical record of the artefacts of a single scientist to be found anywhere.

Much has been written about Faraday and much more will be written — and read — not only because of the enormous significance of his discoveries and the profusion of historical material, but also because his life has a romantic 'rags to riches' quality and a nearness to perfection which will forever be an inspiration to those whose love for science may seem to be unmatched by opportunity or formal education.

I hope that these studies will encourage scholars to 'rediscover' Faraday and to understand better the ways of working of his great mind. The new aspects of his life and achievements revealed here will also be of interest to the many people by whom he is revered throughout the world.

The Royal Institution, July 1985

GEORGE PORTER, FRS
Director and
Fullerian Professor of Chemistry

For our families

Preface

There are many studies of the life and work of Michael Faraday (1791–1867). None of these are definitive and this book does not aim to be so. Our title, *Faraday Rediscovered*, recalls John Tyndall's *Faraday as a Discoverer*, the first account of Faraday's considerable experimental achievements. It conveys our intention to promote a fresh approach to Faraday, whose work has been obscured by preconceptions about science and by heroic myths about its practitioners. We have brought together recent essays on Faraday which point the way for future studies of Faraday and of nineteenth century science generally.

Earlier versions of these essays were presented at the conference 'Faraday Rediscovered' held from 19 to 21 September 1984 at the Royal Institution, with one morning session at the Institution of Electrical Engineers. The conference was a forum in which new work was discussed and criticised. A strength of the meeting was its emphasis on the performance of experimental demonstrations. However, since not all demonstrations and lectures lent themselves to a literary rendering, some have, we regret, been omitted. The central place of experiment in Faraday's work is none the less a dominant theme in several that we have included.

The demonstrations were a striking feature of the conference. They also showed the unique contribution that the Royal Institution continues to make to British intellectual life. No other institution in the country combines a major scientific collection, demonstration skills, conference and library facilities and the personnel that allowed the conference to develop in the way it did.

Not all the demonstrations were successful, as the case of one of us (DG) illustrates. His experiments had been set up before we went to the Institution of Electrical Engineers for the morning session. We returned to the Royal Institution through a heavy rainstorm. Fifty wet historians increased the humidity in the lecture theatre so much that none of the electroscopes functioned. This illustrates Coates's law of electrostatics: 'keep your audience dry'. One of the themes of this book is that failed experiments often provide as much information as successful experiments do.

All the other demonstrations worked. We are particularly grateful to Professor Sir George Porter and Professor Ronald King for their demonstration lectures respectively on Faraday's chemical experiments and his electromagnetic induction experiments. We thank Bill Coates, Senior Experimental Officer, and his staff for the immense effort they put into providing these demonstrations.

Contributors make their acknowledgements at the end of each essay, but we would like to make our joint acknowledgements here. We thank the Director of the Royal Institution, the Council of the Royal Institution and the Steering Committee of the Royal Institution Centre for the History of Science and Technology for supporting the conference and this book. DG wishes to thank them particularly for appointing him a Visiting Research Fellow of the Centre. He also thanks the School of Humanities and Social Science of the University of Bath for a study leave during the spring term of 1984, and the Royal Society for financial support during that period. We acknowledge the award of a travel grant by the British Academy for Dr Nancy Nersessian that allowed her to attend the conference. We thank Lenore Symons, Archivist of the Institution of Electrical Engineers and Irena McCabe, Librarian and Information Officer of the Royal Institution for their support during the conference (the latter, especially, for organising a display of Faradaiana in the library) and for their subsequent patience in dealing with our many editorial queries of the Faraday holdings in both archives.

We thank the Royal Institution for permission to reproduce Plates 1, 3–10, 12–14; the Institution of Electrical Engineers, Plates 11 and 15; Glasgow University Library, Plate 2 and the National Portrait Gallery, Plate 16.

Bath and London, 27 March 1985   DG
                                                                                    FAJLJ

Introduction: Faraday Rediscovered

David Gooding and Frank A.J.L. James

Michael Faraday straddled the eighteenth and nineteenth centuries. Born in a world where light was particulate, as a young man he saw it turn into a wave in a solid aether. He himself laid the foundations of aetherless electromagnetic radiation. Born in a world where magnetism was peculiar to a few metals, he left it as a universal phenomenon. Born in a world where electricity was a fluid substance and a public spectacle, he left it as a species of action, described mathematically by Maxwell, and well on the way to being a public utility. Who can imagine what life would be like without the technological applications of his discoveries?

Faraday presents the historian with a variety of problems. While not unique to Faraday these are perhaps more challenging here than elsewhere. To take the most obvious problem first: Faraday's range of scientific interests were immense even by the polymathic standards of the nineteenth century. To his major contributions to electricity and magnetism must be added his work on field theory, optics, chemistry and metallurgy. To understand what Faraday was trying to achieve with a particular research programme the historian needs to be familiar with these and many other aspects of science in the nineteenth century.

If this seems obvious it is worth reminding ourselves that Faraday's published writing, manuscripts and his surviving instruments are so extensive that it has been quite possible to write about Faraday without looking further afield. Lack of attention to the context in which Faraday lived and worked has been a major weakness. Several of the essays included here address Faraday's context, nineteenth-century society and science.

One reason why such a consistent, self-contained picture of Faraday could appear in the nineteenth century is that he had a clear concern for the image he wished to project, as Prescott shows in her essay. The portraits of Faraday which survive must make him one of the most photographed men in the early history of photography. Faraday had become a popular figure, in this country at least, by the 1830s. This is shown by the large number of biographies of him which have appeared in the past hundred and twenty years.[1] In this respect he is better served than either Darwin or Maxwell, the two nineteenth-century scientists who have received the most attention from modern scholars. On the other hand a recent opinion poll placed Faraday seventh on a list of the best known scientists in this country: Darwin came last and Maxwell appeared not at all![2] What has made him so well known but so little studied? Faraday captured public attention during his life and that has sustained an interest ever since. His contributions to the development of technology are stressed to every school child. This started when the electric telegraph began to have an impact on society which it is now difficult to appreciate. The image of Faraday as a scientist in tune with technological advance was a powerful one. Also seen as a disinterested scientist seeking after knowledge for its own sake, Faraday epitomised a widely held belief of the first half of the nineteenth century about the scientific approach to nature. The essays by Bowers and Gooding describe these aspects of Faraday the public scientist.

In our view scholarly neglect of Faraday and of the context in which he worked has distorted the historiography of nineteenth-century science. Faraday studies can remedy two particular deficiencies. First, study of Faraday can cast light on the way creative scientists work (we return to this point below). Second, Faraday studies can elucidate and broaden general problems of concern to historians of the nineteenth century. Faraday was involved in issues of importance to the modern historian such as the relations of science and religious belief and the relationship between science and the State. Most of the recent literature on the relationship of science and religious belief has tended to concentrate on how geology and evolutionary biology militated against a literal interpretation of the Bible, and the consequences this had. Little attention has been paid to the attitudes of physical scientists towards religion. Since most were believers this has provided a very lopsided picture.[3] In Chapter 4 Cantor contributes to a correction of this bias by showing how intimately related Faraday's religion was to his science. Another important topic, the relationship between science and the State, is not discussed in detail in any of the essays; an omission we were unable to avoid. We would like to emphasise here that there is a need for an extended study of for example, Faraday's work at the Royal Military Academy at Woolwich, at the Board of Trade and for Trinity House, and his role in the Whig versus Tory controversy over the patronage of science. Another topic needing attention is the use of Faraday's expertise in resolving issues of public concern, such as the safety of mines and the way in which science teaching should be introduced. Further, in an age when the value of knowledge was increasingly seen in economic as well as moral terms, the ability to sell his expertise enhanced his status and influence. The economics of scientific knowledge in the nineteenth century deserves further study.

1 Recovering Faraday

Scientists seem to be inveterate myth builders.[4] The word myth is not meant in any perjorative sense: myths do two things for science. They simplify and so allow scientists to discuss problems about their own history in general terms without worrying about details. Myths also provide an ideal, a target for scientists' aspirations. Once these myths have been established they acquire a life of their own. They do however represent for scientists a valid way of interpreting the social world which they inhabit. The construction of a myth is a complex historical process, whose development for Faraday has yet to be examined.

Once Faraday came to be regarded as a great man, much less attention was paid to the way he worked. So, his experiments have been made to seem straightforward, as if he produced them in a ready made, textbook form. This is one of the many myths which surround Faraday. They have served to keep his reputation before the public. But it is also important to go behind the myth to examine Faraday's life and work, to learn something about how a scientist worked and thought. This will also tell us why he became a great man through his research and his lecturing.

The chapters by Gooding and by James show that Faraday's experimental discoveries were by no means straightforward. His interest for historians lies not only in the undoubted intellectual and practical importance of his discoveries but also in the methods by which he studied nature. To this end several of these essays make extensive use of Faraday's laboratory *Diary*. Extending over 40 years and seven printed volumes, the *Diary* allows us to see how a scientist worked day by day, sometimes hour by hour. There is really nothing comparable with it in the history of science. Gooding, James and Tweney all use the *Diary* to construct accounts of the discovery and invention of new science. We think that detailed accounts will have important implications for cognitive psychology, philosophy of science and perhaps for science education as well.

Another myth, which seems to have originated with his early biographers, is that he worked apart from the rest of nineteenth-century society. While it is true that in the laboratory he worked alone or with a single assistant, his other spheres of activity were very much connected with the society in which he lived. Every chapter shows, in different ways, how Faraday interacted with other scientists, other professional groups, and with the public at large. We suspect that his early biographers simply concentrated on his most spectacular results and allowed these to overshadow the rest of his life.

New work on Faraday raises new questions. These are good reasons for a new book on Faraday. However, the problem of such a collection is that it exacerbates an imbalance, the tendency of students of nineteenth-century British science to focus on the major performers and to ignore the supporting cast. Even Faraday's major contemporaries (e.g. Brewster[5] or Herschel) and scientists of the next generation (Thomson and Stokes) still await careful studies (Maxwell is an exception here). Our ignorance of their contributions distorts our understanding of the context in which Faraday worked — to the detriment of our understanding of Faraday. In James's chapter Faraday's work is made an integral part of nineteenth-century optics.

Faraday's reputation was after all conferred upon him by his peers. His success shows that he was working on problems important to his contemporaries. Why was this not obvious? Again it would seem that the myths surrounding Faraday, the 'great man', have prevented his biographers from enquiring into why he was a great man and to whom.

2 Faraday Recovered

The range of Faraday's contributions to science and their influence on our culture is reflected in the diversity of the content and approaches of the essays included here. Prescott draws attention to an important but neglected aspect of Faraday's life, integrating the personal and the scientific in two ways. First, she shows how Faraday was seen by his contemporaries, using the evidence of his own collection of portraits as a means of interpreting the many images of Faraday that survive. Together with Faraday's comments on imaging processes, these show how he wished to be seen. They also show that he wished to be seen in a certain way, taking a more active part in decisions about posture and props to be used in sittings than was usually the case (see Plates 2, 13 and 16). Second, Prescott draws attention to Faraday's close association with and encouragement of, painters and graphic artists and his keen interest in traditional methods of creating images and in new ones such as photography. These connections with the world of graphic art are an important reminder that Faraday's scientific activity was enriched and influenced by a wider, contemporary culture. The range of contacts and resources on which he drew is further indicated by Bowers's description of Faraday's collaboration with Wheatstone, who represented several different spheres of activity — musical instruments, electricity and technologies of communication. Both essays invite further study: Bowers, of the way Faraday drew on the practical and craft skills of those such as Wheatstone and Sturgeon[6] and Prescott's, of his contribution to the techniques of the artists who consulted him and of their influence on the way Faraday perceived the natural world.

Faraday's interest in the visual arts and his interest in the truthful representation of nature were linked in ways that we have yet to explore. An important source of his search for ever closer agreement between 'the natural truth and the conventional representation of it'[7] is discussed in Cantor's essay, and its effects are illustrated in those by Gooding and by Williams. His approach to representation was an important stimulus to his development of the visual style for which he is well known — the pictorial language of lines of force. The emergence of this style has been described in an engaging essay by

Howard Fisher.[8] The subsequent development of Faraday's lines by William Thomson and James Clerk Maxwell has also been widely discussed.[9] Faraday's approach to representation is dealt with in different ways by Cantor and by Gooding. Gooding shows how Davy and Faraday actively constructed images and devices which guided their understanding of their exploratory work on the new phenomenon of electromagnetism in 1820 and 1821. This was an early example of Faraday's adherence to the evidence of experiment. His demand that theorising should be constrained by experience reflected his belief that 'experiment, like analysis, must lead to strict truth if rightly interpreted, and . . . is in its nature far more suggestive of new trains of thought and new conditions of natural power'.[10] For the scientist, error could be avoided ultimately only by empirical rather than intellectual means. Hypotheses were mental constructions which would allow observers to 'outrun fact and lose the information directly before' their eyes.[11] One of the earliest instances of this was his critique of Ampère's interpretation of electromagnetic phenomena, discussed in Williams's essay.

Gooding shows how Faraday transformed the 'suggestive' and truly exploratory work into reliable, demonstrative procedures which made phenomena observable and real. He argues that Faraday's success was largely due to his ability to turn experiences first produced in the privacy of his basement laboratory into accessible, reproducible public facts. Faraday's dedication to experiment displays a faith in observation as the foundation of human knowledge of the created order. Cantor's chapter on the Sandemanian origins of his concepts of law, experience and meaning offers valuable new insights into the source of Faraday's demand for diligent and faithful rendering of observation and other results of experiment. His religion was also a source of his belief in the possibility of objectivity. Crawford argues that to Faraday, objectivity required being honest about the effect of ones desires and emotions upon whatever one is doing. He recognised that the difficulty of coming to terms with one's subjective tendencies and dependencies, is a real obstacle to objectivity.

Cantor's is the only essay that draws directly on eighteenth-century sources. He identifies some striking similarities of emphasis between Faraday's work and that of eighteenth-century dissenting theological writers such as Glas and Hutchinson. Cantor is more interested in parallels, whose value consists in their contribution to our understanding of Faraday's life and work, than in assessing the evidence of the direct influence of particular texts. This approach reveals interesting similarities between Faraday's meticulous, apparently pedantic choice of words and his habitual, occasionally extreme caution over the way the book of nature was to be read, on the one hand, and the Sandemanian emphasis on plain style in the verbal rendering of scripture, on the other. It engendered attitudes that could hardly fail to influence Faraday's daily, working life. Cantor's essay puts paid to the misunderstanding that Faraday kept his science apart from his religion.[12]

Faraday tried to live a religion that was so distrustful of the use of human intellect in the interpretation of scripture and so confident of the possibility of direct revelation of God's word through the Bible that it had no place for theological interpreters or clergymen and therefore had no church hierarchy. All Sandemanians were, in this respect, equal before God. Perhaps Faraday believed that all scientists were equal before nature. A better understanding of his religion and of his fellow Sandemanians would throw light on other facets and attitudes of the man. His uncomprising stance on the 'Decline of science' controversy in the early 1830s and his reluctance to assume high office in what he perceived as the 'church scientific' probably owed as much to his religious convictions as they did to life experiences such as the lessons he learned from Davy, described in Knight's essay.

Faraday's extensive record of his laboratory work and the preservation of a quantity of his apparatus make him a particularly suitable subject for studies of the developing relationship between action, representation and thought in science. Several essays emphasise the importance of understanding what Faraday did in the laboratory to the interpretation of what he wrote or drew. This was a prominent theme of the symposium. Whereas Gooding and James emphasise observational practices and the exploration of possibilities inherent in experimental apparatus, Tweney is concerned to provide a way to analyse the intervention and development of procedures and concepts. His analysis brings cognitive psychology into play as a framework for historical recon-structions of discovery processes and as a new source of criteria for evaluating such reconstructions. It also makes the structure of scientific discoveries accessible to cognitive science as real-life examples of experimental scientists at work.

Understanding the success of science as a learning process calls for a more realistic view of scientists' activity. Several essays therefore emphasise practice.[13] One result is to expose the inadequacy of the still widely held view that the only interesting or important use of experiment is to test the predictions of theories. Gooding shows that Faraday, one of the greatest experimentalists ever, had to learn how to perform his experiments. James's account of Faraday's discovery of the magneto-optical effect and later of diamagnetism provides another example of Faraday's learning process. In this case Faraday had to learn how to make all matter susceptible to magnetism without the mediation of light. Learning how to do experiments entailed three things: making observations whose theoretical significance was often far from clear, varying the experimental arrangements and, as Tweney also shows, altering the research strategies that directed these variations. On this last point, Tweney's clear account of Faraday's recognition of the need to combine confirmatory and falsifying strategies counters the naïve view that the only alternatives to hard-headed falsification are induction, intuition or trial and error.

In addition to questions about why Faraday's science was so productive of reliable knowledge, it is also necessary to ask why his methods were so productive of new theories and of new ways of seeing natural phenomena. Although Faraday's field conceptions of electricity and magnetism were not invented solely by him, his work is a detailed and important example of a conceptual change made over several decades. Sources of new conceptions are addressed again by Gooding, James and Tweney, while Nersessian and Crawford deal with obstacles to recovering the process of development itself. Nersessian identifies historians' neglect of the Lockean task of clearing away the underbush of unexamined assumptions as a major obstacle to historical understanding. In particular, she argues that historians' failure to examine assumptions about the nature of concepts and the way they come to have and change their meaning is to blame for their contradictory conclusions about when Faraday 'had' or articulated the field conceptions attributed to him. Historians interested in the ways that concepts are expressed and how meanings change need to address the question of what they take such concepts to be. We think that her proposal for a flexible, non-essentialist theory of meaning provides a more realistic answer to it.

Crawford identifies a quite different problem: the assumption that scientists must work within an overarching, preferably logical framework, has prevented Faraday scholars from reading his *Diary* as the traces of processes in which he came to terms with the limitations of his own thought. A lack of coherence or clarity in Faraday's *Diary* should be taken at face value, as evidence of *how* Faraday was thinking. It is not something to be explained away as a lapse. Her argument results in a shift (similar to that implied by Gooding's treatment of experiment) towards the question, how did Faraday make such good decisions and get so many good results from such 'imperfect' methods and processes?

Other approaches to more familiar problems of biography are developed in the papers by Knight and by Forgan. Knight portrays Faraday's changing relationship to Humphry Davy and to Davy's brother, John. Humphry began as Faraday's mentor and teacher and eventually became a collaborator. Knight shows that Davy realised that he should take the further step of becoming Faraday's patron, and explains his failure to act upon this in terms of factors which led to their eventual estrangement. One was the web of conflicting loyalties and commitments exposed when, after his spectacular success in discovering electromagnetic rotation, Faraday was proposed for election to the Royal Society. Forgan deals with the relationships between Faraday the individual, his friends and colleagues and the Institution with which he was and is so strongly associated. She shows that the Royal Institution was home and refuge, workplace and public platform. Addressing the problematic relationship of individual to institution she shows that this is as much a problem of characterising the institution as it is of recovering an individual from an overlay of historical interpretations,such as Faraday as the proponent of pure, disinterested research[14] or Faraday as an instrument of the interests of the rising, professional middle classes.[15]. Recognising that Faraday was not necessarily constrained by the fact that the interests of the Royal Institution Managers often did not coincide with his own and that, even from the mid-1820s he was an important force within the Royal Institution, Forgan's treatment argues the need for a more subtle approach to the task of unravelling the strands that made up Faraday's instutitional context. In addition to the material and financial resources Forgan discusses, we should draw attention to the fact that the Royal Institution provided a rich environment as a favoured meeting place for those interested in new discoveries and inventions and their applications. It was a place where Faraday could expect to find much of the scientific world, and a useful share of its resources, coming through his door.

That it was, for a time, *Faraday's* door, is difficult for us to appreciate because of our sharper distinction between the personal sphere and the public, institutionalised sphere of activity. By contrast to Darwin's later seclusion at Down,[16] Faraday crossed the boundary between the private and the public spheres nearly every day of his scientific life, *within* the house of the Royal Institution. Gooding notes that Faraday's discoveries made their passage upwards from the basement laboratory to the famous lecture theatre on the first floor. He points out that their journey from a private to a public space corresponds to a change in their epistemological status, from the realm of novel and personal experience to that of publicly witnessed, demonstrable fact. This juxtaposition of facilities for producing new knowledge and those for disseminating it made the Royal Institution unique and made Faraday more visible than he would otherwise have been. Few scientists have been able to discover, perfect and publicise their results within the same building that contains their home.

Perhaps this unique institutional setting reinforced the self-assurance Faraday so often displayed, even from relatively early in his career. This assurance also owed something to an essentially religious attitude, the humility which gave Faraday an ability whose importance is argued by Crawford: the ability to suspend the need to order and interpret one's experiences; i.e. to tolerate disorder as a threat to one's existing understanding (or, as Faraday called it, one's 'favourite notions'). Following John Keats she calls this 'negative capability'.

Williams's chapter suggests a contrast, both in self-assurance and in institutional context, to Ampère. His account of the impact on Ampère of Faraday's discovery of electromagnetic rotation reveals that Ampère had similar concerns. He argues that Ampère felt that he was being outpaced by other members of the Académie des Sciences and was determined to enhance his reputation by making some major contribution to science. Not surprisingly, he chose the exciting new field opened up by Oersted's discovery of electromagnetism in 1820. This choice was unfortunate because he later lost the experimental initiative, not to his colleagues in Paris, but to Faraday. Although compared with Ampère, Faraday was a relative newcomer to science, he was a better experimentalist. He made criticisms that forced Ampère to change the course of his work. Faraday was largely responsible for what might be called Ampère's retreat from experiment into mathematics. There is an ironic twist in the fact that Ampère did not acknowledge the fundamental status of Faraday's rotations in his theory and that, although Faraday never believed the theory, he often used Ampère's ideas in his work.

3 Mathematics, Rationalism and Empiricism

Faraday's attitude towards mathematics and mathematicians appears in several chapters. Cantor argues that Faraday's suspicion of mathematics can be traced to a Sandemanian reluctance to manipulate signs given by God. This distrust of mathematics was reinforced in Faraday's later scientific experience. Williams points out that Ampère, who was mathematically trained, proposed numerous physical hypotheses to describe and explain electromagnetic phenomena, unconcerned about the experimental implications. James observes that his criticism of the luminiferous aether in 1846 occurred just as two mathematicians — Challis and Stokes — were battling over the explanation of stellar aberration, an issue crucial to the structure of the aether. Yet Faraday was not a simple opponent of mathematics. Gooding has pointed out elsewhere that William Thomson's use of mathematics changed Faraday's mind about aspects of diamagnetism.[17] Maxwell remarked that Faraday had a well-developed ability to think geometrically.[18] In his chapter Gooding shows how in 1821 Faraday transferred a two-dimensional thought experiment into a three-dimensional real experiment. This geometrical process of thought allowed him to discover the electromagnetic rotations that so perplexed Ampère.

Faraday doubted that mathematics could by itself tell us much about the natural world. This set him apart from most of his physicist contemporaries and makes him appear, perhaps, unsophisticated and a little anti-intellectual. But this characterisation says more about our cultural preference for head over hands, than it says about Faraday. This reminds us of a tension that has existed in western intellectual life since the fourth century BC, between Aristotle's commitment to empirical observation of the world and Plato's belief that real knowledge of the world, which exists only in the reality of forms, can be rationally constructed by mathematical thought alone. In the twentieth century most historians and philosophers have tended to project their preference for logically ordered theorising over empirical explorations of phenomena onto science. This has affected historical approaches to scientists such as Faraday. He has been neglected by comparison with great intellects such as Newton, Maxwell and Einstein. Another effect is that Faraday's development has often been characterised in terms of intellectual traditions, to the exclusion of a variety of other sources and influences. Some, such as the practical side of his intelligence and his mastery of the techniques and instrumentation of science, have until recently been dismissed in favour of more lofty aspirations. (As the late Derek Price remarked, most philosophers and historians of science are 'born-again theorists'.[19]) Finally, the emphasis on the literary and intellectual side of science is reinforced by the popular beliefs mentioned earlier about how and why scientists do their work. Faraday is portrayed as pursuing knowledge for its own sake and as a master experimentalist for whom phenomena emerged straight from nature.

The essays in this book show that such descriptions do not fit. Faraday's discoveries cannot be interpreted through the simple dichotomies of reason and experience and of thought and action implied by the Platonic and Aristotelian positions. Several of the essays show that we can develop new frameworks with which to analyse and describe Faraday's work and his approach to nature.

4 New Resources

New approaches to Faraday use new resources and give a different emphasis to those that have been used before. Sources examined here for the first time include his portrait albums, his copy of Paris's *Life of Davy*, eighteenth-century dissenting literature, nineteenth-century weekly periodical literature and his bound copy of the *Experimental Researches*. Prescott uses the two albums of photographs and letters that Faraday bound, as a source of evidence about his connection with the art world and his interest in various forms of graphic representation. Knight uses the letters that Faraday bound in Paris's *Life* to trace the course of Davy's relationship with Faraday from their years of collaboration to their ultimate estrangement. He also uses it as a metaphor for this process. Crawford shows that the interleaved copy of the *Experimental Researches in Electricity* which Faraday bound in 1839 records his attempt to deal with difficulties in his theory of electric and magnetic induction. She uses his system of notation and cross-references here and in the *Diary* as evidence of how he thought and felt, to recover his own assessment of the importance of problems and of his solutions to them.

Though there are many manuscripts that still require study and appreciation, we do not have to rely on them to make new resources available. Cantor uses the writings of eighteenth-century dissenting theologians to understand the Biblical exegesis of the Sandemanians. As remarked earlier, he points out interesting analogies between this and Faraday's scientific work. A source rarely used by historians of science is daily and weekly periodical literature. Prescott uses such literature to establish the market of, and interest in the commercial portraits that Faraday collected. Weeklies such as the *Athenaeum* and *Literary Gazette* have been used extensively by historians of literature. Here James uses lecture reports in these weeklies to discern changes in the language, content and structure of different versions of Faraday's discourses, especially those on matter in the 1840s. He also uses the reports of the 1846 'Thoughts on Ray-vibrations' to demythologise the context of its presentation. Bowers uses this type of periodical literature to trace Wheatstone's early career and his relationship with Faraday.

Resources used previously, but not fully, include Faraday's *Diary*, the *Chemical Manipulation*, his historical and theoretical analysis of electromagnetism and the minutes of meetings of the Managers of the Royal Institution. Forgan uses the Minutes to trace Faraday's changing institutional role within the Royal Institution. In Tweney's chapter, Faraday's notebooks and the *Chemical Manipulation* are a source for his cognitive approach. This shows that Faraday used increasingly complex operations ('scripts') in his investigations of nature. Williams uses Faraday's anonymous *'Historical Sketch of Electro-magnetism'* as a source for his early attitudes to the interaction of theory and experiment. He analyses Faraday's rotation paper in terms of its adverse criticisms of Ampère's electrodynamic theory. Gooding traces Faraday's route to well-known discoveries and instruments using a rather neglected resource: his *Diary*. The magnetic rotations and Faraday's cage emerge from his manipulations and practical problem solving. He draws attention to what Faraday must have done in an experiment as part of the context necessary to textual interpretation. Here he was helped by another under-used resource — the artefacts of Faraday's laboratory. Few scientists have a museum devoted exclusively to them.

5 Faraday's Schooling

Like many of his scientific contemporaries Faraday did not have what could be regarded (in his time or ours) as a normal education. Faraday attended a day school until the age of 13. But this education consisted of 'little more than the rudiments of reading, writing, and arithmetic'.[20] In 1805 at the age of 14 he began a 7-year apprenticeship with the bookseller and binder George Riebau. This gave him access to an extensive library. His reading was given some order from 1809 by Isaac Watts's *The Improvement of the Mind* which recommended, among other things, that those wishing to improve their minds should keep a common place book and correspond with friends to learn to articulate their ideas. Both of these Faraday did, corresponding with Benjamin Abbott at great length. From 1810 he followed another piece of Watts's advice, attending weekly meetings at the City Philosophical Society. There he heard and gave lectures on various natural philosophical topics. Riebau also allowed him to do experiments at the back of his shop. Although Faraday had the support of friends and colleagues he was still largely self-taught. Darwin, Thomson and Maxwell were all at Scottish Universities and later at Cambridge at the age at which Faraday was still a bookbinder.

Conventional school and university education does two things. It provides knowledge to which all members of a community have access and instils a shared critical approach to that knowledge. Faraday had to develop the latter himself. It is easier to acquire knowledge than the mental tools by which it can be evaluated and so Faraday remained, for a time, uncritical. For example, in a lecture to the City Philosophical Society in 1810 he supported strongly and somewhat naïvely, the two-fluid theory of electricity. Shortly after this Faraday read Jane Marcet's *Conversations on Chemistry* and promptly changed his interests from electricity to chemistry — a sure indication that his allegiances were not yet formed.

However, an instilled critical approach can lead to prejudice and so restrict the available options for new approaches to a problem. This is perhaps best seen by comparing Faraday with John Herschel. Although he became as eminent as Faraday, Herschel's mathematical tripos education at Cambridge prejudiced him against alternative approaches to nature, in a period when, even without Faraday, science was undergoing profound changes.[21] Herschel always tried to adopt the analytical, mathematical approach. Even when this failed, he argued that it would eventually have to be applied. Faraday, without the handicap of a Cambridge education or the benefit of a Scottish one,[22] had to work out his own procedures for evaluating whatever knowledge he gained. This meant that he was able to construct his own critical abilities in step with contemporary scientific change.

While Faraday was an apprentice the resources to develop his critical ability were limited. If Cantor's argument about the parallels between Faraday's religion and his science is correct then it is possible that Faraday's Sandemanianism became an important resource. Sandemanians rejected all non-literal interpretations of the Bible, as based on fallible, human understanding, and took their beliefs directly from a literal reading of the Bible. Perhaps Faraday came to criticise scientific theories because they, too, were human interpretations of nature. Certainly he tried harder than most to read the Book of Nature directly, as the essays by Gooding and by Williams illustrate. As Knight notes, when he and Davy were in Paris Faraday was already insisting on experimenting before accepting the theories of French scientists. Once Faraday was at the Royal Institution and had access to other resources he was able to develop his ability to evaluate knowledge and the means of acquiring it.

It was Faraday's good fortune that he did not have the conventional approaches to knowledge instilled in him when young. Faraday had to learn over a period of many years how to explore nature. An example of this development can be seen in his paragraph numbering system. In 1821 when he discovered electromagnetic rotations he numbered for a while the paragraphs of his *Diary*. These remained private to his *Diary* and were soon abandoned. In 1831 when he discovered electromagnetic induction he again began to number his *Diary* paragraphs, stopped and then began the series which continued for three decades ending in 1860 with paragraph 16041. In 1831 he also began numbering the paragraphs of his published *Experimental Researches in Electricity*. He thereby acquired a powerful tool of reference, especially as he indexed both *Diary* and *Researches* from time to time. Faraday's learning process was a continuous one. It allowed him to increase his exposure to nature which, as Gooding shows, he saw as an important tutor.

The success of Faraday's self-schooling shows that he must have had a vast amount of self-discipline. It is difficult to acquire knowledge *and* the ability to evaluate it without continuous encouragement and a standard of critical comparison. But once Faraday had developed his own approach to the natural world he retained it for the rest of his life. As Tweney points out, there are concepts and techniques which recur throughout Faraday's life but which are continually elaborated. His self-education must have given him some insight into the learning process which allowed him to go on making important experimental discoveries and conceptual innovations. He was 30 when he discovered electromagnetic rotations, 40 when he discovered induction and 54 when he discovered the magneto-optical effect and diamagnetism. The latter allowed him, in his late fifties, to articulate and defend his 'field' conception of forces. Not many scientists have begun their creative lives so late or continued for so long.

His insights, expressed throughout his writings but especially in his lecture on 'Mental Education', are an important resource for our understanding of the psychology of learning. He knew that the problems he identified were not peculiar to scientists. His spectacular success did not prevent him from appreciating the difficulties of others in understanding science. Compared with the three Scottish- and Cambridge-educated scientists mentioned earlier, Faraday is universally acknowledged to have been the best communicator. He was careful to tailor both his writing and his lectures to the intended audience. This implies that his audience's opinion of him was important to him. This may have had an important consequence: Knight points out that he had the example of Davy, who had not recognised that some would not welcome his assuming important offices. With Davy's experience before him Faraday did not risk public office. Faraday's unusual education may have advanced his scientific career by preventing a public career.

Notes

(See Bibliographical Notes for use of notes.)

1. For example Bence Jones (1870a, b), Gladstone (1872), Tyndall (1884, 1894), Thompson (1898), Appleyard (1931), Martin (1934), Kendall (1954), Williams, L.P. (1965).
2. 'What do people think of science?', *New Scientist*, (21 February 1985), 12–16, 16.
3. Turner (1978) is an example of this lopsided approach. He fails to mention Faraday's, Thomson's or Stokes's religious belief and seems embarassed by Maxwell's. Wilson (1974, 1984) is one of the few authors who address the religious beliefs of nineteenth century physicists.
4. For a case study of the development and function of a myth see James, F.A.J.L. (1985).
5. There is now a collection of studies on Brewster. See Morrison-Low and Christie (1984).
6. J.O. Marsh, 'Sturgeon and the discovery of electro-magnetic induction' (unpublished), read to the 'Faraday Rediscovered' symposium. Hodkinson (1979).
7. Faraday (1852a), 3075.
8. Fisher (1979) is an excellent introduction to the constructive and rhetorical character of Faraday's experimental work. More detailed treatments of its context and elaboration of the lines can be found in Gooding (1982b, 1985b).
9. Wise (1979b) is a clear and accessible account; more technical discussions are Wise (1979a), Buchwald (1977) and Heimann (1970b).
10. Faraday (1852a), 3159.
11. Faraday, *Diary*, 19 December 1833, **2**, 1207.
12. Based on a misreading of Faraday to [Countess of Lovelace], 24 October 1844, in Bence Jones (1870a) **2**: 192–6, 193, that 'there is no philosophy in my religion'.
13. Hacking (1983), Price (1980), Rescher (1980).
14. Russell and Goodman (1972).
15. Berman (1978).
16. For Darwin's earlier public career see Rudwick (1982).
17. Gooding (1982b).
18. Maxwell (1892), **1**: ix–x.
19. Price (1980), 75.
20. Bence Jones (1870a), **1**: 8.
21. Cannon (1978).
22. Davies (1961), Olson (1975).

Plate 2 Michael Faraday reading a newspaper. John Watkins. Carte-de-visite studio
picture, c.1863, Glasgow University Library, Special Collections, Ferguson Collection
(Bh19h.6). Albumen print from collodion negative.

1

Faraday: Image of the Man and the Collector

Gertrude M. Prescott

The nineteenth and early twentieth centuries mark the transition from a visually starved to a visually overloaded culture. In centuries before our own, public figures were known primarily through the written word and secondarily through the visual portrait. Even in the nineteenth century, biographers devoted long passages to describing the presence, manner and dress of prominent persons.[1] In contrast biographers today tend to provide a series of photographs, usually snapshots, of contemporary individuals; captions only briefly contextualise this primary visual information.[2] Further, the reportage of events has become intrinsically visual. On television, edited film footage frequently takes precedence over the construction of the verbal story and the narration of dramatic events is often — and sometimes incongruously — accompanied by a still portrait of the chief protagonist taken at an unrelated moment; but this image, familiar to the audience through its repeated use, has come to stand for the individual, whatever the context.

Technological innovations effected the shift in the way we perceive people and events.[3] The development of steel-plate engraving, lithography, wood-pulp paper, photography, photomechanical reproduction, film and satellite communication have made the image progressively more accessible.[4] The pace and volume with which visual records of public figures are produced significantly distinguishes our experience from that even of Victorians and this is reflected in our attitude towards images. We take the image for granted, quickly disposing of newspapers which daily feature photographs and we go about our chores all but ignoring the familiar face as it is flashed upon the television screen. In contrast, Victorians, noted for their curiosity about public figures which was fueled by the expansion of the media, were passionate collectors of memorabilia.[5] They purchased and treasured visual representations of their men and women of mark. The appearance of a newly published engraved or photographic portrait of a celebrity was a newsworthy item.

While our press might occasionally notice the unveiling of a major oil painting of a public figure, the issuing of graphic and photographic portraits of a variety of individuals was reported in such diverse publications as *The Church of England Magazine, The Lancet, The Photographic News*, the *Times*, the *Graphic*, the *Art-Journal*, the *Athenaeum* and the *Illustrated London News*.[6]

The appetite for portrait collecting was not limited to the Victorian public at large. Prominent individuals themselves collected images of their acclaimed contemporaries and colleagues. Some of these albums, publications and portfolios have been preserved with their provenance intact.[7] We are fortunate that members of Michael Faraday's family preserved two albums of portraits which he assembled and bound and that these albums eventually returned to the Royal Institution, where they were first enjoyed, and now form part of the Archive's treasures.[8] The Faraday albums are representative of the general Victorian phenomenon of portrait collecting. Yet they are also unique in that they reflect Faraday's particular interests and friendships with contemporary colleagues and celebrities.[9] Further, because some of the portraits were sent in response to Faraday's request, they express a mutual regard of sitter and collector.[10]

But the Faraday albums are more than a collection of portraits. The images were assembled precisely during the decades in which steel engraving, lithography and photography revolutionised the availability of portraits.[11] They tell us which images were on the market and which media were employed for representation. Of still greater significance, they permit a glimpse into a previously unexplored facet of Faraday.

1 Faraday and Print-making Techniques

Although Faraday undoubtedly collected the portraits primarily because of his interest in the subjects, he was also keenly interested in the processes which produced them. In particular, Faraday promoted the development of lithography and photography through Royal Institution lectures and personal contacts with innovators who developed the processes and the techniques of manipulation.

Lithography

Around 1818 the artist Charles Joseph Hullmandel came to Faraday to study chemistry because he realised that the technical improvements which he envisaged for lithography would depend on a thorough understanding of the chemical properties of the materials employed.[12] In order to achieve greater effects in the medium, knowledge of more than the basic antipathy of grease and water was needed. In lithography a drawing is made on stone in greasy ink and the surface is dampened with water which settles only in the non-greasy areas; printing ink is then rolled on and adheres to the greasy drawing which is transferred to paper in the printing process. Hullmandel's more thorough understanding of his materials and how to make alterations in their composition, and of the very technical manipulations, enabled him to refine the process further by etching and scraping the stone's surface, using washes of lithographic ink and dabbing techniques to apply the ink.[13] As a result, lithography was better able to reproduce the range of effects which characterised watercolours. Hullmandel published folios reproducing works by some of the major landscape painters of the day, including Clarkson Stanfield, David Roberts and George Cattermole.[14] Faraday also encouraged and supported Hullmandel in his efforts by publicising and describing Hullmandel's improvements at the Royal Institution and by publicly endorsing a new method, the details of which Hullmandel, for commercial reasons, kept secret.[15]

Photography

Faraday made the first public announcement in England regarding the new art of photography. This placed also him at the forefront of artistic and technological developments.[16] Faraday intended to establish the claim of William Henry Fox Talbot to the invention of photography, a claim which he held to be equal to that of Louis Jacques Mandé Daguerre.[17] At the end of the Friday evening discourse on 25 January 1839, Faraday proclaimed, 'No human hand has hitherto traced such lines as these drawings displayed; and what man may hereafter do, now that dame Nature has become his drawing mistress, it is impossible to predict'.[18] Following the discourse, the audience inspected examples of Talbot's photogenic drawings in the library.[19] These were images which had been obtained by superimposition, that is, by placing objects directly on paper which had been sensitised to the action of light by silver chloride. While Faraday supported Talbot's initial scientific claim, he later rejected his monopolistic ones. Talbot asserted that his patent for the calotype process (which involved the taking of a paper negative in the camera from which positive prints were then made) extended to the collodion process which used a glass negative support. Faraday's refusal to support Talbot's claim may be linked to the suggestion that Talbot be offered a baronetcy to relinquish his claim — an honour that Faraday himself had declined — and to the monetary issues which were involved with Talbot's patent.[20]

Faraday was a willing participant in the image-making process and sat for many photographic portraitists. Some of the images are noteworthy in their reference to Faraday's particular scientific interests or his desire to be portrayed in a pose departing from standard studio types. One portrait, taken and published by the firm of Maull and Polyblank in 1856, shows Faraday as a lecturer, demonstratively holding a bar magnet (Plate 16). He was also depicted in the role of scientific investigator by the firm of William Walker and Son, seated beside a table laden with equipment relating to his experiments (Plate 13). But there was also the 'off duty' Faraday, shown by John and

Charles Watkins as seated, reading a newspaper with the sole of his shoe inelegantly exposed as if in defiance of the formal portrait tradition (Plate 2). A moment later the same photographers depicted him standing next to the chair, paper under his arm. The amateur photographer, author and mathematician, Charles Lutwidge Dodgson (Lewis Carroll) depicted him in a more thoughtful pose.[21] Another image of Faraday appeared in the context of a Friday evening discourse when his portrait was taken on 6 May 1864. On that occasion Alfred Brothers demonstrated taking photographs by magnesium light during a lecture by Henry Enfield Roscoe.[22] Once again Faraday was witness and participant in technological developments in the history of visual representation.

2 Faraday and the Art World

We can develop the theme of Faraday as an interested observer of artistic processes by examining aspects of his life which have been neglected by biographers more intent on Faraday, the man of science. As a youthful apprentice to the bookbinder Riebau, Faraday made early-morning expeditions to examine the contents of gallery windows as well as to seek scientific curiosities.[23] Also while at Riebau's, Faraday attempted to master the technique of perspectival drawing by studying and copying treatises by Brook Taylor, at the suggestion of the painter John James Masquerier.[24] Subsequently, through Hullmandel, he met many artists, among them, apparently J.M.W. Turner.[25] Faraday's brother-in-law, George Barnard, was a noted watercolourist, with whom he evidently enjoyed the convivialities of Hullmandel's circle.[26] Later in life he continued to attend the annual dinners at the Royal Academy, an important exception to his withdrawal from almost all evening public engagements.[27] Through his marriage to Sarah Barnard in 1821 Faraday also was related to the artist and inventor Cornelius Varley. Varley shared his religion as well as his technological curiosity.[28] At the Royal Institution Varley exhibited his graphic telescope, devised to aid mechanically the accurate rendering of portraits and views. The discourse he delivered on his invention was only the fourth evening lecture at the Royal Institution; Faraday had immediately preceded his appearance.[29] One portrait in the Faraday collection can be used to exemplify Faraday's general interest in mechanical aids to artistic transcription. Francis Chantrey's portrait of William Hyde Wollaston which appeared in the album was executed with the help of the camera lucida (Plate 8),[30] a more popular device than Varley's. In the context of the discussion at the Royal Institution of such devices, Faraday's inclusion of the portrait takes on a significance beyond the subject to suggest his interest in the method by which the portrait was created.

In Barnard, Faraday found an enthusiastic travel companion. Together they explored Switzerland, where Barnard executed sketches in preparation for his drawing manuals while Faraday went on lengthy walks.[31] A close bond developed between the two and during Faraday's declining years, it was Barnard who handled all practical arrangements for travelling.[32] According to Thompson, this relationship extended to the laboratory as well. Barnard was reported present when Faraday observed the electric wire revolve around the pole of a magnet.[33] Faraday must have watched Barnard prepare his drawing manuals for publication. Barnard considered Faraday his mentor and, after the success of one of his treatises on drawing, he dedicated the later editions of the book to Faraday in a touching tribute.[34] He particularly cited Faraday's encouragement as deriving from the belief that the book would be a 'real and useful' work. Barnard dwelt not only on the aesthetics of drawing, but also on colour theory and a variety of techniques. His manuals were beautifully illustrated by means of lithography, the graphic medium which Faraday had encouraged.

Faraday was also involved with the artistic world by virtue of the advice he gave to the British Museum, the National Gallery and Westminster Abbey about problems of conserving sculpture and architecture.[35] He also counselled artists, among whom allegedly was the great scenic painter J.M.W. Turner, on subjects such as the permanency of pigments.[36] Pursuing these connections within the art world, we can number among Faraday's circles of friends and acquaintances the art critics Lady Elizabeth Eastlake, wife of the President of the Royal Academy, and Anna Jameson; the portraitist and scientist William Brockedon; the portrait painter Henry William Pickersgill and the amateur photographer Julia Margaret Cameron.[37] Faraday did not limit his interest to the respected and élite artists, but extended his concern to the younger generation. In addition to Barnard, he encouraged the young Glaswegian artist Alexander Blaikley, helping him to find patronage.[38] Perhaps in form of a tribute, Blaikley executed a painting and lithograph depicting Faraday's Christmas lecture in 1855 before a distinguished audience including the Prince Consort and the Prince of Wales (Plate 9).[39] Faraday also recommended to Jane Davy that she select an aspiring painter to execute a copy of the Humphry Davy portrait at the Royal Society, rather than an established artist, for whom such a commission would be of less benefit.[40]

Such evidence allows us to place Faraday within a context in which art theory and practice and technological developments in the visual arts were being seriously discussed and promoted. Faraday was not a naïve observer who would have looked at the portraits he collected only in terms of their content, the likeness. Those who have studied Faraday's life with the purpose of writing scientific biographies have dismissed his connections with the art world. For instance, Thompson wrote in 1898 that 'Faraday does not . . . appear to have any very direct connections with the world of art. . . . Though a sufficiently good draughtsman to prepare his own drawings, he had little or no knowledge of the technicalities of painting'.[41] Thompson's bias has influenced others. Williams assigned Faraday's consultations with museums concerning the conservation of art to a section on Faraday's 'fallow years'. The implication is clear: when Faraday was not pursuing great scientific research, then what he was doing was unimportant![42] In light of our new knowledge of Faraday's interest in the technology and chemistry of art, we must reinterpret such activities as being characteristic rather than being something which Faraday pursued by default; for example, when his health did not permit him to devote himself to his 'true' calling.

3 Faraday as a Collector

With this re-evaluation of Faraday we can now turn to delineate Faraday the collector. The images will allow us to explore Faraday from this new point of view. His interests and friendships also permit us to discern further layers of contextual meaning for the very images he assembled. Let us first look at the albums themselves, their make up and content. As remarked earlier the two albums of manuscripts and portraits were arranged and bound by Faraday himself.[43] They are a poignant reminder that Faraday was first trained as a bookbinder and that he introduced himself to the great man of science, Humphry Davy, by means of a carefully bound transcription of Davy's lectures at the Royal Institution. In the albums, portraits of and letters from the subjects are frequently mounted on adjoining pages. Occasionally the letters pertain directly to the portraits which he preserved. But usually the manuscripts and portraits are not precisely contemporary in date. Faraday apparently selected those letters which were readily available or which were of special interest to him. The two volumes contain approximately 135 letters and manuscripts and 250 portraits executed in line engraving, lithography, photography, mezzotint and watercolour. Images and letters from personal friends, individuals within the Royal Institution inner circle, British and foreign colleagues, royalty and actresses and actors were arrayed for perusal.

Amongst the many men and women of science represented are Humphry Davy, D.F.J. Arago, John George Children, John Dalton, Mary Somerville (Plate 3), J.B.A. Dumas, C. Matteucci, Alexander von Humboldt, G.G. Stokes, Michael Eugene Chevreul, and Thomas Graham. Artists such as Sir Francis Chantrey, William Wyon and Thomas Phillips also corresponded with Faraday, as did the actor, William Charles Macready, a favourite of Faraday's. Royalty (the Prince of Wales and Prince Louis Napoleon), medical men (Henry Clutterbuck and Henry Holland) and the men of letters (William Jerdan) are also preserved in letter and likeness.[44]

Faraday purchased some images, received others from the artists or publishers, and was sent still others by the sitters, sometimes at his request. Many of the portraits were readily available on the market. One of the letters explains that when Faraday's purchase of a portrait was made known to the subject himself, he hastened to write to Faraday that he would have been happy to present the portrait, had he known of the great man's wish.[45] The Royal Institution's proximity to the major art and print dealers in the Bond Street area meant that popular and fine art prints were easily accessible. Among the dealers were Colnaghi's on Bond Street and Pall Mall, and John

Plate 3 Mary Somerville. After J. Phillips. Royal Institution, Faraday Album, H:10. Lithograph.

Murray on Albemarle Street, both of whom forwarded prints to Faraday.[46] During the 1830s when Faraday seems to have been particularly active as a collector, Thomas McLean of Haymarket published the popular series of lithographs entitled 'Athenaeum Portraits' which featured contemporary notabilities. Faraday was of course included amongst these subjects. The published lithograph reproduced a bust of him sculpted by E.H. Baily (Plate 10). Faraday's collection contained a number of portraits from the series. Many of these depicted men noted in scientific circles, with whom Faraday was actively corresponding.[47] McLean's series thus proved to be a convenient source of images for Faraday. One wonders whether he placed a standing order with the publisher or whether the firm forwarded images which it felt would interest an influential man of science. Unfortunately, neither the manuscripts nor the prints provide conclusive evidence.

Faraday's albums also contain images issued in limited edition form, intended to hold special appeal for collectors. One print, showing the engineer James Walker, is listed as a subscriber's copy;[48] another was issued from a private plate.[49] Others were 'proof prints'; an example is the portrait of the botanist A. Bourke Lambert from the series entitled the 'Professional, Scientific and Literary Portrait Gallery'.[50] In the nineteenth century this term came to refer to an impression printed before the main edition and offered to collectors at a higher price.[51] The added value placed on these particular prints is indicated by the Countess of Lovelace's pointed apology for sending Faraday one of the main edition prints. She felt it necessary to explain that none of the proofs remained in her possession.[52] Documentation occasionally reveals that Faraday received portraits from the artists responsible for the depiction. The engraver and artist Charles Turner forwarded his portrait of Brockedon.[53] The engravaing was published in 1835, the year after Brockedon's election as Fellow of the Royal Society and 4 years after Turner's execution of a portrait drawing depicting Faraday, now in the National Portrait Gallery.[54] Brockedon's portrait would have been of particular interest to Faraday because Brockedon was pursuing technological experiments intended to benefit the practice of art.[55] Brockedon was attempting to utilise waste lead in the manufacture of pencils; Faraday saved and mounted a letter from Brockedon in which Brockedon enquired about some samples of Cumberland lead.[56] Brockedon's other projects included a rest for artists engaged in minute work. Such a device would have been a great aid to artists who copied works on the steel plates from which engravings (such as Faraday collected) were printed. One wonders if Turner forwarded the print at Brockedon's request, following a wish earlier expressed by Faraday, perhaps during Faraday's sitting for Brockedon. In other instances, Faraday's requests for portraits was only fulfilled at a later date when a portrait became available.[57] Faraday's portrait exchanges also included artists such as the portrait medallist and chief engraver at the Royal Mint, William Wyon and the painter, Thomas Phillips, both of whom also portrayed Faraday.[58]

Faraday also received engraved portraits after oil paintings from the portraitist W.H. Pickersgill.[59] As testimony to the friendship which arose between them, the artist inscribed the prints 'To Michael Faraday Esqr. From his friend W.H. Pickersgill'.[60] The portraits included a depiction of Cuvier and the botanist and librarian of the Linnean Society, Robert Brown.[61] Evidently it was Pickersgill who advised Faraday on the selection of an artist who would copy the original portrait of Davy which hung in the Royal Society rooms.[62] Thomas Phillips, who depicted many prominent Victorians, also presented Faraday with an image which would be of personal interest.[63] This was a portrait of Davy executed as a mezzotint (Plate 6). Faraday preserved the letter which accompanied Phillips's portrait. It expresses Phillips's intent in forwarding the print as well as his esteem:

> Pray do me the favour to accept the accompanying print of Sir Humphrey [sic] Davy engraved by Reynolds from a picture which I painted about 1818.
>
> Who so worthy to possess a memorial of that eminent man than is Michael Faraday.[64]

The print which Phillips sent is a fine mezzotint executed by a skilled engraver.[65] The mezzotint process was noted for its faithful evocation of the tonal range of paintings. This surpassed the effects which the cheaper method of line engraving could achieve. Victorian collectors accordingly placed greater value on mezzotints. Although Phillips's letter is undated, it must have been written after the print was published in 1822. Faraday later collected another version of Phillips's Davy portrait reproduced by a different engraver in line (Plate 7).[66] A comparison of the prints graphically shows the greater illusionistic effects which the mezzotint, chosen by Phillips, created. (Faraday would also accept yet another portrait engraving of Davy, this one after a painting executed by James Lonsdale.[67])

The Davy portrait is only one of several documented contacts between Faraday and Phillips. Further evidence of the intermingling of artistic and scientific circles is given by the letter Phillips wrote to Faraday in May 1838. He expressed the gratification and enjoyment which he received from listening to Faraday's illustration of the nature and properties of carbonic acid gas.[68] In 1841 Phillips was working on a portrait of Faraday for which Faraday gave several sittings. The painting was completed in 1842.[69] This portrait was not commissioned and was presumably undertaken on the artist's initiative. Phillips subsequently gave it to the inventor and engineer John Scott Russell.[70] An indication of the mutual respect and regard between Faraday and Phillips is that Faraday preserved a portrait of Phillips which he mounted in his album facing the artist's letters.[71]

One of the few images in Faraday's albums which departs from the portrait of a particular subject depicts a type. It shows the image of 'A Collector' (Plate 4).[72] In the light of our understanding of Faraday as a collector, the image can be interpreted as revealing the role in which Faraday cast himself when compiling the albums. In the engraving the archetypical connoisseur sits alongside a table and cabinet ladened with curiosities and treasures; his scholarly reading interrupted by our intrusion. We can easily imagine Faraday in the setting of the Royal Institution rooms relaxing and enjoying the images and letters which paid tribute to the friendships he had established over the years. But for Faraday the enjoyment was not necessarily the isolated activity which such a portrayal suggests. A letter from the glass manufacturer Apsley Pellatt shows that Faraday shared his collection with his friends and colleagues. Evidently some of the individuals provided portraits at Faraday's request, knowing that they would be so enjoyed:

A COLLECTOR.

Plate 4 'A Collector'. Royal Institution, Faraday Album, H:51. Engraving.

> Several years since you shewed me a number of portraits of your friends &
> acquaintances & asked me if I could give you a Lythograph [*sic*] of my own, which
> I did not then possess; if you think the accompanying Photograph would answer
> the same purpose I shall deem it an honour to be placed among the eminent
> worthies in your Portfolio undeserving as I may be of the favour.[73]

The letter also reveals a problem which ultimately affected the composition of
Faraday's portrait collection. Before photography became widespread, only a
narrow sector of society commissioned portraits or had portraits available for

engravers to copy; fewer yet had ready access to multiple copies of their portrait to share with friends.

The Pellatt letter and the portraits in Faraday's album suggest that Faraday specified lithographs in some of his requests for portraits and that the lithographic process had extended the circle of individuals for whom portraits were available. I have already noted that the lithographic series of the 'Atheneaum Portraits' was well represented in Faraday's collection. But Faraday received lithographs depicting eminent individuals from abroad and from various walks of life as well. His collection contains a number of images drawn by the French lithographer Z.-F.-J.-M. Belliard of which his portrait of Justus von Liebig is representative (Plate 5).[74] Other individuals appearing in lithographic portraits include J.J. Berzelius, Emil Dubois Raymond, Mary Somerville, the aeronaut Charles Green, Pierre Simon Laplace and Heinrich Rose.[75] Among sitters who signed their lithographic portraits to Faraday were John Haviland Burke, Edward Daniell, L.W. Dillwyn and J.B.A. Dumas.[76]

At times the letters and portraits in Faraday's album represent a process of exchange as well as a response to specific one-way requests. A letter from Francis Gore dated 9 February 1836, addressed from the Athenaeum Club reads:

> You will oblige me very much, by favouring me with your signature, for the purpose of placing it with the Portrait of a Gentleman for whose Public and Private Character, I have so high an esteem.[77]

Faraday mounted this letter opposite a portrait of Gore himself. Faraday may have complied with a request for the autograph by expressing the wish to have in return an image of Gore. One wonders whether he sent his portraits to some of the other celebrities who forwarded portraits to him? Only extensive research will bear further information.

Faraday's taste?

How discerning a collector was Faraday? It would be a mistake to compare Faraday with the great print connoisseurs of the day. They competed for rare portrait prints and would have been little interested in mass-produced portraits of contemporary figures, such as the 'Athenaeum' series. Although fine mezzotints and proof prints exist in the collection, it is impossible to establish whether Faraday sought these specifically for their fine art value. We would misrepresent the collection if we analysed the portraits as evidence of Faraday's aesthetic sensibilities because of the variety of sources from which he received portraits. Not only did artists and publishers forward prints to him, but also the subjects themselves sent some.[78] The latter should be considered as reflecting the taste of *sitters* rather than of the collector.

Yet Faraday should not be characterised as a collector who was insensitive to the manner in which the image was created and the mode by which it was reproduced. In one instance his response to images sent to him was recorded. Faraday was evidently delighted with the photographic portraits executed by

Plate 5 Justus Liebig. Z.-F.-J.-M. Belliard. Royal Institution, Faraday Album, H:43.

a Munich photographer, sent to him by Justus Liebig. He wrote to Liebig on 1 May 1856:

I have to thank you . . . for your kindness in sending me a photograph of Mr Barlow [Plate 14]. Your Munich Photographs delight me very much; for I am not fond of those which I see about in London, coloured up so highly that all simplicity is taken away from them, I suppose the owners think them fine and elaborate, I think them commonplace and often vulgar.[79]

Faraday's album shows that this group of Munich photographs were by Franz Hanfstangel, a prominent portrait photographer, whose work is still esteemed today.[80] Besides portraits of John Barlow and his wife, Liebig also sent portraits of himself and Robert Wilhelm Bunsen.[81]

The wording of this letter to Liebig gives a crucial insight into Faraday the collector. He says nothing about the worth of the subjects who were pictorially documented; nor about the pleasure of having their images; nor finally, about the accuracy of the likenesses themselves. Victorian observers frequently focused on such issues when discussing portraits.[82] Instead the very appearance of the images is what stimulated his interest and delight. Simplicity was preferred over adornment. Elaboration was classified as commonplace and vulgar. His wording shows him setting his taste apart from that which he attributed to the ordinary consumer who did not appreciate the qualities of the photograph itself.

Perhaps Faraday was unfair in his sweeping characterisations of London photographers and their clientele. Some firms were executing beautiful straight photographs comparable in quality with those of Hanfstangel. An example is the striking portrait by Maull and Polybank of Faraday gesticulating with bar magnet in hand. Faraday was undoubtedly aware of other portraits by this firm.[83] His comments suggest that he was responding to some of the portraits on display in shop windows and galleries. Retailers may have been more eager to show coloured portraits since they generated more return to the photographers and shops. Additional charges were made for hand colouring photographs and the images attracted a clientele which wished for a photographic portrait having the appearance of the more expensive miniature.

4 Conclusion

Faraday's portrait albums thus span the crucial decades from the mid-1820s through to the mid-1860s when the impact of technological developments significantly increased the availability of images and widened the circle of people whose images were available on the market. Steel engraving, lithography and photography made social exchange through portraiture possible on a scale previously unprecedented. Faraday's albums are more than an assemblage of likenesses. He was keenly interested in the very processes which made the visual revolution possible. Through the Royal Institution and his friendships with leading artists and inventors, he supported and helped the advances. As a collector with insight into the processes by which images were produced, Faraday would have appreciated the portraits as testimony to what man and nature could create.

Notes

I thank Irena McCabe at the Royal Institution, Lenore Symons at the Institution of Electrical Engineers, Nigel Thorp and Elizabeth Watson at the Glasgow University Library,

Andrea Gall and Terrence Pepper at the National Portrait Gallery London and William Schupbach at the Wellcome Institute for the History of Medicine for help with working on images and manuscripts in their care.

1. For a representative example see the reminiscences of Hall, S.C. (1871). Samuel Carter Hall (1800–1889) was an author and editor in the literary and artistic field of publishing. As editor of the *Art-Union Monthly Journal*, beginning in 1839, and later the *Art-Union Journal*, he was responsible for helping encourage the collecting of prints by Victorians. He was, as G.C.Boase observed in 'Samuel Carter Hall', *DNB*, **24**: 87–9, intimate with most of the celebrities of the day.
2. Mariani (1981).
3. Benjamin (1970).
4. McLuhan (1964).
5. White, J. (1857). Album of Photographs and Autographs compiled by Miss Harriet Lowe, sold at auction, Sotheby's (London), 29 June 1984, lot 236.
6. For examples relating to photography see *The Church of England Magazine* (18 December 1858), **45**: 430; *The Lancet* (24 October 1863), **ii**: 485; *Athenaeum* (31 October 1857), 1359; *Ill. Lond. News*, 1856, **29**: 508. Parallel announcements appeared for images in other media including engraving and lithography.
7. See Sylvanus P. Thompson's albums of portraits and memorabilia in IEE MS and the albums of photographs of John Tyndall compiled by his wife (RI MS T 4/B12) (presented to the Royal Institution by Granville Proby, nephew of Mrs Tyndall, *Proc. Roy. Inst.*, 1944, **33**: 187). Sarah Faraday, in November 1867, presented a copy of T.S. Maguire's lithographic *Portraits of Hon. Members of Ipswich Museum*, in which Faraday was featured, to Harriet and Julia Moore, intimates of the Faraday family circle (RI MS F1 K, purchased Sotheby's, December 1971).
8. Volume one (RI MS F1 H) was bequeathed by Thomas J. F. Deacon of Newcastle to the Royal Institution on his death, 8 September 1901 (*Newcastle Daily Journal* (29 October 1901), 4 and *Proc. Roy. Inst.*, 1902, **17**: 43). Volume two (RI MS F1 I) was presented to the Royal Institution by D.J. Blaikley from the bequest of J[ane] Barnard (niece of Faraday) at her express wish (*Proc. Roy. Inst.*, 1911, **20**: 251).
9. Among the notable individuals who will not be discussed in this paper are the following: (NB references to material in the two volumes of Faraday albums will be made by an H or I, the H album beginning with the portraits of the royal children, with the page number subsequently listed). Mary Somerville (I: 56), P.M. Roget (I: 118), Prince Albert Edward (H: 2), Harriet Moore (I: 160), J. Dalton (H: 37), W. Whewell (I: 70), David Brewster (I: 22), Thomas Graham (I: 32), among many others.
10. Among these are Biot (I: 63), A. Quetelet (I: 62), Bunsen (H: 50), John Haviland Burke (H: 55), Edward Daniell (H: 59), Francis Gore (H: 59), A. Dumas (H: 63), Edward Hawkins (H: 64), John Poole (H: 69) and J. Hachette (H: 85).
11. See Griffiths (1980), Godfrey (1978) and Twyman (1970).
12. C.J. Hullmandel (1789–1850). Bryan (1927), **3**: 84–5 and Bénézit (1976), **5**: 665.
13. Godfrey (1978), 91 and Twyman (1970), 125–6.
14. C. Stanfield (1793–1867), D. Roberts (1796–1864), G. Cattermole (1800–1868).
15. Faraday presented the results of Hullmandel's improvements at the Royal Institution on 3 March 1826 while Hullmandel exhibited and demonstrated his process ('Proceedings of the Royal Institution', *Quart. J. Sci.*, 1826, **21**: 134–5). Faraday would later again present Hullmandel's discoveries in the official forum of the Royal Institution; see *Lit. Gaz.*, (18 June 1842), 424–5. For Faraday's unusual endorsement of a secret process see Faraday to Hullmandel, 12 April 1827, in Twyman (1970), 133–4. The Royal Institution possesses a lithographed circular of April 1829, with eight plates, in which Hullmandel displayed the effects of which his particular improvements were capable; we can assume that this entered the collection during the Hullmandel –Faraday association.

16. Buckland (1980), 39 and Gill (1967), 54.
17. W.H.F. Talbot (1800–1877), L.J.M. Daguerre (1787–1851).
18. 'Royal Institution', *Lit. Gaz.* (2 February 1839), 74–5, 75.
19. *Ibid.*, 74.
20. Gernsheim (1955), 180. Faraday characteristically refused to enter into disputes concerning patent rights, see [Pollock, J. and W.F.] (1867), 282. (For the authorship of this see Pollock, W.F. (1887), **2**,: 167.)
21. C.L. Dodgson (1832–1898). Collingwood (1961), plate 28.
22. Roscoe (1864), 290. Gill (1967), 65–6.
23. Riebau to? [October or November 1813], RI MS F1 BA. Faraday evidently 'kept by him', Ireland's Graphic Works of Hogarth and copied interesting plates which clients brought to the firm for binding. There were two relevant works about the great graphic artist William Hogarth (1697–1764) to which Faraday may have had access: Ireland, S. (1794–9) and Ireland, J. (1791–8).
24. Bence Jones (1870a), **1**: 12 and Thompson (1898), 7–8. Brook Taylor's treatises were popular in Faraday's youth. The Royal Institution has Malton (1778). Faraday's biographers have characterised J.J. Masquerier (1778–1855) as a poor emigré artist. Art historical references depict another story. Masquerier was born in Chelsea in 1778 of French parentage; he trained in England as an artist (Royal Academy) and in France (in the atelier of Horace Vernet). On a second trip to Paris in 1800 he executed a portrait of Napoleon which, upon his return to Britain, created a sensation since it was the first portrait from life to be exhibited in Britain. This began his career as a successful portrait painter; he executed some 400 portraits in 28 years and was able to retire in comfort to Brighton and died there in 1851. When Faraday visited him in Brighton in 1851 (Jerold (1892), 109), it was a celebrated man of science visiting a successful artist.
25. Thompson (1898), 246–7. J.M.W. Turner (1775–1851).
26. *Ibid.* George Barnard (1807–1890).
27. *Ibid.*, 246.
28. *Ibid*, 5. C. Varley (1781–1873).
29. *A brief notice of the life of and labours of Cornelius Varley*, London (c. 1874), 9. Faraday presented Varley (1845) to the Royal Institution in 1855 (*Proc. Roy. Inst.*, 1855, **2**: 137 and *Quart. J. Sci.*, 1826, **21**: 133–4).
30. H: 86.
31. Thompson (1898), 224. Williams, L.P. (1965), 102.
32. *Ibid.*, 492. Tyndall (1894), 90. Faraday to Andrews, 27 July 1856, *Correspondence*, **2**: 637.
33. Thompson (1898), 51. See also [Bollaert], (1867), 389 who also claimed to have been there but made no mention of Barnard. For the authorship of this see Brock (1968).
34. Barnard (1885). The dedication stated: 'My dear Michael,/ When I first undertook this Volume, your conviction that it would prove a "real and useful work" encouraged me in its progress./ I much wished at that time to dedicate it to you, who from boyhood have been my kind friend and adviser; and I hesitated only lest it should not prove worthy of your acknowledgment./ Now that it has met with approval, and a new edition is called for, I feel encouraged to place your name on this page; and to express in this manner how sincerely we, who have the advantage of your intimate friendship, recognize and esteem and qualities of heart which endear you to us, and in comparison with which even your distinguished fame holds but a subordinate place./ Ever your affectionate Brother/ George Barnard'. A copy of the first edition of this treatise was sent by the publishers to the Royal Institution and was accepted by the Royal Institution on 5 February 1855 (*Proc. Roy. Inst.*, 1855, **2**: 25). The book went through various editions and Barnard's dedication must have been added after the first edition but during Faraday's lifetime. That the dedication should continue to be printed in later editions is an indication of Faraday's continuing fame and the importance with which Barnard held his association.

35. For bibliographical references to the reports see Jeffreys (1960) entries 385, 459, 467 and 471. See also Thompson (1898), 246 and Williams, L.P. (1965), 479–82.

36. Thompson (1898), 246. I have been unable to substantiate Thompson's assertion that Faraday advised Turner. However, Turner frequented the circles of artists in which Faraday was included, such as Hullmandel's and Varley's. See Thompson (*ibid.*) and *A brief Notice of the Life and Labours of Cornelius Varley*, London, (c.1874), 6.

37. Pollock (1887), **2**: 14, reported that on 18 April 1852 he spent an evening at Mrs Carrick Moore's at which present were Faraday, Babbage, the Lyells, Anna Jameson (1794–1860), Lady Eastlake (1809–1893) (wife of Sir Charles Eastlake, President of the Royal Academy), John Murray and Sir C. Fellows. Harriet Moore was a competent artist and her watercolours depicting Faraday and his laboratory hang in the Royal Institution. Photographic portraits of her were also included by Faraday in his portrait albums (I: 103). The fashionable portrait painter, George Federick Watts, asked the photographer Julia Margaret Cameron (1815–1879) to approach Faraday to request that he sit to a portrait which would be included in Watts's 'Hall of Fame'; unfortunately the sitting never occurred. (Watts, G.F. (1975), 6).

38. Faraday to Andrews, 27 July 1856, *Correspondence*, **2**: 637. A. Blaikley (1816–1903).

39. Lithograph and a nineteenth century photographic copy are in the Royal Institution archives. The original painting belongs to the Royal Society of Chemistry.

40. Jane Davy to Faraday, 23 August 1847, *Correspondence*, **1**: 356.

41. Thompson (1898), 246.

42. Williams, L.P. (1965), 479–82.

43. The binding was created by Faraday himself according to the *Newcastle Daily Journal* (31 October 1901), 4. The arrangement appears to be Faraday's and does not follow any apparent system — chronological or by subject — other than the matching of portraits and manuscripts. Occasionally portraits of the same individuals appear in different places in the album. Manuscript notations regarding the sitters' identity had been added subsequently by different hands, presumably family members.

44. H. Davy (1778–1829), D.F.J. Arago (1786–1843), J.G. Children (1777–1852). J. Dalton (1766–1844), M. Somerville (1780–1872), J.B.A. Dumas (1800–1884), C. Matteucci (1811–1868), A.v. Humboldt (1769–1859), G.G. Stokes (1819–1903), M.E. Chevreul (1786–1889), T. Graham (1805–1869), F. Chantrey (1781–1841), W. Wyon (1796–1851), T. Phillips (1770–1845), W.C. Macready (1793–1873), H. Clutterbuck (1767–1856), H. Holland (1788–1873), W. Jerdan (1782–1869).

45. Henry Storkes to Faraday, 31 July 1839, I: 108.

46. Lithograph (by E.U. Eddis and M. Gauci) of Edward Hawkins forwarded to Faraday by Colnaghi (H: 23). Stipple engraving (from a drawing by James R. Swinton) of Mary Somerville presented to Faraday by the publisher, John Murray (I: 57).

47. Charles Lyell (I: 111); Roderick Murchison (I: 111), W.H. Pepys (I: 152); and Charles Daubeny (I: 119).

48. J. Walker (1781–1861). I: 66.

49. I: 21.

50. A.B. Lambert (1761–1842). I: 135.

51. Goldman, P. (1981), 11.

52. Countess of Lovelace (1816–1852) to Faraday, 16 June 1840, H: 13.

53. I: 80–1. Charles Turner (1774–1857) executed a portrait of Faraday as well; Iconography collection, Wellcome Institute for the History of Medicine, listed in Burgess (1973), 144, entry 938.5.

54. Ormond (1973), 168, entry 2515.

55. Redgrave (1874), 53.

56. Brockedon to Faraday, 27 October 1845, I: 81.

57. Apsley Pellatt (1791–1863) to Faraday, 14 October 1857, I: 82 and Issac D'Israeli to Faraday, 20 August 1839, I: 120.

58. I: 14, 114 and 160.

59. W.H. Pickersgill (1782–1875).
60. I: 11 and 41.
61. Cuvier (1764–1832); R. Brown (1773–1858).
62. Jane Davy to Faraday, 23 August 1847, *Correspondence*, **1**: 356.
63. T. Phillips (1770–1845).
64. Phillips to Faraday, 23 June 1841, I: 160.
65. The mezzotint after Phillip's painting which he forwarded to Faraday was executed by the engraver Samuel William Reynolds (1794–1872); for Reynold's stature as a Victorian engraver see Engen (1979), 162–3. Reynolds's daughter was married to William Walker, engraver and photographer, to whom Faraday sat for photographic portraits.
66. W.T. Fry after Phillips, I: 19.
67. J. Lonsdale (1777–1839), I: 23.
68. Phillips to Faraday, 20 May 1838, I: 160. See Jeffreys (1960), entry 283.
69. Ormond (1973), 168, entry 269. Faraday to Phillips, 27 January 1844, in the collection of the Wellcome Institute for the History of Medicine.
70. Henry W. Phillips to George Scharf, 5 May 1868, 13 June 1868 and 29 June 1868 in National Portrait Gallery collection. In 1868 Russell (1808–1882) sold it, with the help of the artist's son, to the National Portrait Gallery where it remains.
71. I: 160.
72. H: 51.
73. Pellatt to Faraday, 16 October 1857, I: 82.
74. Z.-F.-J.-M. Belliard (b. 1796); J.v. Liebig (1803–1873), H: 43.
75. J.J. Berzelius (1779–1848), I: 46; E.D. Raymond, H: 16; M. Somerville, H:10; Charles Green (1785–1870), H: 27; P.S. Laplace (1749–1827), H: 45; H. Rose (1795–1864), H: 44.
76. J.H. Burke, H: 55; E. Daniell (1804–1843), H: 459; L.W. Dillwyn (1778–1855), H: 25; J.B.A. Dumas, H: 63.
77. Gore to Faraday, 9 February 1836, H: 58.
78. Countess of Lovelace to Faraday, 10 June 1840, H: 13, the Countess was responding to a request which Charles Babbage had conveyed from Faraday. Pellatt to Faraday, 14 August 1857, I: 82. I. D'Israeli to Faraday, 20 August 1839, I: 120. John Poole to Faraday, 24 February 1836, H: 68: 'My dear Faraday./ Accept the accompanying *proof* — that I have not forgotten your flattering request. I think you will allow it to be a better likeness than the one of which you are already the fortunate possessor, in as much as it is *considerably handsomer*. Personal beauty is a point, however, upon which I am, and always have been, utterly indifferent, and unaffectedly now, I scarcely think mine a subject of sufficient interest or importance for a *regular course* of lectures. *Pray remember that*. But with such a document in your possession as the one I send you if you choose to take it up *just for one of your Friday evenings*, or do, I am not aware of any particular objection to your doing it'. Writing from the Garrick Club, Poole was, of course, speaking tongue in cheek.
79. Faraday to Liebig, 1 May 1856, *Correspondence*, **2**: 631. J. Barlow, I: 39.
80. F. Hanfstangel (1804–1877).
81. J. Barlow, I: 39; Mrs Barlow, I: 38; R.W. Bunsen (1811–1899), H: 50; Liebig, H: 77.
82. For contemporary response to published portraits see *Ill. Lond. News*, 1856, **29**: 508; *Athenaeum* (6 October 1866), 239 and (12 January 1861), 55.
83. Faraday's portrait was published in Maull & Polybank (1856–9) in October 1857. Other celebrated individuals who appeared in this series — which featured photographic portraits and biographies — were Richard Owen, Sir B.C. Brodie, T. Graham, George Cruikshank, Lord Brougham, W.E. Gladstone, D. Livingstone, to mention a few.

Painted by T. Phillips Esq. R.A.   Engraved by S.W. Reynolds.

SIR HUMPHREY DAVY BAR^T

President of the Royal Society &c. &c. &c.

Pub.^d by T. Phillips March 1822.

Plate 6 Humphry Davy. Samuel William Reynolds after painting by Thomas Phillips (1818). Royal Institution, Faraday Album, H:21.

2

Davy and Faraday: Fathers and Sons

David M. Knight

It has been said of Bergman and of Davy that their greatest discoveries were Scheele and Faraday. This is a rather backhanded kind of compliment. Davy at least would not have relished it and it has a curiously reductive aspect if we group his great discoveries as Potassium, Chlorine, Faraday and the Safety Lamp and solemnly try to decide which was the greatest. The relationship of Davy and Faraday was highly ambiguous. Probably the most familiar characterisation of it is Bence Jones's remark in his biography of Faraday, that Davy was hurt by success, that he had little self-control, method or order, and that:

> he gave Faraday every opportunity of studying the example which was set before him during the journey abroad, and during their constant intercourse in the laboratory of the Royal Institution; and Faraday has been known to say that the greatest of all his great advantages was that he had a model to teach him what he should avoid.[1]

This is a thoroughly catty remark, surprising at first sight in one whose contemporaries praised him as possessing all the virtues. Yet the tone is familiar in the complaints of sons about overbearing fathers.

Bence Jones was unhappy with this simple view, and wrote in the following year in his book on the Royal Institution:

> Whenever a true comparison between these two Nobles of the Institution can be made, it will probably be seen that the genius of Davy has been hid by the perfection of Faraday. Incomparably superior as Faraday was in unselfishness, exactness and perseverance, and in many other respects also, yet certainly in originality and in eloquence he was inferior to Davy, and in love of research he was by no means his superior. Davy, from his earliest energy to his latest feebleness, loved research; and notwithstanding his marriage, his temper, and his early death, he first gained for the Royal Institution that great reputation for original discovery which has been and is the foundation of its success.[2]

Plate 7 Humphry Davy. W.T. Fry after painting by Thomas Phillips. Royal Institution, Faraday Album, I:19. Steel engraving.

The biographer's love of comparisons, however odious they may be to the rest of us, has meant that we have tended to see Davy through the unflattering eyes of Faraday.

What Faraday needed to avoid is indicated in a chatty column in *Fraser's Magazine* of February 1836, which is devoted to him as number sixty-nine in a 'Gallery of literary characters'. Davy, wrote the columnist,

that great and good man (so abominably caricatured by the ass Paris) rushed to
the rescue of kindred genius [Faraday]. Sir Humphry immediately appointed him
an assistant in the laboratory; and, after two or three years had passed, he found
Faraday qualified to act as his secretary . . . and he is now what Davy was when he
first saw Davy — in all but *money*. . . . The future Baronet is a very good little
fellow — a Christian, though, we regret to add, *a Sandemanian* (whatever that
may signify) — a Tory (as might have been inferred from Rat Lamb's hostility).[3]

Like many sons, Faraday did not want to walk in his father's footsteps or to
live in his shadow. He married an *hausfrau*[4] rather than an heiress, and refused
Presidencies and titles.[5] This is only part of the story.

Another biographer, John Tyndall, wrote:

We have heard much of Faraday's gentleness and sweetness and tenderness. It is
all true, but it is very incomplete. You cannot resolve a powerful nature into these
elements, and Faraday's character would have been less admirable than it was had
it not embraced forces and tendencies to which the silky adjectives 'gentle' and
'tender' would by no means apply. Underneath his sweetness and gentleness was
the heat of a volcano.[6]

As Tyndall knew him Faraday was not slow to anger, but he was highly self-
disciplined. He showed a curious mixture, or perhaps we should say
compound, of humility and pride.

It is fun to try to get inside the psyches of the dead and distinguished, and we
shall return to it; but it is best to begin with a look at the context in which Davy
and Faraday inosculated, to their mutual pleasure and pain. In the early
nineteenth century there was no obvious way into science as there was in the
major professions. While there have been in science some dynasties, like the
Becquerels, the Huxleys and the Wollastons, it is less of an hereditary activity
than the classic professions, the Church, the Law, the Services, and Medicine
— where at Edinburgh students were subjected to the Monro doctrine for
more than a century. This may be just because science became a profession
much more recently, or because it is not really a profession, or because it is
more intellectually demanding than the others.

1 Faraday, Sir Humphry Davy and Patronage

Davy, as a poor boy with little education, had been apprenticed to an
apothecary-surgeon.[7] This would have led to a skilled-craftsman status only,
unless he had been able to upgrade himself by going to university. His father
was a woodcarver, often out of work, who died when Davy was young. Thus
far his background was not so very different from Faraday's. He did not have
the Nonconformist conscience which drove Faraday, and belonging to
Church rather than Chapel he was more open to the attractions and perils of
the Establishment. The patronage on which Davy drew was less obvious than
Faraday's: Gregory Watt, Davies Giddy (later Gilbert, and his successor as

President of the Royal Society), Thomas Beddoes and his circle in Bristol, and possibly the mysterious Tepidarians talked about by J.A. Paris in his biography.[8] Beddoes came nearest to being his patron, but from the start the relationship was curiously equal.[9] Beddoes was converted to Davy's theory of phosoxygen and Davy's researches on the oxides of nitrogen were far in advance of anything Beddoes was capable of. Davy was hurt by some critical reviews of his speculations which Beddoes had published, and may have looked on Beddoes as an example of what to avoid. He seems to have seen in Beddoes a case of energy being dissipated.

Perhaps Davy's brilliance was apparent from the start. Chemistry was so incoherent and fluid that one could get to the frontier of knowledge sooner in 1799 than when Faraday came on the scene in 1812. Davy's relationship with Beddoes was very different from Faraday's with Davy. Davy was soon tempted away to the Royal Institution, and Beddoes died not long afterwards. There was no problem of Davy having to grow up in his patron's shadow.

Another point of comparison between Davy and Faraday is their upward social mobility. Faraday's contemporaries stressed his career from rags to riches, or rather to eminence. Bence Jones in the first edition of his biography portrays him receiving a handout of a loaf of bread each week in the hard times of 1801.[10] In fact he was from the respectable or deserving poor. This was why he later found beggars so offensive. Bence Jones later retouched the picture by pointing out that the bread came from Faraday's parents, not from the parish.[11] Berman's recent 'portrait' of Faraday is vitiated by the belief that someone from the artisan class in the early nineteenth century should think like a student of the class of 1968.[12] Davy's climb was much greater for he ended up trying to fill the niche vacated by Sir Joseph Banks, a landed grandee. Davy was thus presiding over his betters in a highly stratified society.[13] Not everybody likes being governed by their social inferiors, however brilliant. While Davy was a *parvenu* Faraday did not take such risks.

Davy's reputation suffers from the judgements *de haut en bas* of contemporaries. In an era when science was not yet professional, they would have expected the aspirations of someone of Davy's background to be lower. It is hard to see how at that time anyone aiming at the highest place in science could have behaved very differently. Davy and Faraday may have been nature's gentlemen but they were not gentlemen of science.[14] Perhaps what Faraday learned to avoid were ambitions that threatened this group. Both Davy and Faraday moved into a social milieu very different from that in which they had grown up, and were fish out of water. There is always a price to pay for social mobility.

Society in the early nineteenth century worked by patronage. Faraday's method of writing to a great man was not unique. Nor was his first choice, Banks. He had helped a number of young men, sending naturalists on voyages and finding them employment at Kew and at botanical gardens around the world. Davy noted of Banks: 'He was always ready to promote the objects of men of science; but he required to be regarded as a patron, and readily swallowed gross flattery'.[15] Patronage is a hit-or-miss business. To young men of Faraday's station Banks could never have been a father: a patron, a fairy godfather perhaps, putting up on occasion with grumbling, but never involved in a relationship ripening into a kind of equaltiy. On applying to Banks, Faraday was told 'no answer'.[16] Other notables of the day failed to recognise youthful talent: the young Boussingault had found a menial job in Thenard's laboratory through a friend, and when Thenard discovered how young he was he threw him out.[17] When Boussingault returned from South America, Thenard did become his patron. In many cases such support would have come too late, like Chesterfield's patronage of Johnson.

As Tyndall put it, 'Davy was helpful to the young man, and this should never be forgotton'.[18] Even in the days before there were chemist breeders,[19] Faraday was unusual in getting his chemistry entirely through apprenticeship or pupillage. It was also unusual to pick upon the most brilliant chemist of the day. Those who worked with Berzelius had already had some training, and were not with him very long. Their relationships were more like that with a supervisor for a higher degree. Berzelius took his pupils one at a time, but Thomson and Liebig had considerable numbers going through their hands. As the century went on the difference in size of scientific families made a crucial difference. A professor might have a favourite son out of several dozens, but this is a different relationship from that with an only child. The process begins to look more like raising cattle than like raising a family. Yet there was often a close and emotional relationship between the professor and the student, and between the band of brothers who had learned their science together. There were good sons, who kept the professor's reputation green and continued his work; and bad ones, who assailed both. Some of the history of nineteenth-century science (for example, physiology) has the aspect of family rows.[20]

There is a classic case of an adoption in science, Berthollet's relationship to the young Gay-Lussac.[21] Berthollet, a protégé of Macquer, encountered Gay-Lussac as a pupil at the École Polytechnique. He asked him to be his son in science. Since Berthollet already had a son, the whole thing looks a trifle complicated. But the younger Berthollet removed himself by a scientifically planned suicide, and the ceremonial sword came to Gay-Lussac as the mantle of Elijah came to Elisha. With it probably also went a double portion of his spirit. Gay-Lussac was undoubtedly a good son. He learned his science from Berthollet, who got him good posts, got him into the Institut, and launched him on a very distinguished career. How far he was able to emerge from the shadow of his parent is harder to say. His reluctance to admit the elementary status of chlorine seems undoubtedly due to excessive deference to Berthollet's views. His rapid promotion may well have made him overcautious. When what was needed were testable conjectures along the lines of Laurent's *Chemical Method*, Gay-Lussac was looking for laws.

2 Faraday and John Davy

Faraday's relationship to Davy is perhaps more like that of David to Saul, whose attitude to his destined successor was ambiguous. The problem there was that Saul had a son already. The interesting thing about Davy was that although his marriage was childless he had two sons in science. The first, older than Faraday by about a year, was Davy's younger brother John. He was to be the good son, fighting skirmishes on Humphry's behalf over chlorine, editing his posthumous *Consolations in Travel*, and fighting battles (particularly with Faraday and with Babbage) for his reputation. Of the *Consolations*, John Davy wrote: 'His whole life it may be said was a kind of preparation for the last work, which contains as it were the essence of his intellect in relation to most of the subjects on which he had not previously published'.[22] John wrote a *Life* of his brother, and edited the nine volumes of Humphry's *Collected Works*. After the death of Jane Davy, who had been a cruel stepmother to him and Faraday, he brought out a volume of *Fragmentary Remains* as a supplement to the *Life*.

John Davy was born in 1790.[23] His father died when he was 4 and after going to school in Penzance until 1808, he came to the Royal Institution to work with Humphry. In 1810 he was sent to Edinburgh to prepare for a medical career. In 1815 he joined the Army, and went on to become an Inspector General of Army Hospitals. On graduating MD in 1814 he was elected to the Royal Society. Obtaining a higher degree is like crossing a Rubicon and no doubt this made an appropriate point to terminate his apprenticeship in science. His time at the Royal Institution was, he used to say, one of the happiest and best employed of his life. Despite his excellent start in scientific life, John never did any particularly distinguished research. His obituarist remarked that: 'It is much to the credit of Dr Davy's moral nature that no shadow of mortification or jealousy ever darkened his meditations on his brother's achievements, into comparison with which he was so constantly forced to bring his own'.[24] He also remarked more darkly on 'the great reputation which, in spite of all efforts to the contrary, has settled round the name of Sir Humphry Davy'.[25] He attributed the protection of Davy's reputation as due in part to John Davy's efforts.

Blood is thicker than water. Readers of *The Selfish Gene* will know that it is as rational to help a brother as a son.[26] John Davy was a distinguished scientist of his day; he was genial, energetic and methodical, but he must have lacked that volcanic quality necessary to the outstanding scientist. The Davy brothers were both very keen fishermen, and Humphry seems in later years to have really only relaxed with rod (or occasionally gun) in hand: his closest friends were his fishing companions.[27] For Faraday, we have George Barnard's testimony that: 'Faraday did not fish at all during these country trips, but just rambled about geologising or botanising'.[28] He lacked a key to Davy's heart.

John Davy and Faraday died within 6 months of one another and nearly 40 years after Sir Humphry. So it is important to remember that they did not belong to different generations, being only 11 and 12 years younger than

Davy. In different ways they behaved like sons. It was the good son, John, who rushed to attend Humphry in his last illness in Italy and in Switzerland. But to see Faraday simply as the bad son (from Davy's viewpoint if not our own) would be to miss various interesting ambiguities. Faraday wrote that: 'These polemics of the scientific world are very unfortunate things; they form the great stain to which the beautiful edifice of scientific truth is subject. *Are they inevitable?* They surely cannot belong to science itself, but to something in our fallen natures'.[29] And again, on family rows: 'We may well regret such incidents. It is not that they are not to be expected, for they belong to our nature, but they ought to be repented'.[30] One of the last acts of his life was to subscribe 'most liberally to the fund for raising a monument to Sir H. Davy at Penzance'.[31]

3 Faraday and Davy's early relationship

In 1812, when he was twenty one, Faraday went as a journeyman bookbinder to De la Roche, leaving the fatherly Riebau for this 'very passionate man'[32] who gave him a great deal of trouble. But De la Roche said: 'I have no child, and if you will stay with me you shall have all I have when I am gone'.[33] Faraday's choice of Davy instead meant that he inherited a position but not possessions. Although in 1812 John was at Edinburgh Davy does not seem to have felt any particular need at that time for an apprentice. The story is now familiar:[34] Davy granted Faraday an interview, told him that science was a harsh mistress in the pecuniary point of view, and smiled at his notions of the superior moral feelings of philosophic men. The upshot of it was that in March 1813 'through his good efforts' Faraday went to the Royal Institution as assistant in the laboratory — thus doing something rather more interesting than the work which W.H. Pepys advised Davy to give him: 'Put him to wash bottles; if he is good for anything, he will do it directly; if he refuses, he is good for nothing'.[35] In this instance, Davy perceived that menial tasks were not appropriate to Faraday. Gassiot reported to Tyndall that Davy, on giving up his post at the Royal Institution 'insisted that Faraday should be appointed Director of the Laboratory, and, as Faraday told me, this enabled him on subsequent occasions to hold a definite position in the Institution, in which he was always supported by Davy'.[36]

There is a fascinating source for insight into Faraday's time under Davy. Besides the correspondence which Faraday wrote during these 10 years and the various biographies, which have drawn on the letters and journals, there is Faraday's copy of Paris's *Life* of Davy.[37] Faraday was one of Paris's informants for this official biography. What is striking about it is its debunking tone which duly outraged John Davy. Into his interleaved copy, Faraday bound a whole series of manuscripts. These include a doodle; remarks on space and time; a geological sketch; drafts of scientific papers; and letters from Davy. The volume is an extraordinary monument to a relationship, and one cannot go through it without feeling a variety of emotions.

The many manuscript comments by Faraday are striking; his neat handwriting contrasts completely with that of Davy. Davy complained of the want of neatness and order in his laboratory. But his own notes of experiments are scrappy and haphazard. The experiments we are told were often done with a rapidity which astonished the beholder, as pieces of apparatus were put to previously unimagined uses in a burst of inspired activity. It is no wonder that Davy needed Faraday as an amanuensis. In the Paris volume there is a manuscript on iodine, annotated by Faraday on 7 January 1832: '*An original paper by Sir H. Davy*. It was my business to copy these papers. Sir H. Davy was in the habit of destroying the originals but on my begging to have them he allowed it and I now have two volumes of such manuscripts in his handwriting'.[38] (This is why so many of Davy's papers in the Royal Society are in Faraday's hand.) The iodine manuscript is on paper of different sizes, but shows Davy in excellent form, reasoning from analogy and no prey to the sterile virtue of tidiness. As Gooding shows in Chapter 6, Faraday also developed a flair for creative play with apparatus. This made it impossible that he should remain an amanuensis.

The continental tour

It was in this capacity that Davy took Faraday with him on his continental tour from 1813 to 1815. Because Davy's valet dropped out at the last moment, Faraday also had to do some jobs appropriate to a servant. He was by no means treated simply as a servant. But the name of valet rankled: it was white-collar rather than blue-collar status which mattered to Faraday. In fact, Davy 'having been in an humbler station, and not being corrupted by high life, had very little occasion for a servant of that kind':[39] the whole affair may simply go to prove the truth of the (French) saying, that no man is a hero to his valet.

On the tour, Faraday began to impress a few of the men of science they met:[40] notably the elder De la Rive, and also Dumas who wrote: 'We admired Davy, we loved Faraday'.[41] Though this was in the Éloge of Faraday, it is very likely true of reactions at the time. Faraday had never been more than 12 miles from London, but because of the French wars travel abroad had been almost impossible even for aristocratic Englishmen right through his lifetime. Her experience of the continent made the Edinburgh salon of Jane Apreece, the future Lady Davy,[42] so noteworthy and desirable. The chief fact normally remembered from the tour is her disagreeable behaviour to Faraday, putting him in what she conceived to be his place.[43] The young Faraday stood upon his dignity and outfaced her, glad when seasickness stopped that flow of conversation which had delighted Edinburgh. What is striking about the tour is that Faraday had, when they stopped anywhere, one or more servants under him, and was in charge of the practical arrangements for the party.

Before they went, Faraday had assisted Davy with experiments on nitrogen trichloride; some safety precautions were taken. They wore glass masks which fortunately were not shattered by explosions that cut their faces through leather.[44] The experience of assisting with research continued on tour: 'Sir H. is now working on the old subject of chlorine, and, as is the practice with him goes on discovering'.[45] Davy's 'example did great things in urging the Parisian chemists to exertion'.[46] Over iodine he wrote,

> The French chemists were not aware of the importance of the subject until it was shown to them, and now they are in haste to reap all the honours attached to it; but their haste opposes their aim. They reason theoretically, without demonstrating experimentally, and errors are the result.[47]

This was a partisan comparison of Davy and Gay-Lussac, but it does show that what struck contemporaries about Faraday's method, his insistence on experimental demonstration, was learned early. Davy may have gone to Paris demonstrating that science was above politics, but when shown the loot in the Louvre, or 'Galerie Napoléon', he and Faraday refused to be impressed. They were patriots rather than philistines.[48] Their competition with the French was a kind of intellectual warfare carried on in the enemy capital.

Faraday noted that books were cheaper in Paris, that type faces were squarer, that stereotyping was in vogue.[49] In Rome he noted that bookbinding was poor.[50] 'Sir H. Davy kindly explained to me'[51] about Vesuvius and other places of interest, and 'by a high favour'[52] included letters of Faraday's with his own to be sent back by a courier. Faraday was aware of 'the glorious opportunity I enjoy of improving in the knowledge of chemistry and the sciences with Sir H. Davy'.[53] All the references to 'Sir H. Davy' are a reminder that Faraday never knew plain Mr Davy; he was already knighted and married and had published his *Chemical Philosophy* in 1812 and his *Agricultural Chemistry* in 1813, the year Faraday was appointed.[54] Faraday was with him in his work on iodine, on the diamond and in the research leading to the safety lamp; but Davy's great theoretical work was already done, published in journals and then in books, by the time Faraday joined him. On their return Davy was still a hero in many respects, as well as tutor and patron.

4 Faraday becomes an equal

Once back at the Royal Institution, with thoughts of a return to bookbinding dismissed[55] (luckily in view of the impending appearance of machine-made binding cases, which were a factor in the great cheapening of books by about 1830), Faraday assisted Davy with his work on the safety lamp. In a lecture on this, Faraday said that it was,

> the result of experimental deduction. It originated in no accident, nor was it forwarded by any, but was the consequence of a regular scientific investigation . . . an instance for Bacon's spirit to behold. Every philosopher must view it as a mark of subjection set by science in the strongest holds of nature.[56]

In his copy of Paris's *Life* Faraday bound in various papers connected with the safety lamp.[57] In 1816 Davy gave him an analysis of same caustic lime from Tuscany,[58]

> at a time when my fear was greater than my confidence, and both far greater than my knowledge; at a time also when I had no thought of ever writing an original paper on science. The addition of his own comments and the publication of the paper encouraged me to go on making, from time to time, other slight communications . . . their transference from the 'Quarterly' into other journals increased my boldness.[59]

In papers on the lamp and on the flame Davy referred to Faraday's assistance.[60] This candour was and is not always found in eminent men of science, and we can see Davy bringing along a promising student. Faraday later acknowledged Sergeant Anderson's assistance, but he never encouraged him to write a paper: Davy was treating Faraday as more than a mere assistant. In 1817, Davy also recommended 'a gentleman' to take private tuition from Faraday, in the manner of a supervisor giving an opportunity to a research student. Faraday wrote to Abbott: 'I am engaged to give him lessons in mineralogy and chemistry thrice a week in the evening, for a few months . . . our lessons do not commence till eight o'clock, and, as my gentleman is in the immediate neighbourhood, I am at liberty till that hour'.[61] Faraday was therefore teaching him at his house.

In letters bound into the Paris volume, Davy wrote from Frankfurt on 5 June 1818 to Faraday, who was holding the fort in London. The letter has no heading, and ends 'I am very sincerely yours, H. Davy'[62] rather than anything more affectionate. Humphry's letters to John Davy, by contrast, always began 'My dear John', and ended in a variety of ways, including on 18 March 1814: 'Tell me what you are doing, and what you wish; and command me as your affectionate friend, and love me as your very affectionate brother'[63] to the more usual, on 11 August 1821: 'Pray . . . believe me to be, My dear John, Your affectionate Brother and Friend, H. Davy'.[64]

Other letters to Faraday from this European trip, however, began to be less formal. Writing from Rome, he asked Faraday to buy annuities and was delighted to get independent confirmation of his student's capacities: 'Mr Hatchett's letter contained praises of you which were very gratifying to me & Sir believe me there is no one more interested in your success and well fare than your sincere well wisher and friend H. Davy'.[65] Charles Hatchett's opinion, like that of an external examiner, changed the tone of the correspondence from that of a master and pupil to that of senior and junior colleague. Davy's letters now generally began, 'Dear Mr Faraday', and ended 'I am dear Mr Faraday your sincere well wisher and friend H. Davy', making his status not so different from John's. The new tone is shown in a letter from Italy of 13 May 1819: 'Pray when you write me give me any scientific news — for neither journals nor transactions reach this place'.[66] And 2 days later, for he was a good correspondent, he groused to Faraday about W.T. Brande, Professor at the Royal Institution. Brande had published without authority what Davy had written on manuscripts found at Herculaneum. Davy was 'more vexed . . . than I can well express', and hoped he would not again be treated 'with so little ceremony', but asked Faraday not to take it further.[67]

Now that Faraday was in his confidence, he could discuss chemical theory as with an equal:

> Be so good as to say to Mr Brande that I have received his letter & that I do not consider myself as *adopting* the opinion of Berzelius in regarding silica as acting the part of an acid. I think Mr Smithson is the first person who made this statement, & long before Berzelius I pointed out the analogies between the silicious & Boracic bases — whatever perfectly neutralizes an alkali may be regarded as possessing the opposite chemical powers; but the term *acid* applies to physical properties such as sour &c. & I certainly never meant to attribute any acid qualities to silica but merely to express that it acted the part of an acid in producing solution of an oxide &c.[68]

Faraday's interest in and approach to scientific terminology followed Davy's example. Davy chose names for potassium and chlorine and iodine, rejecting 'azote', and restricting 'acid'.

Davy's Presidency of the Royal Society

In June 1820 Davy returned hurriedly from Italy. Banks was dying and after Wollaston (the caretaker President) had withdrawn from the contest Davy was easily elected President of the Royal Society in November.[69] We may sympathise with those like Dalton and Faraday who declined responsible positions in the scientific establishment to pursue research, but there is nothing immoral in turning in middle life towards the management of science, and even enjoying the exercise of power. The election of a man without a university training and of obscure provincial origins seems at first sight astonishing. Through Banks's long reign — he had been elected a few days before Davy was born — Paris had been the centre of the scientific world. However, Davy, who in his juvenile notebook had written 'Newton & Davy'[70] had made chemistry as much a British as a French science. Davy was idolised for his sheer brilliance and was the only man of the day to be knighted for his scientific work. He was an apostle of applied science who had invented the safety lamp. His position at the Royal Institution was no doubt an advantage given its close connection to the Royal Society. These are discussed by Sophie Forgan in her chapter. Contemporaries entertained great and impossible hopes for a new President,[71] the Newton of chemistry perhaps, who would reconcile the disparate interests within the Royal Society. Newton had not always been aimiable and straightforward in his dealings and Davy soon found himself between hostile camps.

In 1821 Faraday got married and was made a full member of the Sandemanian Church. Of his marriage Davy wrote to him, in a letter bound in Paris's volume: 'I hope you will continue quite well & do much during the summer & I wish you in your new state all that happiness which I am sure you deserve'.[72] In May of that year Faraday became Superintendent of the House and Laboratory at the Royal Institution. In part one of the *Philosophical Transactions* there appeared his first paper to be published by the Royal Society.[73] All these things might have indicated Faraday reaching maturity. Davy knew what he ought to do, for that summer he watched eagles and wrote a poem:

> Their memory left a type and a desire:
> So should I wish towards the light to rise,
> Instructing younger spirits to aspire
> Where I could never reach amidst the skies,
> And joy below to see them lifted higher,
> Seeking the light of purest glory's prize.[74]

The prospect of marriage, however, began to detach Faraday from Davy. He wrote to Sarah in December 1820: 'As I ponder and think of you, chlorides, trials, oil, Davy, steel, miscellanea, mercury, and fifty other professional fancies swim before and drive me further and further into the quandary of stupidness'.[75]

Things began to go wrong between Davy and Faraday when Faraday ventured into electromagnetism. During Wollaston's brief tenure of the Presidency of the Royal Society, the Council (which included Davy) awarded the Copley Medal to Oersted for his discovery of electromagnetism. Both Davy and Wollaston (plate 8) were highly interested, as veterans of electrochemistry. Though friends (Davy converted Wollaston into a keen fisherman, and portrayed him and Babington in his dialogues) they were also rivals. For example Wollaston was the preferred Presidential candidate of the active men of science in the Royal Society. Wollaston hoped to make a wire rotate on its axis when it carried a current in a magnetic field, and tried the experiment with Davy at the Royal Institution, with no result.[76] Faraday may or may not have been present: see Williams's and Gooding's discussions in Chapters 5 and 6. In September 1821 Faraday succeeded in producing an electromagnetic rotation.[77] Davy persisted in regarding this as merely completing Wollaston's experiment, and friends of Wollaston saw Faraday as trespassing. Then came the liquefaction of chlorine.[78] There the kind of note from Davy which had been welcomed with Faraday's first paper was not now welcome. Davy had not allowed any of his credit to go to those who vaguely believed potash to be compound or all forces to be one. Now Faraday was not allowing any of his credit to go to Davy or Wollaston for predictions that he saw as equally vague.

In 1823 Faraday let his name be put forward for the Royal Society. The certificate was organised by Phillips. Davy's friend Babington was one of the proposers. The President did not by convention propose candidates. But Banks had expected to be consulted and had been free with his opinions. To Banks and Davy this seemed vital if unworthy candidates were to be

Plate 8   William Hyde Wollaston. R.J. Lane after drawing by Francis Chantrey made with camera lucida. Royal Institution, Faraday Album. H:86.

excluded.[79] The lack of consultation was an affront to Davy. A new President who failed to wield a veto in such a case would have seemed weak, so to Davy the affair must have looked like a deliberate challenge to his authority. It was particularly unfortunate that his own protégé was being thus proposed, because the air had not been fully cleared after the charges of unfairness to Wollaston. We do not need to suppose extreme jealousy in Davy when it is obvious that embarrassment was to be expected. The Royal Institution was felt by some to be too powerfully connected to the Royal Society. To put up a

Royal Institution man who had affronted a Cambridge man was unwise from
Davy's point of view. It forced him into being against Faraday's nomination
because he would otherwise be assumed to be behind it.

The last item in Faraday's copy of Paris is a draft of a note by Davy. In the
hands of both Faraday (who drafted it) and Davy, this clarified the latter's
remarks about Faraday's alleged plagiarism of Wollaston.[80] Then in
Faraday's hand there is a chronology of these events.[81] Then a complete blank.
Paris's volume has nothing more of Davy in it. This does not vindicate the
confidence in the 'superior moral feelings of philosophic men'[82] that Faraday
had expressed to Davy when they met in 1812. Nor does it support Tyndall's
belief that 'the differences of really honourable and sane men are never beyond
healing'.[83] Faraday wrote in 1835:

> I was by no means in the same relation as to scientific communication with Sir
> Humphry Davy after I became a Fellow of the Royal Society as before that
> period; but whenever I have ventured to follow in the path which Sir Humphry has
> trod, I have done so with respect and with the highest admiration of his talents.[84]

On this chilly note, and with further ripostes to John Davy over priority at
various times, the relationship ended.

5 Conclusion

What did Faraday learn to avoid? One thing was the responsibility for running
science which Davy had welcomed. He thus avoided clashes between personal
feeling and obligations to other institutions. He also avoided being made to
feel socially out of place. Davy's continuing respect for Faraday is indicated
by his getting him appointed as Secretary of the Athenaeum in 1823[85] and the
Directorship of the Laboratory of the Royal Institution in 1825. Sophie
Forgan shows in her chapter that Faraday assumed considerable responsibility in running the scientific activities of the Royal Institution. Faraday
also learnt that he must avoid the sort of entanglements which he had had with
Davy. When, for example the young Huxley, believing that he had a key to
perpetual motion, came boldly to see Faraday, he received courtesy but no
fathering.[86] Walter White, Assistant Secretary of the Royal Society, recorded
in his diary a conversation with an eminent chemist in 1872: 'Dr Stenhouse
says Faraday was selfish and narrow-minded. That a man once went to him, as
he himself had gone to Davy, and that F. sent the young man to [Thomas]
Graham, of which incident Graham made a standing joke'.[87] Faraday worked
on his own with Anderson as not much more than a pair of hands. He wrote
that he could never work, as some professors did, through students[88] and he
made it a rule never to write testimonials. Although Tyndall was in various
ways his heir Faraday's involvement with him was much less than Davy's had
been with Faraday. This proud and humble man was prickly about his honour
in a way those of higher social standing had no need to be. In this

respect Faraday was friendly but private — being in this way not unlike Davy, trailing lonely around Europe at the end of his life. Sylvanus Thompson found magnanimity in Faraday's later attitude to Davy.[89] Most of us might deplore its absence on both sides, regret the end of a story which had involved generosity and affection, and mark how inarticulate two of the greatest orators of science found themselves in an emotional crisis. As with the Gosses,[90] the clash of two temperaments led to no offer of compromise or truce.

Notes

I thank the Royal Institution for permission to work on the papers of Davy and Faraday.

1. Bence Jones (1870a), **1**: 210.
2. Bence Jones (1871), vii.
3. 'Gallery of literary characters. No. LXIX. Michael Faraday, F.R.S., Hon.D.C.L. Oxon, Etc. Etc.', *Fraser's Mag.*, 1836, **13**: 224.
4. Bence Jones (1870a), **2**: 458.
5. Thompson (1898), 273.
6. Tyndall (1894), 43.
7. Fullmer (1969), 17 list the biographies of Davy; see also D.M. Knight, 'Humphry Davy', *DSB*, **3**: 598–604 and Forgan (1980).
8. Paris (1831), 33–5, 80.
9. Levere (1984); Stansfield (1984), Chapter 9.
10. Bence Jones (1870a), **1**: 8.
11. Bence Jones (1870b), **1**: v.
12. Berman (1978), Chapter 5.
13. Miller, D.P. (1983).
14. Morrell & Thackray (1981).
15. Davy, J. (1836), **2**: 126.
16. Bence Jones (1870a), **1**: 14–15; contrast Caley (1967), Chapter 1.
17. McCosh (1984), 4ff, 58ff, 69.
18. Tyndall (1894), 4.
19. Morrell (1972).
20. Lenoir (1982), 188ff, 195ff.
21. Crosland (1978, 1980).
22. RI MS HD 21d, 269; Fullmer (1969), 17.
23. R. Siegfried, 'John Davy', *DSB*, **3**: 604–5; R. Hunt, 'John Davy', *DNB*, **14**: 195–6; 'John Davy', *Proc. Roy. Soc.*, 1867–8, **16**: lxxix–lxxxi.
24. *Ibid.*, lxxxi.
25. *Ibid.*
26. Dawkins (1976).
27. Knight (1980).
28. Bence Jones (1870a), **1**: 420.
29. Faraday to Matteucci, 3 March 1853, in Bence Jones (1870a), **2**: 319–21, 321.
30. Bence Jones (1870a), **2**: 447.
31. *Ibid.*, 445.
32. *Ibid.*, **1**: 46.
33. *Ibid.*
34. Faraday to Paris, 29 December 1829, *Correspondence*, **1**: 97.

35. Gassiot to Tyndall, 28 November 1867, in Tyndall (1894), 4–5.
36. *Ibid.*
37. Paris (1831); Faraday's copy (RI MS F8) was the quarto edition, in one volume.
38. RI MS F8 282ff; cf RI MS HD 10, Davy's Laboratory Notes, 1805–1809, 1809–1812, bound and annotated by Faraday in 1829, and his Papers, bound and annotated 1832. On Davy's technique, Paris (1831), 96ff.
39. Faraday to Abbott, 25 January 1815, *Correspondence*, **1**: 26.
40. Thompson (1898), 20.
41. Dumas (1885), 72.
42. W.P. Courtney, 'Jane Davy', *DNB*, **14**: 193–4.
43. Faraday to Abbott, 25 January 1815, *Correspondence*, **1**: 26.
44. Faraday to Abbott, 9 April 1813, *Correspondence*, **1**: 15.
45. Faraday to Huxtable, 13 February 1815, in Bence Jones (1870a), **1**: 193–5, 195.
46. *Ibid.*, 194.
47. Faraday to Abbott, 23 February 1815, in Bence Jones (1870a), **1**: 195–8, 198.
48. Bence Jones (1870a), **1**: 92.
49. *Ibid.*, 97.
50. *Ibid.*, 122.
51. *Ibid.*, 135.
52. Faraday to his mother, 14 April 1814, in Bence Jones (1870a), **1**: 123–6, 123.
53. Bence Jones (1870a), **1**: 209.
54. Davy, H. (1812, 1813).
55. Bence Jones (1870a), **1**: 209.
56. *Ibid.*, 240–1.
57. RI MS F8.
58. Faraday (1816).
59. Note added by Faraday in reprinting Faraday (1816), *ERCP*, 1–5, 1.
60. Davy, H. (1816), 4; (1817), 61; (1818a), 171; (1818b), 319 get steadily warmer — the last two are in the text rather than a note. Cf Thompson (1898), 96f.
61. Faraday to Abbott, 25 November 1817, in Bence Jones (1870a), **1**: 252.
62. Davy to Faraday, 5 June 1818, RI MS F8 326.
63. H. Davy to J. Davy, 18 March 1814, in Davy, J. (1836), **1**: 481–3, 483.
64. H. Davy to J. Davy, 11 August 1821, in Davy, J. (1836), **2**: 156–7, 157.
65. Davy to Faraday, 29 October 1818, RI MS F8 358c and e.
66. Davy to Faraday, 13 May 1819, RI MS F8 364g.
67. Davy to Faraday, 15 May 1819, RI MS F8 364j. In this letter Davy also wrote 'It gives me great pleasure to hear that you are comfortable at the Royal Institution & I trust you will not only do something good and honourable for yourself; but likewise for Science' (368c).
68. Davy to Faraday, 16 November 1819, RI MS F8 368b and g.
69. Hall, M.B. (1984), 16–22.
70. RI MS HD 20b, 182.
71. Lyons (1944), 122; Miller, D.P. (1983); Fullmer (1980); Hall, M.B. (1984).
72. Davy to Faraday, 18 July 182[1], RI MS F8 376.
73. Faraday (1821a).
74. Davy, J. (1836), **2**: 157.
75. Faraday to S. Barnard, December 1820, in Bence Jones (1870a), **1**: 322.
76. Williams, L.P. (1965), 153ff.
77. Faraday (1821b).
78. Faraday (1823a).
79. Crosland (1983), 176, 185 (n.10); Lyons (1944), 183, 198, 211, 213, 231; Weld (1848), **2**: 154, 163. Thompson (1898), 56–9 is misleading; Williams, L.P. (1965), 160 seems right in saying Davy was offended.

80. RI MS F8 382.
81. RI MS F8 392.
82. Faraday to Paris, 23 December 1829, *Correspondence*, **1**: 97.
83. Tyndall (1894), 48.
84. Bence Jones (1870b), **1**: 340.
85. Personal communication from Dr Frank Greenaway. Faraday gave this position up once the club was established.
86. Huxley (1900), **1**: 22.
87. White, W. (1898), 256; but cf 69, 120f.
88. Faraday to Becker, 25 October 1860, *Correspondence*, **2**: 749.
89. Thompson (1898), 59.
90. Gosse (1907).

3

Faraday — From Servant to Savant: The Institutional Context

Sophie Forgan

On 25 August 1867 the revered Faraday died. His funeral was, in the words of his niece Jane Barnard, a 'strictly private and plain' affair.[1] The simple funeral cortège left the house at Hampton Court, and, on its way to Highgate Cemetery where the philosopher was to be laid to rest, proceeded up Albemarle Street, paused outside the Royal Institution to pick up some mourners, and then continued on its way. John Tyndall noted it is his diary, but stayed away along with the rest of the scientific community at the request of the family.[2] Thus for the last time the paths of Faraday and the Royal Institution intersected. It was a richly symbolic occasion and encapsulates key characteristics of the man himself and of his relationship to the Institution.

There are, however, problems when attempting to analyse those characteristics and to examine the relationship between any individual and an institution. If one focuses primarily on the individual, the institution is apt to become merely 'context', of secondary importance, relevant in so far as it aided or obstructed the individual in his chosen course. The individual's work and achievements form the main subject of interest. If, by contrast one is more interested in the institution, a different set of questions arises. The danger here is that the individual may become reduced to the role of hapless pawn, swept along by the larger forces of institutional direction. These forces are often construed as historical processes. Nevertheless, individuals and histories of institutions are both still often treated in the biographical idiom. After all, both have personalities, whether corporate or individual; they are born, grow, have anniversaries, weddings and jubilees, enlarge their houses, suffer financial crises and grow thin or prosperous with age. In this idiom it is easy to identify an individual too closely with the institution, or to invest the institution with the individual's personality. Recently much original work has tended to favour the collective biography or the institutional study. We are now used to examining context, and familiar with the dangers of being either too limited or misleading in approach. However, with regard to an individual, one needs to consider afresh the precise ways in which historically one can look at a person in context. What is the significance of the context? What is the extent of the relevant context? Is it simply descriptive in nature? Or does it have an obligatory, imperative force?

The problem is complicated in this case by the Royal Institution's own recent historiography. In this work, *Social Change and Scientific Organization*, Morris Berman offers a radically different interpretation of the Institution's significance.[3] Through the Royal Institution, he argues, the landed aristocracy attempted to contain social unrest. Then, in the 1820s and 1830s, the middle classes of utilitarian sympathies used science to reinforce their professional ambitions. He sees the Institution as developing into a metropolitan powerhouse of expertise for the scientific management of the problems of an industrialising society. In this analysis, men such as Faraday were used to provide technical solutions to what were really social and political problems. According to Berman, Faraday was forced to spend a large part of his time on work which diverted him from scientific research so that he was torn between his personal scientific quest and dutiful loyalties to Government and Institution. For Berman the context is imperative, not descriptive. His view rightly emphasises aspects of the mentality of the period, the importance of certain groups in the management and the sheer amount of time Faraday had to spend on practical work. His interpretation does, however, ignore other important aspects of the Institution's history. It postulates a chronology which ends the 'significant' history of the Royal Institution in 1844, and it omits much of the essential context of metropolitan science in the nineteenth century. Berman's portrait of Faraday does present us with real problems. This is not the place for a lengthy discussion, but I shall try to deal with some of the main questions in this essay. Did the Royal Institution prevent Faraday from doing the work he wanted, or did it direct him in particular ways? Or by contrast, was Faraday's experimental career possible only in the Royal Institution context? What characterised the relationship between Faraday and the Institution and what effect did he have on the Royal Institution's development? To what extent did his view of the Royal Institution's proper objectives differ from that of the Managers or from his colleague and fellow professor, W.T. Brande.

I propose to discuss these questions by looking at the resources available to Faraday, the demands made on this time, and the degree he was subject to managerial control. Finally, I shall examine those intangible factors which turned his environment into a fruitful workplace and a nursery of ideas, and will suggest a way of looking at the very unusual nature of Faraday's institutional context.

1 Faraday's resources

Faraday's resources included salary, laboratory facilities, apparatus, materials and the services of an assistant. As an assistant in Davy's laboratory

Faraday's starting salary in 1813 was twenty one shillings per week.[4] On his return from Europe in 1815, he was reappointed at thirty shillings per week with the official title of 'Assistant and Superintendent of the Apparatus of the Laboratory and Mineralogical Collection'.[5] This grandiose title meant that apart from laboratory duties he was to look after the increasing stock of apparatus and mineralogical specimens. Faraday was also given rooms in the House of the Institution. During this period, he assisted Davy and Brande, as well as preparing experiments for the lectures given at the Royal Institution. When Davy withdrew from active work within the Institution, the chemist apothecary Brande became the dominant professorial figure. In 1821 Faraday was appointed 'Superintendent' of the house and laboratory under Brande's direction.[6] In 1825 he was appointed Director of the Laboratory after Brande had obtained a post and a house at the Royal Mint.[7] Faraday's salary was £100 per annum. This was reasonable when compared with Brande's £150 per annum, a sum reduced from £200 in 1824 in one of the Royal Institution's periodic economy drives.[8] His rooms were more than adequate, with coals and candles provided (a perk worth £30–50 per annum). His salary as Director of the Laboratory remained the same for nearly 40 years. It was not until 1853 that it was raised to £300 per annum.[9] However, his income through the Royal Institution was increased in 1833 by the Fuller endowment. This nominated Faraday as the first 'Fullerian Professor of Chemistry', at a salary of £100 per annum.[10] Salary alone may seem to have been inadequate, especially for a married man, but it should be noted that Faraday received considerable income for lectures given in the Royal Institution. He received £100 for any Christmas course of Juvenile lectures, and usually a sum of 100 guineas (50 in the 1830s) for any afternoon course of lectures. He also carried out commercial, consultancy and analytical work. From 1835 he received a Civil List pension of £300 per annum.

It is easy to over-emphasise the importance of the size of his income. Faraday's way of life was simple, any excess he gave to charity, and the absence of reference to money matters suggest that he was unburdened by financial matters. What is important was his perception of its fitness and appropriateness. The evidence suggests that he was quite aware that his official salary as Director of the Laboratory was derisory, but that he was unconcerned on his own account and anxious not to impose any burden on an institution which was in debt for nearly 40 years.[11] The Managers in 1832 regretted not being able to pay a more fitting salary, though they then happily forgot about it for another 20 years.[12] As Faraday put it in 1858, 'It was only quite recently that the thought of bettering it had occurred to the authorities'.[13] However, the thought of suggesting an increase did not occur to him either.

Faraday was rather more fortunate with regard to laboratory space and facilities. The Royal Institution was one of the very few well-equipped laboratories in London in the 1810s. The London Institution did not finish building until 1819 and its Managers were extremely cautious about commencing laboratory work and appointing permanent staff. It was not until 1840 that W.R. Grove was appointed as its first professor.[14] University College and King's College with their laboratories only came into existence in the late 1820s. The Surrey Institution was in a state of decline and had collapsed by 1823. The Russell Institution appears never to have had a laboratory. Apart from the patronage occasionally offered by wealthy patron–practitioners, at the time Faraday was seeking a scientific position opportunities were very few.[15] At the Royal Institution Faraday had a laboratory of 80 square metres in the basement. This had all the expected facilities (furnace, gas supply, etc.) as well as an impressive collection of apparatus and mineralogical specimens.[16] At some time soon after 1820 the old servants hall was converted into a new laboratory of 30 square metres specifically for Faraday's magnetic researches. He therefore had a personal laboratory specifically for his own work. Assistance in the laboratory was also paid for by the Institution. From 1827 Faraday had the ideal assistant in the person of Sergeant Anderson — silent, obedient, careful and faithful.[17] The Institution also paid for chemicals and apparatus; and expenditure for these items ran between £100 and £200 annually in the 1830s. When expensive pieces of apparatus were needed, the normal procedure was to launch a special fund. In later years this sometimes led to the unhappy spectacle of a professor contributing to a fund for his own apparatus.[18] Experimental research was not expected to cost large sums of money. It could not in any case be predicted what sums might be required, but when a specific piece of apparatus was needed, the patronage of managers and members of the Institution was relied upon. The exercise of restraint with regard to cost became the natural habit of its professors. To Faraday, frugality and deft mechanical ingenuity were part of his character and religious outlook which abhorred extravagance and ostentatious show. But it was the norm in the London scientific world, for apparatus and specimens to be borrowed or lent freely. As apparatus became more complex and expensive the professors of the Institution increasingly made do with 'sealing wax and string'.[19] For Tyndall, Faraday's successor, this was almost a manly attribute, as proper a characteristic in the physicist as hardiness in the geologist who tramped miles over moor or mountain.[20]

2 Duties and obligations

The demands on Faraday's time were numerous. J.H. Gladstone, one of Faraday's earliest biographers, paints a charming picture of Faraday's working day.[21] In Gladstone's account, Faraday started off with breakfast at 8.00am. Afterwards he did the rounds of the house to see that all was in order before going to the laboratory. He might then be interrupted by some visitor, but normally worked until dinner at 2.30pm. The afternoon was spent writing letters in his study or going to the council meeting of a learned society. He then returned to the laboratory until evening approached when he retired upstairs again to his family. This description is less than revealing about the nature of the demands on his time. Such an agreeable schedule was derived from Gladstone's knowledge of Faraday in later life. It contrasts sharply with the references, especially frequent in the 1820s, to the lack of time on account of lectures, private work, journal business, experimental researches, and the many callers who felt free to call upon him at any time. As he complained in 1828, 'there is no end to them in this house'.[22]

Demands on his time varied in type and intensity throughout his years at the Royal Institution. Some he could control, others he felt an obligation to fulfil. From 1821 Faraday became assistant–superintendent of the House (the 'assistant' later disappeared from the title). This unpaid post meant that Faraday was generally responsible for seeing to the upkeep of the building and the smooth running of the Institution. The servants were under his control, drunk or sleepy porters had to be sacked, new servants engaged and emergencies coped with. During the summer recess, estimates for repairs authorised by the Managers had to be obtained and the work carried out. Minor requests for new shelves, cases, seat cushions occurred throughout the year. On occasion the work included more detailed investigation. An example was the vexed question of ventilating the lecture theatre, which was prone when crowded to send its audience to sleep or chill them with induced draughts in an effort to keep them awake. In general such work comprised what the head of any medium-sized establishment would carry out as a matter of course. Naturally every penny had to be accounted for. Faraday, careful and meticulous in this respect as in all others, does not appear to have had difficulties with the Treasurers of the Royal Institution.[23]

The lecture programmes had highest priority in the eyes of the Managers and were altogether more demanding. Several types of lecture were presented concurrently; these included Brande's morning laboratory lectures for medical students, the afternoon courses of lectures, the Friday Evening Discourses and the Christmas series of Juvenile lectures.[24] Here I am concerned with the impact of the lectures on Faraday's time and not with their content and purpose. The lecture season ran from January to June, with the exception of the morning laboratory lectures which started in October. From 1824 Faraday began to share the morning laboratory lectures and from 1831 he started giving a regular afternoon course most years. The Friday Evening Discourses were to a large extent his own personal creation. These latter, as Berman has noted, proved to be a 'winning formula' for the Royal Institution, instrumental in attracting new members, and in providing a superb vehicle through which scientific discoveries could be publicised and newsworthy practical discoveries applauded.[25] In total Faraday gave more than 100 discourses, the first in 1825 and the last in 1862, with perhaps four per season. After 1850, he rarely gave more than two per season, generally the opening and closing sessions. He also gave a course of afternoon lectures until 1853 (excepting 1841). Courses varied in length but normally consisted of 6–8 lectures. In addition he contributed to the Juvenile lectures (six in length) giving a total of nineteen series between 1827/28 and 1860/61. Therefore

Faraday's lecturing year included the following: 30–40 laboratory lectures (in 1835 this was reduced to 12 and stopped altogether in 1840); six afternoon lectures; four or five discourses and perhaps also the Christmas lectures. A high proportion of these were one-off lectures. Only the laboratory lectures were repeatable, though some of the courses covered the same areas in different years. A second important feature of the lectures, particularly of the discourses, was the number and quality of experimental demonstrations. Faraday's lecture notes show up to 30 or 40 experiments and diagrams used in a single lecture.[26] As David Gooding points out in Chapter 6 this involved time-consuming preparation and careful rehearsal.

Apart from actually performing in the lecture theatre (a subject I will return to) Faraday had to devote a certain amount of time and effort to the general organisation of the lectures at the Royal Institution. In 1828, a Lecture Committee was established, consisting of several Managers together with Brande and Faraday. They had few problems finding people prepared to lecture; offers to do so were numerous, so that it was a question of deciding whom to accept. A Committee also arranged the Friday Evenings, but here the choice and details of arrangement often fell on Faraday. Later, when the Royal Institution Secretary was an active and efficient person, such as John Barlow or Henry Bence Jones, the resident Professor received much assistance.[27]

The Friday Evenings were complex and varied occasions; additional demonstrations in the Library were sometimes put on, and an interesting selection of objects exhibited. From 1826 Faraday recorded all these objects in a notebook and was probably responsible for this aspect of the evening's entertainment.[28] After 1840 Faraday's record stops and in that decade it became a duty of the assistant-secretary to seek out objects for the Library table.[29] Such exhibitions were one of the ingredients which went into making the Friday Evenings such successful occasions. Equally important was the role of the resident Professor. His presence, sociability and affability to all present enhanced the occasion and lent it a distinctive quality. Faraday was alive to the importance of setting the right tone. In the General Monthly Meetings of members (when new members were admitted and presents received), he often gave a little demonstration or short talk to enliven these otherwise quite routine occasions.

Finally, there were many demands on Faraday's time for practical advice, commercial analysis, expert testimony and for public service duties in general. In the 1820s these practical activities were wide ranging and extremely time consuming.[30] Some were due to Brande's presence and professional interests. Another was work commissioned by the Royal Society. In the 1820s the Royal Institution may be considered the workshop of the Royal Society. The links between the two were close: Davy was the President of the Royal Society, Brande one of the two Secretaries from 1816 to 1826; Davies Gilbert (Davy's successor as President of the Royal Society) was also a Royal Institution

Manager, and his brother-in-law, John Guillemard, the Royal Institution's Treasurer for two brief spells. Such interconnections may be multiplied. Since the Royal Society had no laboratory facilities, it was natural to turn to the Royal Institution for people who had the facilities available or the space to have them constructed. Faraday's work on optical glass is the best-known example, but refusal to continue with it together with his support for John Herschel's unsuccessful campaign in the 1830 Presidential election, signalled an end to the close connection between the two bodies. He was elected to the Royal Society Council in 1833 and 1834, but declined nomination finally and permanently after that time. By contrast Faraday never refused to give advice and do practical work for the Government. To Faraday as a very loyal subject this was patriotic. But it was also a moral duty, to use science in the service of man.

The uses of science

It would have been very odd if Faraday had *not* been consulted about problems to which, erroneously or otherwise, it was believed that science might provide a solution. As Gooding has shown, in the 1820s among men working in electrical science, there was no clear differentiation between theoretically motivated investigation and interests relating to technology.[31] This was made all the more true for those who knew little about science but were surrounded by the technological marvels of the steam engine and the electric telegraph. Another reason is that reliable advice was not readily available elsewhere. The medical profession, for example, was notoriously partisan and quarrelsome. When there was a serious explosion in 1843 at the Royal Gunpowder Factory at Waltham Abbey, it was natural to turn to the well-established and independent figure of Faraday for advice on the safety of the buildings.[32] That episode probably persuaded the Home Secretary to appoint Faraday with Charles Lyell as the investigators of the Haswell Colliery explosion in 1844 (there was no School of Mines until 1849, and the Geological Survey had only been set up in 1835). Faraday continued to serve in this sort of role but grew increasingly cautious about becoming embroiled in thorny problems such as the ventilation of the new Houses of Parliament, or with the wilder flights of fancy of the War Office.[33]

Another type of request made of Faraday was to analyse substances chemically. These were sent in to him by a great variety of people, some Royal Institution members, but the majority not. Such requests were the result of the open-house, expert consultant policy Brande had fostered in the 1820s. These requests diminished by the end of the 1830s but continued to trickle in through the 1840s and 1850s. During these decades the requests mirrored changing concerns. For example, preoccupation with water analysis was replaced with problems of speculative archaeology, such as whether earth from mounds in Jerusalem contained ancient ashes (Faraday thought not[34]). Faraday was

never free from requests for advice. Though he could decline the most irksome
of these and did so from the 1830s, the majority of demands for practical work
certainly had nothing to do with his research interests. Some were mildly
interesting from a chemical point of view, and others furnished good material
for Friday Evening Discourses.[35] Faraday was quite clear about the need to
dispose of his time both economically and in his own interests. He was, for
example, extremely firm about the conditions on which he would consent to
teach cadets at Woolwich. 'Time is my only estate', as he wrote to Thomas
Drummond in 1829.[36]

Yet certain of Berman's conclusions are debatable. I doubt that Faraday,
despite his 'true Sandemanian self',[37] presented as coherent a utilitarian image
as Berman claims. Berman also over-emphasises the importance of the Royal
Institution when asserting that virtually single handedly it made science into
an instrument of utilitarian policy. In any case, far from being a single-minded
entity, the Royal Institution operated at several levels and in quite different
ways. Even though physically in one building, the various departments of the
Institution led a semi-independent existence, separately financed and accounted for. For example, the laboratory had two capital accounts. Only one of
these was under the direct control of the Managers, and the other had its own
Treasurer distinct from the main Royal Institution Treasurer. The Library
retained a proprietorial structure far longer than the rest of the Institution.[38]
The Board of Managers, responsible for running the Royal Institution and
appointing its staff, though containing members of certain definable interest
groups, continued to be a remarkably mixed body. One must therefore ask
whether Faraday was subject to control by the Managers. How did his
relationship with them change? And to what extent did his views of the proper
functions of the Institution differ from theirs?

Faraday in the Royal Institution

During his early years Faraday was the apprentice and journeyman. His
position was a humble one as laboratory assistants were not highly regarded.
As the Institution became more associated with Brande's utilitarian interests
in the 1820s, Faraday became more involved in the management. He was
present at Managers meetings and served on committees, but also he was
disillusioned by what he saw as Brande's excesses. By the end of the 1820s the
Managers regarded Faraday as Brande's equal though his junior in professorial years. Berman makes much of the fact that there is no mention of
Faraday's research achievements in the Managers Minutes.[39] But this is not
surprising. Research was regarded as the professors' own affair. Hence the
minutes were not the place where comments or congratulations about it would
be made. However, from 1831 Faraday was one of the brightest stars of
London's scientific world; a discoverer internationally acclaimed. This is
reflected in a subtle change in the tone of the Managers Minutes; there we find

Faraday was gradually transmuted from plain 'Michael Faraday', to 'Mr Professor Faraday' and finally to 'Professor Faraday'.[40] The Managers were well aware how much they owed Faraday. During his breakdown of health in the 1840s, Faraday was relieved of many of his lectures, and moreover the appointment in 1842 of an active and efficient secretary, John Barlow, took over much of the day-to-day business

The Managers, however, considered the diffusion of useful knowledge by means of lectures to be vital. The Institution needed also to be seen to flourish in that social sense, as a species of club, which signalled to contemporaries its general success and usefulness. There was no reason to make any overt policy changes. The Institution was doing very well as it was, the idea of any other sort of organisation specifically for the support of research was foreign to the Managers. It was only towards the end of the 1840s that consideration arose again of the objectives and proper activities of the Institution and the role of the professors within it. By this time the educational activities of the Royal Institution (such as the morning laboratory lectures) were being displaced by the activities of new professional and educational institutions. The diffusion of knowledge by means of general lectures needed revitalising.[41] The result was the statement, for the first time, that disinterested scientific research was the prime function of the professors.[42] In 1853 Faraday ensured that the man chosen to replace Brande, who would probably be his own successor, Tyndall, was one for whom research came uppermost.[43] The lecture programmes were gradually directed towards including, in addition to natural science and newsworthy topics, the best of the new human sciences which were so characteristic of the vigorous culture of mid-Victorian Britain.

During the 1850s the character of the Board of Managers underwent another sea-change. Increasingly men were elected who were properly knowledgeable about science. A number of these included Faraday's personal friends or scientific colleagues: W.R. Grove (first elected 1845), Charles Wheatstone (1847), J.P. Gassiot (1853), Warren De la Rue (1856), J.H. Gladstone (1860) and Henry Bence Jones (1854). Bence Jones was Faraday's personal physician, solicitous friend and a notable enthusiast for the cause of scientific research. All of these were amongst the most active Managers. During these later years the Managers were differential and concerned in their attitude towards Faraday.

The keynote of Faraday's attitude towards the Institution throughout his life was loyalty. This is shown in his decision in 1827 not to accept a chair at University College. He wrote to Richard Phillips in 1828 'I am so indifferent to most things except the success of this particular house (The R Institution)'.[44] He never expressed any criticism of the Managers' decisions in public. Even in private he was the soul of discretion. Where matters of institutional policy were concerned, he gave entire support to the Managers, as for instance in his efforts to get the new Royal Institution *Journal* off the ground in 1830. In 1843 the proposal to establish a school of practical chemistry in the Institution could have threatened both his position and his occupation of the main laboratory. Yet there is no evidence that he gave any thought to such a possibility.[45] He was, however, prepared to nudge the management along the path towards the disinterested 'Advancement of science for its own sake' and used his diplomatic and linguistic skills to this end. He was also a master of the nuances of a managerial resolution, the wording of a final minute, or the drafting of a 'note', an ability perhaps obscured by the charm and sweetness of his character so apparent in his letters. However, he never forced the issue, remaining content to state objectives as he saw them and leave the initiative in the hands of the Managers.

This picture of Faraday, certainly in the last three decades, is not that of a man torn between conflicting loyalties. This is because, despite certain drawbacks, the Royal Institution was uniquely advantageous. The main laboratory quickly became his own personal territory. His magnetic laboratory had independent access from the back stairs, so that he could shut himself away in it. In the 1820s access to visitors and callers may have been easy, but I do not believe that this was so from the mid-1830s. Faraday's method of working was solitary: 'I do not think I could work in company, or think aloud, or explain my thoughts at the time'.[46] Anderson's great merit as an assistant was his silence, and days might pass with only a few words exchanged between them. As pointed out earlier the Management's attitude to the laboratory was one of non-interference. This is shown in the 1832 economy drive, when they were 'of the opinion that no reduction or observation is called for'.[47] His salary might be small considering the extensive demands on his time, but in the key area, the laboratory, Faraday had space and a freedom from interference which was invaluable.

3 The private man and the public scientist

The Institution became his real home, the place from which he could face the world or withdraw from it. Sarah lived there after their marriage in 1821. It was common to live over the shop in nineteenth-century England. It saved much time in travelling and there was no tyranny of the timetable, and last train home. But work and home were even more entwined for Faraday than one might expect in an institutional setting, and especially in his later years. At least one of his personal physicians was a Manager. Benjamin Vincent, a relative and co-religionist, filled another key position within the Institution, that of Librarian and Assistant Secretary. Vincent was doubly related to Faraday. His aunt had married Faraday's brother Robert and Vincent married as his second wife a niece of Sarah Faraday, Ellen Barnard. He was knowledgeable, efficient, loyal and his presence must have added considerably to the harmonious running of the Institution.[48]

Faraday did not retire from the Institution. He did not vacate his rooms there and remained Superintendent of the House although in the years before his death he spent increasing amounts of time at Hampton Court once the season had ended. As he declined into senescence, his duties were not taken over as we might expect by his younger colleague Tyndall. Rather they were carried out by members of his own family; Sarah Faraday and her nieces. The petty cash account books are written in Jane Barnard's hand.[49] The Institution *was* and remained both family and home.

At this time the home was more and more emphasised as the source of virtues nurtured in decent privacy as the nature of the distinction between public and private changed.[50] While it was home for Faraday, the Royal Institution was also part of the public domain. Members could come in from 10.00am to 10.00pm to use the Library; they came to hear public figures speaking in the lecture theatre; and their own distinctive social gatherings took place on Friday evenings. For Faraday, the public and private domains were not only adjacent; they overlapped. This is why Faraday's apparent withdrawal from 'public life' in London (e.g. his reluctance to dine out) should not be interpreted only as a reaction to lack of time, or to a distaste for wasting time with frivolous people. It was his way of managing and controlling this fluid division between the two domains. Withdrawal was not a retreat into solitude. It simply meant that he was not available for certain purposes. What he was available for was thereby brought into much sharper focus. People still called upon him. If it was a young man with a bright idea, Faraday generally came downstairs to the hall to talk to the caller.[51] A call upstairs to the private apartments was something to be approached in a very different spirit. This is well caught by the young Cornelia Crosse recounting her first visit in 1850:

A feeling of awe overcame me, as we ascended the long flight of stairs leading to the Upper Chambers of that famous house in Albemarle Street. With the knowledge that we were approaching the Arcana of Science, I was in no condition of sympathy with the fools who rush in, but rather felt restrained by the reverent spirits of those who fear to tread, on sacred ground. The very sound of the homely door-knocker rapped on my heart.[52]

Once inside what impressed her most was Faraday's normality, the fact that he was reading a novel, 'a touch of nature, delightfully reassuring'.[53] The contrast between the private man and the public image was thrown into sharp relief. On other occasions, the favoured might be ushered upstairs to the privacy of the apartment, after a Friday Evening Discourse for example. Meanwhile Faraday sometimes forgot and became closeted in conversation whilst his wife and niece searched for him and the intended guests, as Faraday amusingly apologised to Richard Owen: 'Oh Owen! I got into a sad hobble last night. All the time I was talking with you they were searching for me (and you & Mrs Owen) to take you upstairs'.[54]

Faraday delivering one of his Christmas Juvenile Lectures in 1856 with the Prince Consort in the Chair accompanied by the young Prince Albert (later Edward VII) and his brother

Plate 9   Faraday lecturing during the 1855/6 Christmas lectures. Alexander Blaikley.

Faraday's lectures

To most outside the private domain, public gaze centered on the lecture theatre. Success in the lecture theatre was until the last quarter of the nineteenth century a necessity for any scientist. It is well known that Faraday carefully analysed the ingredients that made up success. From the 1830s he drew large audiences, and by the 1840s was regarded as one of the finest of London's scientific speakers.[55] How did this prince among lecturers affect his listeners, and how did this ability affect Faraday's public image and the reputation of the Royal Institution? First of all, Faraday was identified with the Royal Institution. Apart from teaching commitments at Woolwich, his early lectures to the City Philosophical Society and an exceptional course of lectures for the London Institution in 1827[56], he lectured only at the Royal Institution. Unlike his contemporaries, he did not give courses or even single lectures elsewhere. Nor did he give speeches at prize givings or at ceremonies opening new buildings and the like. The theatre of the Royal Institution was the only place where his public performance could be seen. As a result, his public image became associated exclusively with the Royal Institution; it was the framework through which Faraday was seen. Second, there were elements in his performance which give us a clue as to why his hearers were powerfully affected, and there is no doubt that they were. It is commonplace to contrast Faraday's use of plain language with Davy's more flowery eloquence.

However, we should not take the contrast too far for many commentators remarked upon Faraday's passion, and his vivacity of facial expression. This suggests a man so consumed by belief and passion for his subject that his whole body was physically animated by it. Cornelia Crosse commented on 'that wonderful mobility of countenance so peculiar to him',[57] while Juliet Pollock spoke of his gleaming eyes, the hair streaming out from his head, his moving hands and irresistible eloquence.[58]

Lectures such as these were a communal experience, not just an individual one — as Juliet Pollock said, 'His audience took fire with him, and every face was flushed'.[59] This helps us better understand his impact on the audience. This was also an age in which people believed that interchanges in society were disclosures of personality.[60] Such public performances were therefore a most powerful revelation of personality, which may help explain the common addiction to public lectures. It may also explain why, although his audiences did not always understand what Faraday was saying, at the time they felt they did. The subject matter of the lecture was to some extent less important than the quality of the performance. As Tyndall put it, '. . . his Friday evening discourses were sometimes difficult to follow. But he exercised a magic on his hearers which often sent them away persuaded that they knew all about a subject of which they knew but little'.[61]

This manner of influence suggests that the title of sage might be as appropriate as that of savant.[62] His lectures won Faraday a place in the pantheon of eminent Victorians. He was a seer, a man of great energy and enthusiasm, endowed with a philosophical and cosmic awareness verging on the metaphysical. His output was prodigious and stimulated the work of many people. Tyndall called him a prophet although not entirely in a complimentary way. He was referring to the 'entangled' meaning of Faraday's language which he found untranslatable into the scientific idiom of the time.[63] Prophets do indeed speak in other tongues. Faraday appealed principally to the imagination, both public and scientific, quickening his audiences to a new capacity for experience. As Cornelia Crosse said:

> No attentive listener ever came away from one of Faraday's lectures without having the limits of his spiritual vision enlarged, or without feeling that his imagination had been stimulated to something beyond the mere exposition of physical facts.[64]

The conviction that one's spiritual awareness was being addressed, confirmed the authenticity of the message. Its meaning was somehow to be found within the individual himself, arising out of his own experience and history. The nature of the occasion, a powerful communal experience packed with a strong spiritual charge, was one which could send men and women away from the lecture theatre to tramp the streets at night in a state of mind akin to that of religious inspiration. Juliet Pollock commented that '. . . with some listeners the impression made was so deep as to lead them into the laborious paths of philosophy'.[65] For them the road to Damascus was down Albemarle Street.

To other scientists, the effect was not necessarily the same. The meaning of his lectures should have been clear though not necessarily expressed in the expected language of scientific exposition.

4 Conclusion

Faraday's institutional context was rich, varied and complex. One cannot say that the Royal Institution's significant history ended after 1844. It entered the final third of the nineteenth century stronger than ever, out of debt, with a healthy surplus, more members, greater public appeal, larger laboratories and more work being done on the premises. Of course there were constraints, in terms of money, the utilitarian interests and demands for practical advice. But there were also great advantages; the facilities available and the increasing freedom from any interference. The Royal Institution also provided a stage on which Faraday, self-made in an age which favoured self-improvement, appeared to a younger generation as the true embodiment of science. More subtle but equally significant was the way his lectures appealed to the imagination. Their content seemed far removed from utilitarian considerations. Together with his major discoveries, these paved the way for an emphasis on disinterested research. It is not surprising that the Institution became closely associated with the idea of the advancement of science for its own sake at a time when pure research was becoming a touchstone for the new professional scientific man. Finally for more than 40 years the Royal Institution provided a home for Faraday, a home which he entered as Davy's servant and in which he flourished, and grew old as Britain's best-loved savant.

Notes

I thank the Royal Institution for permission to work on the papers of Davy, Faraday and Tyndall.

1. J. Barnard to Bence Jones, 3 September 1867, in Bence Jones (1870a), **2**: 482.
2. RI MS T 2/C8, Journal, **8a**, 416.
3. Berman (1978). See chapter 5 in particular for Faraday.
4. RI MM, 1 March 1813, **5**: 355.
5. RI MM, 15 May 1815, **6**: 58. Erroneously stated in Bence Jones (1870a), **1**: 209, as 7 May 1815.
6. RI MM, 21 May 1821, **6**: 328.
7. RI MM, 7 February 1825, **7**: 6.
8. RI MM, 5 July 1824, **6**: 450.
9. RI MM, 4 July 1853, **11**: 27.
10. RI MM, 14 January 1833, **8**: 64 and 4 February 1833, **8**: 67.

11. Faraday to Lardner, 6 October 1827, *Correspondence*, **1**: 88. 'The Institution has been a source of knowledge and pleasure to me for the last fourteen years, and though it does not pay me in salary for what I *now* strive to do for it, yet I possess the kind feeling and good-will of its authorities and members, and all the privileges it can grant or I require; and moreover, I remember the protection it has afforded me during the past years of my scientific life'.

12. RI MM, 10 December 1832, **8**: 50–1. This appears in a report of a Committee appointed to inquire into all aspects of Institution's expenditure 'with a view to its reduction'.

13. RI MS T 2/C7, Journal, 20 February 1858, **7**: 275.

14. Cutler (1976) and Hays (1974).

15. Hays (1983), especially 94–5. Inkster (1977), especially 10–11. Carnall (1953–4).

16. Chilton & Coley (1980).

17. From 1827 to 1830 Anderson (c.1790–1866) worked on the Royal Society's optical glass project and was then employed by Faraday himself until 1832 when he was appointed an assistant by the Royal Institution. Faraday to ?, 3 February 1865, in Appleyard (1931), 135–6. RI MM 5 November 1832, **8**: 28.

18. Chilton & Coley (1980), 192–4. Both Faraday, Tyndall and later Dewar contributed to funds for the purchase of scientific apparatus.

19. J.P. Gassiot and Charles Wheatstone were among those who shared or provided apparatus for Faraday's work. There was a standing arrangement with the Royal School of Mines from the 1850s to borrow specimens and apparatus, and the Managers Minutes record repeated requests from other London institutions to borrow particular pieces, generally for the purpose of lectures.

20. See the self help tone of Tyndall to Lord Rayleigh, 16 December 1887, in Strutt (1924), 232. 'Besides, we were often able to put together, through the exercise of mother-wit, apparatus which, had we resorted to the philosophical instrument maker, would have cost a ten-fold sum. We never lacked the necessary apparatus; but we declined to heap up dead stock'. Tyndall stated that the decision to depend on borrowing whenever possible 'was Faraday's plan, and mine'.

21. Gladstone (1872), 31–2.

22. Faraday to Phillips, 28 August 1828, *Correspondence*, **1**: 91. Similar complaints about lack of time and pressure of work appear for example, in Faraday to Berzelius, 1 July 1823, *ibid*, 64 and other examples are extensively quoted in Berman (1978), 162–3.

23. Tyndall (1894), 174 asserted 'His mode of keeping accounts excited the admiration of the managing board of this Institution'.

24. On this aspect of the Institution's history see Forgan (1977), Chapter 4 and Williams, L.P. (1965), Chapter 8.

25. Berman (1978), 126.

26. RI MS F4 G. These are notes for Faraday's Friday Evening Discourses from 1838 to 1862.

27. John Barlow, honorary secretary 1843–1860 and Henry Bence Jones, honorary secretary 1860–1873. Both played an active role in proposing and choosing suitable speakers.

28. RI MS F4 F. This is a notebook of Friday Evening Discourses from February 1826 to June 1836 by Faraday and detailing the exhibits at each. RI MS F4 E is a similar notebook for Friday Evening Discourses 1837–40.

29. RI MM, 16 November 1846, **9**: 414.

30. Berman (1978), 162ff.

31. Gooding (1985b).

32. Smith (1871), 7.

33. As in the well-known plan put forward by the Earl of Dundonald in 1854 to take Cronstadt by means of ships filled with burning sulphur, driving the garrison out with the fumes of sulphur dioxide. See Faraday to Martin, 7 August 1854, *Correspondence*, **2**: 567.

34. RI MS HD 8b Laboratory notebook 2 (1830–1865), entry for 11–12 October 1855, p. 133–4.
35. For example the Haswell Colliery disaster in 1844, the ventilation of the House of Lords in 1847 and probably the Waltham Abbey explosion featured in his 1847 discourse 'On gunpowder'. See Jeffreys (1960), entries, 329, 357 and 356 respectively.
36. Faraday to Drummond, 29 June 1829, *Correspondence*, **1**: 95. Drummond was Lieutenant Governor of the Royal Military Academy at Woolwich.
37. Berman (1978), 152 and chapter 5.
38. Forgan (1977), 72–82.
39. Berman (1978), 133–4.
40. For example, RI MM, 18 May 1829, **7**: 257, 2 December 1833, **8**: 115, 20 June 1836, **8**: 436 respectively.
41. Berman (1978), 136ff.
42. Forgan (1977), 149–68. See also Bence Jones (1862).
43. RI MM, 23 May 1853, **11**: 13–14.
44. Faraday to Phillips, 29 August 1828, *Correspondence*, **1**: 91. It should however be pointed out that while the sentiment expressed might be quite accurate, Faraday was also politely declining a post with an institution whose future was at the time far from assured, and which would have involved him in heavy, poorly remunerated duties.
45. Forgan (1977), 133–35b.
46. Faraday to Hansteen, 16 December 1857, *Correspondence*, **2**, 673.
47. RI MM, 10 December 1832, **8**: 49.
48. Benjamin Vincent (1818–1899). See the relaxed and intimate tone of Faraday's letters to Vincent which always start 'My dear friend', 25 July 1850, 27 July 1851, 10 October 1860, 7 August 1863, *Correspondence*, **2**: 427, 469, 748, 803. Vincent was an excellent linguist. He produced a revised classified catalogue of the Royal Institution Library in 1857, saw philological works through the press for a firm of publishers, and compiled, revised and edited such works as Haydn (1855) and Vincent (1877). See obituary *Times* (5 May 1899), 10.
49. RI MS F5 F, petty cash book, 1851–1867, signed 'J. Barnard for M. Faraday'.
50. A study which covers many aspects of this topic is Sennet (1977). A useful study of the separation of home and workplace and the resulting emphasis on domestic virtues may be found in Davidoff & Hall (1983).
51. For example, T.H. Huxley called on Faraday as a young man with an idea about perpetual motion. Huxley (1900), **1**: 22.
52. Crosse (1891), 33. She was the wife of Andrew Crosse (1784–1855), well-to-do scientific amateur and electrician.
53. *Ibid.*, 34.
54. Faraday to Owen, 8 February 1851, RI MS F1 D2.
55. See Williams, L.P. (1965), 328–9 and extracts from Faraday's writing quoted in Porter & Friday (1974). Memoirs of the period are full of comparisons of lecturers and their merits. For a typical assessment of Faraday see Pollock, W.F. (1887), **1**: 247.
56. These lectures formed the basis for Faraday (1827).
57. Crosse (1891), 38.
58. [Pollock, J.] (1870), 294. (Williams, L.P. (1965), 334 assigned the authorship of this article to Lady Holland, but Pollock, W.F. (1887), **2**: 167, confirms that his wife wrote the article).
59. [Pollock, J.] (1870), 294.
60. Sennet (1977), 219.
61. J. Tyndall, 'Michael Faraday', *DNB*, **18**: 190–202, 201. Others who similary found his ideas at times 'confused and unintelligible' included the psychologist and logician Alexander Bain in Bain (1904), 129.

62. Faraday was not an intellectual in the sense we normally understand the word. For contemporary use of the word sage see Brock (1969), 82 and Holloway (1965), 4–9.
63. Tyndall (1894), 85–8.
64. Crosse (1891), 42.
65. [Pollock, J.] (1870), 294.

Plate 10   Michael Faraday. W.D. after sculpted bust by Edward Hodges Baily. Royal Institution, Faraday Album, H:71. Lithograph.

4

Reading the Book of Nature: The Relation Between Faraday's Religion and his Science

Geoffrey N. Cantor

> He sees in Nature's laws a code divine,
>   A living Presence he must first adore,
>   Ere he the sacred mysteries explore,
> Where Cosmos is his temple, Earth his shrine.[1]

Like his father and grandfather, Michael Faraday was a Sandemanian. He made his confession of faith in 1821, married into another leading Sandemanian family and became an elder in 1840. In proclaiming his faith, Faraday joined the small company of believers pledged to practise Christianity with fundamentalist purity by living their lives according to the Bible and in imitation of Christ's perfect thoughts and deeds.

Sandemanianism is not for the half-hearted or for those whose practise their Christianity only on Sundays. It is a robust, totally demanding religion. On becoming one of the elect Faraday committed himself to this uncompromising faith. Although superficially indistinguishable from his neighbours in Albemarle Street or his fellow scientists at the Royal Society, Faraday the Sandemanian lived an inner life very different from that of the non-Sandemanians he encountered. Doctrinally, morally and even socially there was an unbridgeable gap between him and them.

Since Sandemanianism was such a significant part of Faraday's life we must ask the question: What type of relationship existed between his science and his religion? It is difficult to articulate this relationship because a sharp contrast is usually drawn between science and *revealed* religion. At first sight it appears remarkable that a Sandemanian should have been an outstandingly successful scientist. A further difficulty is that much of Faraday's science, particularly his detailed researches, seem so independent of his religious beliefs. However, a stronger case can be made about Faraday's general approach towards science; what might be called his metaphysics. But even these general attitudes are not readily related to Sandemanianism, so we must therefore dig deeper to excavate their interrelationship.

Faraday has left little documentary evidence to help the historian. The few extant statements relating to this issue — for example, 'There is no [natural] philosophy in my religion'[2] — have been taken to imply that there was no meeting point between his science and his religion. Despite such apparent disclaimers several historians have turned to Sandemanianism to explain aspects of Faraday's personality and intellectual disposition. James Riley, for example, argued that Sandemanianism was 'the key to so much of Faraday's character' and Pearce Williams has suggested that Faraday's science was rooted in his religion which emphasised the intelligibility, beauty and symmetry of the universe.[3] Others such as Trevor Levere and David Gooding have been less concerned with Sandemanianism than with identifying a number of theological and metaphysical themes which directed Faraday's scientific practice.[4]

While all these historians offer valuable insights, the relation between Faraday's religion and his science needs further exploration. This essay examines one of several ways in which Sandemanianism and science can be interrelated in Faraday's thought. The method adopted here emphasises the close similarities between how Sandemanians *read* the Bible and how Faraday *read* the book of nature. Although this perspective does not explain the details of Faraday's scientific practice, it does help account for some of his metaphysical beliefs and more importantly it demonstrates the unity underlying his religion and his science.

1 The book of revelation and the book of nature

The Sandemanians are 'people of the Book' who study the Bible in depth and base their religion and their daily lives on the Word.[5] Sandemanians have to be thoroughly familiar with the text since, lacking a clergy or priesthood, they adopt the Bible as their sole authority on all issues of principle and practice. Members of the movement, particularly the elders, possess an excellent knowledge of the text and their sermons are composed largely of Biblical quotations with a short linking commentary. Faraday's few extant sermons and sermon notes, together with the annotations in his Bibles, indicate his thorough knowledge of both Old and New Testaments.

Since Sandemanians view the Bible primarily as the guide to religion and morality they tend not to emphasise its interpretation as a natural philosophy text. For example, John Glas, the founder of the Glassite or Sandemanian sect, did not publish on either scriptural physics or scriptural geology. The only article by Glas which even touches on these subjects is a critique of John Hutchinson's exegesis of the opening verses of Genesis which, Hutchinson claimed, specified the physical structure of the universe.[6] Although Glas generally avoided such issues his son-in-law, Robert Sandeman, engaged natural philosophy in the works I shall discuss below and is also attributed with the authorship of *The Philosophy of the Creation* which offers a cosmogony based on Genesis and an account of the physical processes that occurred during the creation.[7]

A case could be make for interpreting Faraday as a scriptural physicist, but a stronger and more interesting argument can be developed from an examination and extension of Sandeman's published views about the relationship between the visible and the invisible realms. The crucial text on this issue is chapter 1, verse 20 of St Paul's epistle to the Romans which was frequently cited by Sandemanian authors:

> For the invisible things of him from the creation of the world are clearly seen, being understood by the things that are made, even his eternal power and Godhead.

Glas briefly glossed this passage in his critique of Hutchinson but did not discuss 'the things that are made'.[8] However, Sandeman analysed this passage in greater depth in *The Law of Nature Defended by Scripture* (1760). He praised John Locke's paraphrase[9] and then proceeded to argue that since 'every machine and contrivance suggests to us an artist or contriver' the book of nature likewise 'sufficiently evinces its author'. Like natural theologians Sandeman appealed to the argument from design, but his legitimation of this argument lay not with the power of reason but with God's revelation. Thus Romans 1:20 provided the scriptural foundation for his claim that the natural world is the reflection of the divine.[10]

Faraday quoted Romans 1:20 before a Royal Institution audience on at least two occasions. In May 1854, when addressing the Prince Consort and other dignitaries on mental education, he stressed the need for humility. He then drew an 'absolute distinction between religious and ordinary belief' and argued that what we can know from religious faith is not incompatible with what we can know from reason. Quoting Romans 1:20 as an article of his own faith Faraday strongly suggested that the physical world manifests its divine origin:[11]

> . . . even in earthly matters I believe that the invisible things of HIM from the creation of the world are clearly seen, being understood by the things that are made, even His eternal power and Godhead; and I have never seen anything incompatible between those things of man which can be known by the spirit of man which is within him, and those higher things concerning his future, which he cannot know by that spirit.[12]

Faraday made a similar point in a lecture on putrefaction and decay some years earlier when he noted that these phenomena are 'full of beauty and of power, and evidences of a wisdom which the more a man knows the more freely will he acknowledge he cannot understand'.[13]

Faraday also quoted Romans 1:20 in a lecture in 1847 which he ended with a survey of the role of central forces in the economy of nature. Such forces seem to account for diverse natural phenomena: the stability of the heavens, the role of heat, the lightning discharge, tidal motions and even life itself.[14] While all these phenomena indicate 'the harmonious working of all these forces in nature' and are manifestations of God's 'mighty purpose' our scientific knowledge is very limited. Nevertheless, the little we do know 'should lead us to think of Him who hath wrought' the phenomena of nature: 'for it is said by an authority far above even that which these works present, that "the invisible things of Him from the creation of the world are clearly seen, being understood by the things that are made, even His eternal power and Godhead".'[15]

The crucial point is that Romans 1:20 provided both Sandeman and Faraday with the scriptural authority for reading the book of nature as comprised of signs which signify the 'invisible things of Him'. The link between the visible and invisible, between creation and creator is not forged by reason — as the natural theologians claimed — but by the Bible which is the key for comprehending the meanings underlying nature. Romans 1:20 also provides another important ingredient in Faraday's science. This is the structural similarity between the physical and the spiritual or moral universes. Just as there is a correspondence between nouns and the things they signify, so visible, natural signs bear a correspondence to the 'invisible things'. I will investigate the details of this correspondence in the next three sections of this essay.

First, however, we must examine a revealing passage in Faraday's lecture on mental education where he attacked the pretensions of the tableturners. Here he vividly portrayed the relation between God, nature and man in a single sentence: 'for the book of nature, which we have to read, is written by the finger of God'.[16] At first sight the phrase 'finger of God' appears out of place in this context since the relevant biblical reference is to Exodus 31:18, which concerns Moses receiving the ten commandments 'written by the finger of God'. By this allusion Faraday extended the metaphor of God as author to imply His authorship of both the book of revelation and the book of nature.[17] Moreover, Faraday likened the investigation of nature to *reading* a book, a metaphor which implies that the act of reading is central to both religion and science; the former is reading the book of revelation and the latter is reading the book of nature.

Faraday was not original in employing the above metaphors. Instead he exhibited a concern, found frequently among theological writers, with the numerous references to linguistic acts in the Bible. For example, God speaks on many occasions; Adam names the animals and there are frequent references to the Word and the word of God. Particularly relevant to the present topic is the first chapter of Genesis where God *said* 'Let there be light. . . . Let there be a firmament in the midst of the waters'. Thus the *logos*, the word, is crucial to the formation of the physical universe.[18] It is not surprising that Biblical resonances can be found in some of Faraday's scientific writings. For example, while discussing matter theory in his memorandum of February 1844 Faraday asked rhetorically whether 'God could not just as easily by his *word speak* power into existence around centres, as he could first create nuclei & then clothe them with power?'.[19]

Such metaphors should not be dismissed as mere embellishments of no significance to the understanding of science. Faraday's references to the book of nature and to God's word are not literary ornaments. Instead they deserve close attention as clues to some of Faraday's deepest suppositions about the physical universe. In the remainder of this essay I argue that these metaphors disclose several surprising and revealing correspondences between Faraday's religion and his science.

2 Sandemanian hermeneutics and Faraday's epistemology

One of the distinctive features of the Sandemanian movement is its insistence not only on the truth of scripture but also on the need to interpret the Bible as literally as possible. From the 1720s John Glas took a firm stand on this issue and chided those divines who indulged their private interpretations of scripture, thereby perverting the Bible's message. Glas charged the reader with discovering the truth inherent in the biblical text by interpreting it as literally as possible. He admitted that metaphorical language is present in the Bible but argued that the reader should use the unambiguous passages to clarify the more difficult ones. In his search for a 'pure and undefiled' religion Glas believed that the Bible was a text whose meaning was manifest to all who sought its truth and were prepared to adopt a form of exegesis which avoided distortions. Scripture was not mysterious — a term frequently encountered in eighteenth-century theology — but was open to a simple interpretation by any man of common sense. Throughout their writings the Sandemanians used the terms 'plain style' and 'clear style' to describe their form of Biblical exegesis. Thus they shared with Locke and the deists a concern with plain language, but unlike these writers they sought to base their Christianity on a literal interpretation of the Bible.[20]

Since the Sandemanians accept that the Bible is written in a plain style we would expect them to attribute similar characteristics to nature. Indeed Faraday assumed that nature possesses an inner coherence and simplicity. For example, he accepted that nature was governed by a set of God-given causal laws. These laws were not merely the result of God speaking his will at the creation, they were also the work of a wise Creator who, avoiding unnecessary complexity, constructed the world on simple, plain principles. Faraday's belief in the indestructibility of force — all phenomenal forces being manifestations of a more basic conserved force — can likewise be interpreted as an instance of this more general principle of simplicity.[21] A third example is his use of the principle of least action, which Gooding suggests expresses Faraday's more basic assumption that nature operates economically.[22] While many other scientists adopted similar metaphysical principles on pragmatic, conventional or psychological grounds it is revealing to interpret Faraday's deployment of these principles as correlates of Sandemanian hermeneutics.

The other area I will examine is Faraday's way of reading the book of nature. Just as the Sandemanians prize every word in the Bible as incorrigible truth not to be misinterpreted by man, so Faraday looked upon scientific facts as the basic words or signs comprising the book of nature. 'A fundamental fact', wrote Faraday in 1854, 'never fails us, its evidence is always true'. However, he recognised that scientists often fail to grasp facts for what they are and he cautioned against adopting 'doubtful knowledge'. As Gooding has pointed out, Faraday believed that all knowledge of the physical world must be acquired as directly as possible by observation or experiment.[23] Faraday's passion for precise, unambiguous experiments can be interpreted as an activity parallel to his belief that the Biblical commentator must respect the integrity of God's word. Although observed facts were the basic signs in the book of nature, these signs had to be read and their significance determined. Just as with the Bible only the plainest and clearest interpretation was likely to lead to truth. Similarly, just as Sandemanians reject misinterpretations of God's word by other theologians, so Faraday was quick to dismiss those who misconstrued nature by letting their imaginations run riot. As he wrote in his *Diary*, 'I must keep my researches really *Experimental* and not let them deserve any where the character of *hypothetical imaginations*'.[24] A certainty close to that of revelation might be attainable, but only by the best founded laws of nature.[25] At the other extreme were the many hypotheses that Faraday treated with contempt or at best with a degree of tolerance. In the first category were the wild phantoms of the tableturners, while in the latter were the many hypotheses which offered reasonable but provisional explanations of physical phenomena.[26]

It is sometimes supposed that Faraday adopted a positivist epistemology in which facts form the foundation of proper science. However, a positivist philosophy is not compatible with Faraday's belief that nature is God's handiwork, nor does it encompass his celebration of the book of nature. Tyndall was surely close to the mark when he wrote:

> The contemplation of Nature, and his own relation to her, produced in Faraday a kind of spiritual exhaltation which makes itself manifest here. His religious feeling and his philosophy could not be kept apart; there was an habitual overflow of the one into the other.[27]

Establishing the factual basis for science involved the formation of ideas as well as observation, and, finally, the distillation of those ideas into words. Faraday was aware of the power and pitfalls of representations from the beginning of his career, as is documented in other chapters in this volume. In a letter to Benjamin Abbott in 1812 he praised letter writing because 'it tends I conceive to make ideas clear and distinct'.[28] Likewise in his lecture on mental education he emphasised that facts have to be formulated as '*clear and precise ideas*' and warmly recommended the habit of framing such ideas.[29] Faraday made a similar case for the habit of 'expressing them [exact ideas] clearly by language' and he argued the need for 'clear and definite language, especially in physical matters; giving to a word its true and full, but measured meaning'. Although scientific words do not achieve this degree of precision when first coined, the progress of science, he thought, involves the refinement of language so that the reference of terms becomes increasingly precise.[30]

Faraday was concerned with the role of language in interpersonal communication both as lecturer and researcher. His lectures were renowned for their clarity and the *Experimental Researches in Electricity* sometimes possesses a transparent quality. Although it would be difficult to argue that Faraday's prose style is consistently clear, particularly where he is speculating beyond the reach of experiment he nevertheless thought that in framing facts the scientist must move from observation to ideas and then to words. In this process a high degree of clarity was required in both ideas and words to guarantee the integrity of the fact. The classic expression of this theory of language is book three of John Locke's *An Essay Concerning Human Understanding*. Locke's theory was reiterated in many subsequent works including the popular writings of Isaac Watts which Faraday studied in his youth.[31] Whatever other influences are pertinent here, it is important to notice the close similarity between the Sandemanian emphasis on a clear style of Biblical exegesis and Faraday's insistence on a clear style in science.

This last theme found expression in Faraday's concern with scientific terminology which he believed must not be infected by association with speculative hypotheses. Instead, the terms used to describe experimental results should be theory-neutral and portray nature with integrity:

> I cannot help thinking it a most unfortunate thing that men who as experimentalists & philosophers are the most fitted to advance the general cause of science & knowledge should by the promulgation of their own theoretical views under the form of nomenclature notation or scale actually retard its progress — It would not be of so much consequence if it was only theory & hypotheses which they thus treated but they put facts or the current coin of science into the same limited circulation when they describe them in such a way that the initiated only can read them.[32]

Here we find Faraday concerned not only with obtaining a true reading of the book of nature but also with the integrity of verbal description. This is closely analogous to the acts of naming related in the Bible, particularly in Genesis 2:20 where Adam gives the true names to the animals. In a sense Faraday was seeking to discover the 'Adamic language' in which the book of nature was written.

3 Laws — moral, natural and physical

The word 'law(s)' occurs over 300 times in the Bible. It was also one of the most frequently discussed terms in Sandemanian writings and sermons. Glas believed that the Bible enshrined numerous moral laws which provided a code for the true Christian who seeks to imitate Christ. By contrast, a person who steals or hates or is covetous or who commits any other sin, is breaking God's law. He also believed the light of nature does not disclose God's laws which are revealed to us only in the scriptures.[33] While Glas sometimes employed the term 'law of nature' this was more widely discussed by Robert Sandeman who even devoted a small book to *The Law of Nature Defended by Scripture* (1760). In it Sandeman argued that a law of nature was a law of divine origin and of universal applicability. By 'natural' Sandeman meant that such laws were consonant with the moral feelings of all mankind. In contrasting natural and unnatural Sandeman offered as an example of a natural relationship 'the common propensity between the sexes'. However, 'a similar propensity between those of the same sex, is unnatural or against nature — so, highly criminal. No other argument is needful to evince this, than an appeal to the human heart'.[34] Like Shaftesbury earlier in the eighteenth century, Sandeman believed that we possess a moral sense which provides us with incorrigible judgments on moral issues. These moral judgments were instances of God's moral law.

Sandeman's book is largely concerned with the first three chapters of St Paul's epistle to the Romans. Not surprisingly he devoted much space to Romans 1:20, noting that the:

> apostle, with propriety, begins his charge, by taking notice of the lesson exhibited to all nations by the visible works of God: for whatever superior instructions were given to Jews and Heathens, they were still chargeable with guilt for every neglect of the common lesson taught by the frame of nature.

The non-Christian has therefore access to God's moral law. After further analysis of Romans 1:20 Sandeman concluded that the book of nature is itself testimony against the idolator, since 'the great frame of nature sufficiently evinces its author'.[35] However, nature offered only a very partial revelation compared with scripture. While God's laws could only be learnt from the Bible and from the guidance of one's conscience, Sandeman allowed that they could be gleaned in part from observing the book of nature.

In one of his sermons Faraday exhibited the traditional Sandemanian concern with God's moral law. He argued that only by submitting oneself entirely to the law of God could one hope to achieve the moral purity exemplified by the life of Christ. The Christian, even the Sandemanian, is constantly aware that he fails to achieve this absolute standard of thought and behaviour, and yet he should value God's perfect law beyond anything in this world.[36]

In Faraday's scientific writings we find that physical laws have a role similar to that played by moral law in his sermon. His scientific career can be described, with only slight anachronism, as being directed towards the discovery of nature's laws. The word 'law(s)' is as prominent in the *Experimental Researches in Electricity* as it is in the Bible. Many of his major discoveries were laws: the law of electromagnetic induction, the general law of electric conduction and the laws of electrolytic action. Faraday was not alone in seeking nature's laws, but unlike most of his contemporaries, he prized laws far above theories and emphatically stated that the laws of nature are 'the foundation of our knowledge in natural things'.[37] Laws of nature were central to Faraday's 1844 memorandum on 'Matter' where he argued that 'God has been pleased to work in his material creation by laws' and went on to state that 'the Creator governs his material works by *definite laws* resulting from the forces impressed on matter'.[38] These particularly revealing passages make the direct connection between God and the causal laws of nature. This connection parallels the laws of God in the moral realm.

The two types of law differ in the necessity of their action. A body under the influence of the law of gravitation has no choice but to move according to that law, whereas we can choose whether to obey moral laws. However, this difference does not destroy the homology between these two types of law. I am not claiming that there was for Faraday an exact analogy between the moral and the physical. The similarity is striking not only because of the importance Faraday attributed to law in his science and in his religion, but also because the laws in question are universal. All bodies are subject to the gravitational force and all men are subject to moral law, whether or not they chose to act in accordance with that law. Only Christ is unique in that he 'came into this world to fulfil' God's law, and to provide an example for good.[39] Like the Sandemanian who should strive to imitate Christ, but should always remain humble, knowing that he cannot fully succeed, the scientist should with similar humility strive to grasp the laws by which God chose to govern the physical world. Of course the laws framed by the scientist are not necessarily those ordained by God. The laws of science are instead provisional, may be proved false and be replaced by better laws.

> How wonderful it is to me the simplicity of nature when we rightly interpret her laws and how different the convictions which they produce on the mind in comparison with the uncertain conclusions which hypothesis or even theory present.[40]

When compared with such 'uncertain conclusions' the laws of nature were 'assured and [of] large character'. [41] Both through the Bible and in nature Faraday's highest aim was to search for God's laws.[42]

4 Mathematics

Faraday was at the height of his powers in the 1830s when large areas of British physics, such as optics, electricity and heat theory, were dominated by mathematical physicists educated principally at Cambridge and at Trinity College, Dublin.[43] The rapid mathematisation of physics rendered many problems and a significant number of publications outside the scope of non-mathematicians. One of the most striking aspects of Faraday's scientific work is his near total neglect until late in his career of mathematical analyses of physical phenomena.[44] His *Diary* and *Experimental Researches in Electricity* show that he seldom recorded and manipulated quantitative measurements and that he rarely used even the simplest equations. While it is tempting to ascribe his avoidance of analytical mathematics to a lack of training in that subject, his failure to use even the most elementary mathematical operations and his stated antipathy towards using mathematics in physics suggest that there may be a deeper reason for his attitude.

There are two promising ways in which Faraday's religion might account for his attitude towards mathematics. First, it is interesting that many

eighteenth-century opponents of the use of mathematics in natural philosophy
were adherents of revealed religion. Hutchinson, a verbose contemporary of
Glas, opposed Newton's natural philosophy, arguing that we know nature
principally through the senses and from the scriptures. If rightly interpreted
these provide an account of the underlying mechanism of the world. The
scientist must first consult the book of revelation and then the book of nature.
Mathematics had no place in Hutchinson's scheme because it was a language
of human invention and not the language of the book of nature.[45] Dismissing
the diagrams in Newton's *Principia* as useless to science — 'cobweb[s] of
Circles and Lines to catch Flies in' — Hutchinson charged mathematicians
with employing an inappropriate language of natural description. He also
claimed that Newton had erred in calling his book the *Mathematical Principles
of Natural Philosophy* since, 'when 'tis examined, it will be found, that . . . they
[mathematics] have no Place, but the last in Science'.[46] Hutchinson's argument
was subsequently adopted by many scriptural physicists, with only minor
variations.[47] Although I have not yet found this argument in works by
Sandemanians, it is likely that Faraday was familiar with this opposition to
mathematics grounded in a literal interpretation of the Bible. It is difficult to
determine whether he was influenced by the Hutchinsonians but it appears
that he shared their view that nature was not written in mathematical
characters. The best evidence for this is the lack of mathematics in his scientific
works. Likewise, Tyndall's comment that 'No man ever felt the tyranny of
[mathematical] symbols more deeply than Faraday' reveals the strength of his
opposition to mathematics as the language of natural description.[48]

   The second approach to Faraday's religion and his attitude to mathematics
is to notice that the Sandemanians argued that the lot is sacred since it is a sign
from God indicating his will. Throughout the Bible there are a number of
references to lots. For example, God instructed Moses to divide the promised
land and to assign the different parts of it by the drawing of lots (Numbers
26:55; 33:54; 34:13). The lot is extensively used in the Sandemanian church,
for example, lots are drawn to indicate where members of the congregation
should sit at the love feast. Since the lot is of divine origin Sandemanians are
prohibited from profaning the lottery by playing cards, dice or other games of
chance.[49] How might Faraday's science be related to this belief in the divine
origin of lots? The Sandemanian attitude towards lotteries does imply a
profound respect for natural signs. Because they share with the lot the
property of being God given they may therefore be regarded as sacred. To
operate mathematically on a sign by, say, squaring it, dividing it by five or
adding it to another sign is to destroy that sign and make it unrecognisable.
This seems to be close to Faraday's own attitude since his real objection was to
the use of mathematical, especially algebraic, operations which alter and thus
impugn the God-given signs that we read in the book of nature.

   Both of these approaches help us understand Faraday's attitude towards
mathematical manipulation and his belief in the primacy of experiment over
mathematics. In his 1857 lecture on the conservation of force Faraday denied
that mathematical physicists possess an advantage over experimentalists 'in

perceiving the nature and power of a natural principle of action [such as the force conservation law]. It [the mathematical mind] cannot of itself introduce the knowledge of any new principle'. The experimentalist alone was capable of making new and important discoveries. He argued that history confirmed this, since experimentalists, not mathematicians, had discovered such important laws of nature as the law of electromagnetic induction.[50] In 1831 Faraday had expressed a similar view in a letter to Richard Phillips: 'It is quite comfortable to me to find that experiment need not quail before mathematics, but is quite competent to rival it in discovery'.[51] Then Faraday was on the defensive because the high regard others had for mathematical physics. After the mid-1840s he acknowledged the power of mathematical approaches, but he never adopted or advocated this style of science. The conviction of the paramount importance of experiment remained the key to his highly personal way of reading the book of nature.

5 Conclusion

I have interpreted Faraday's religion and his science as parallel activities. Given the Sandemanian belief that the word and the works of God are written in similar characters it was natural for Faraday to read them in similar ways. I have identified the Biblical support for this view and have shown that metaphors about writing and reading the book of nature recur frequently in exegetical works. As a Sandemanian Faraday was steeped in a fundamentalist tradition which conceived the physical world as 'written by the finger of God'. It is difficult to demonstrate that in his science Faraday was 'reading the book of nature'. Nevertheless the metaphor reveals and elucidates some of his basic attitudes towards nature. It also expresses structural parallels to Sandemanian hermeneutics. There are several ways in which Faraday adopted the 'plain style' in his science. For example, his emphasis on incorrigible facts, clear language, careful experiments and his suspicion of hypotheses and mathematical operations. Similarly, Faraday's search for the laws of nature, their role and the confidence he placed in them reflects the traditional Sandemanian concern with God's moral law. This suggests that Faraday's way of reading the book of nature reflected Sandemanian attitudes towards reading the book of revelation.

It has often been claimed that Faraday kept his science and his religion in separate, unconnected compartments.[52] Although he did not deploy any simplistic strategy, such as the argument from design, to interrelate the two activities, we can construct the relation between them by using a structural, rather than a causal, idiom. William Barrett was close to the mark when he described Faraday's religion as concerned with 'God's revelation to man of the Divine purpose', and his science as dealing with 'man's revelation of the Divine handiwork'. Barrett continued this analogy:

> But he considered the scientific investigator as a high priest of God, & quite as sacred & noble an office as the expounder or priest of revealed religion, — more so indeed for he hated all sacredotalism & ritual.[53]

The approach adopted in this essay endorses and extends Barrett's analogy by exploring not only the structural similarities between Faraday's science and his religion, but also their interrelation through the metaphorical transfer of such key terms as nature, language and law. It is from this perspective that we can appreciate the unity underlying Faraday's religion and his science.

Notes

I am indebted to Brian Bowers, John Hedley Brooke, Barbara Cantor, Peter Denton, J.W. Glen, David Gooding, Trevor Levere, Irena McCabe and Derek Murray for their help in preparing this essay. For permission to quote from material in their possession I am grateful to the Physics Department, University of Birmingham and to the Royal Institution.

1. Tomlinson (1879).
2. Faraday to [Countess of Lovelace], 24 October 1844, in Bence Jones (1870a), **2**: 192–6, 193. See also Faraday (1854), *ERCP*, 464–5.
3. Riley (1954), 2; Williams, L.P. (1965), 102–6. See also Clark (1967 and 1974); Thompson (1898), 286–99.
4. Levere (1968); Gooding (1980a).
5. The most useful analysis of the Glassite (Scottish Sandemanian) movement is Murray (1976). See also Hornsby (1936); Bogue and Bennett (1808–12), **4**: 107–25; Escott (1960), 17–23. For primary sources see Glas (1782); Sandeman (1757) and other works by Sandeman cited below. Sandemanians used the King James version of the Bible.
    There is another, more secular, sense in which Sandemanians were involved with books. Not only did members of the movement write books but several Sandemanians were printers, publishers or booksellers: for example, the Morison family of Perth who published editions of works by Glas and Sandeman. Faraday's friend and fellow congregant George Whitelaw owned a bookshop in Fleet Street and Faraday himself was initially an apprentice bookbinder. Moreover, Benjamin Vincent became Secretary and Librarian at the Royal Institution and was responsible not only for the Royal Institution Library Catalogue but also for other published compilations (see Forgan (this volume), note 48).
6. Glas (1759) in Glas (1782), **2**: 426–35. On Hutchinson see Wilde (1980); Cantor (1979). For the variety of different interpretations of the Bible see Williams, A. (1948) and Collier (1934).
7. [Sandeman?] (1835).
8. Glas (1759) in Glas (1782), **2**: 426–35, 431 and 435.
9. Locke (1707) in Locke (1824), **8**: 273–427, 284–6.
10. Sandeman (1760) in Sandeman (1857), 273–85, 278–9.
11. Faraday (1854), *ERCP*, 464–5.
12. *Ibid.*, 465.
13. Bence Jones (1870a), **2**: 104.
14. Gooding (1980a), 28–9.
15. Bence Jones (1870a), **2**: 229–30.
16. Faraday (1854), *ERCP*, 471.
17. According to William Barrett in a letter to J.H. Poynting, 6 March 1911 (in the possession of the Physics Department, University of Birmingham), Faraday claimed that the Bible was 'God's revelation to man of the Divine purpose', while science was 'man's revelation of the Divine handicraft'. Here a somewhat different metaphor is employed but with similar connotations.
18. For an insightful analysis of the role of the Word in early-modern chemistry see Hannaway (1975); also Foucault (1970).

19. M. Faraday, 'Matter', IEE MS. Published in Levere (1968), 105–7, 107. Emphasis added.
20. Glas (1739a and b) in Glas (1782), **2**: 395–414, 397–410; Murray (1976), 112–9. There are significant similarities between Sandemanian hermeneutics and the plain style adopted by Puritan divines: see Miller, P. (1971).
21. Faraday (1857b); Heimann (1974).
22. Gooding (1980a), 10; (1982a), 61–4.
23. Faraday (1854), *ERCP*, 468–9; Tyndall (1894), 49; Gooding (1980a), 11 and this volume.
24. Faraday, *Diary*, 19 December 1833, **2**, 1207.
25. Faraday (1854), *ERCP*, 470.
26. Faraday (1853a and b, 1854); Agassi (1971), 117–63.
27. Tyndall (1894), 178. Faraday also differed from the positivist in considering laws to the causal and not mere constant conjunctions.
28. Faraday to Abbott, 12 July 1812, *Correspondence*, **1**: 1.
29. Faraday (1854), *ERCP*, 478.
30. *Ibid.*, 480. See also Faraday (1838a), 1304 and Gooding (1975), 144–8.
31. Williams, L.P. (1965), 12–3; Faraday to Abbott, 12 July 1812, *Correspondence*, **1**: 1.
32. Faraday to Whewell, 21 February 1831, *Correspondence*, **1**: 107. See also Faraday (1840).
33. Glas (1741) in Glas (1782), **2**: 1–42, 35; Glas (1740) in Glas (1782), **2**: 173–9, 174 and Glas (1733) in Glas (1782), **2**: 229–55, 246.
34. Sandeman (1760) in Sandeman (1857), 273–85, 274.
35. *Ibid.*, 276 and 279.
36. M. Faraday, 'Fragmentary notes of a discourse by Michael Faraday, delivered in London, 7th July 1861' in R[orie] (1910), 15–18. See also Faraday's sermon notes RI MS FL8A 101, especially the note beginning 'To the *law* and *testimony*'.
37. Faraday (1854), *ERCP*, 469.
38. Faraday, *op.cit.* (19), 105 and 107. Emphasis Faraday's. See also Williams, L.P. (1965), 103.
39. Faraday, *op. cit.* (36), 15.
40. Faraday to Svanberg, 16 August 1850, *Correspondence*, **2**: 430.
41. Faraday (1854), *ERCP*, 471.
42. Gooding (1975), 310–30.
43. Cantor (1983).
44. Gooding (1982b).
45. Cf. Galilei (1967), 103: 'But with regard to those few (mathematical propositions) which the human intellect does understand, I believe that its knowledge equals the Divine in objective certainty'.
46. Hutchinson (1732) forms volume **5** of Hutchinson (1748–9), 222–3.
47. For example Bate (1740), 71; Jones (1781) forms volume **9** of Jones (1801), 36–7.
48. Tyndall (1894), 63–4.
49. Bogue and Bennett (1808–12), **4**: 113; Hornsby (1936), 167.
50. Faraday (1857b), *ERCP*, 458.
51. Faraday to Phillips, 29 November 1831, *Correspondence*, **1**: 122. As Gooding (1982b), especially pp. 246–8, points out, Faraday called his researches 'Experimental' to express his 'pique' at the 'high mathematicians' who anticipate nature.
52. Thompson (1898), 298.
53. William Barrett to J.H. Poynting, 6 March 1911.

Plate 11   André-Marie Ampère. F. Tonnelat. Institution of Electrical Engineers. Line engraving.

5

Faraday and Ampère: A Critical Dialogue

L. Pearce Williams

A new epoch in the history of physics began in the summer of 1820 when Hans Christian Oersted announced his discovery that a compass needle was affected by an electric current. All over Europe, as the news came to them, natural philosophers repeated, extended and theorised about Oersted's basic experiment.[1] Nowhere was the fever more intense than in Paris where, in a few short weeks, André-Marie Ampère created a new science which he later named electrodynamics. By the end of 1820, Ampère had published a number of papers in which he tried to account for all magnetic phenomena by means of the forces exerted by electricity in motion — forces that he had discovered and which he insisted were completely different from the ordinary and well-studied forces of static electricity. In spite of his striking discoveries and in spite of the apparent ability of his new theories to account for new phenomena, Ampère's ideas were greeted with scepticism. Among those who were not convinced of the basic correctness of Ampère's view was Michael Faraday. In 1821 and 1822 Faraday published papers that criticised Ampère's theories with sufficient force to compel Ampère to modify his views.[2] Ultimately he presented his theoretical results in a manner quite different from those which marked the beginnings of electrodynamics. In this essay I explore in detail the bases of Faraday's critique and point out exactly its effect upon Ampère.

1 Ampère and Faraday compared

Before examining their works, we should look briefly at the two men, for they differed in many ways, both personally and scientifically. Their respective positions reflected these differences. In 1820, Ampère was 45 years old.[3] His life has been marked by a series of emotional crises that had plunged him into despair. His father has been executed during the French Revolution; his wife had died prematurely, leaving him with an infant son who, in 1820, began his unfulfilled worship of Mme Recamier. Ampère's second marriage had collapsed in bitterness and recrimination. Although intellectually weaned on Diderot's *Encyclopédie*, Ampère took refuge from the blows of fortune in an intense faith that, however, oscillated between mystical devotion and sceptical despair. The emotional strain was visible in his work on electrodynamics. The autumn and winter of 1820 were months of exultation in which Ampère's mind leapt from intuition to idea to concept with almost lightning speed. His discoveries resulted from flashes of brilliance rather than from logical and rational deduction. The memoirs that he wrote at this time reflect this. They are at times almost incoherent, as solid fact and speculative fancy followed one another and as accurate description passed into contradiction or obscurity. This did not make it easy for his readers to accept his theories, which were rapidly met with both hostility and severe criticism.

There is a note of desperation in Ampère's responses to his critics. He knew full well that electrodynamics was his claim to scientific immortality. Until 1820 he had published a number of competent but uninspired papers on mathematical physics and mathematics. He had speculated on the nature of matter and its combinations, but without making any serious converts to his views. He was more interested in philosophy and psychology than he was in physics or mathematics as he made clear to all who knew him. Ampère, his membership of the Académie des Sciences notwithstanding, felt he was no closer to achieving scientific eminence than when he had been an adolescent 'mathematical genius'. His failure was undoubtedly placed into sharp focus by his friendship and close association with Augustin Fresnel who lived in Ampère's house in these years. Fresnel was 13 years his junior and had no apparent superiority in talent. Yet, by 1819, he had won over some of Ampère's colleagues in the Académie to *his* new undulatory theory of light.[4] There is no hint anywhere that Ampère was jealous of Fresnel who briefly took up the exciting new subject of electromagnetism.[5] But Ampère's later insistence upon his own originality and upon the essential truth of his new science indicates just how strongly he had felt about his claim to scientific fame. He would fight to his last breath to secure this niche in the history of science as the creator of electrodynamics.

When his dialogue with Faraday began it was not clear which of his theories he would consider crucial to preserve and which he could quietly abandon. It will be useful to spell out briefly, following Hofmann,[6] the 'Lakatosian' research programme to which Ampère was committed. The fundamental aspect of Ampère's new theory, that he consistently reiterated and which was obviously its most important part, was the identity of magnetism with dynamic electricity. He constantly sought to prove this identity. Whenever he learned of a new effect in magnetism or electrodynamics, Ampère immediately tried to show that it was explicable in terms of the motions of electrical currents.[7] This commitment led to two further theoretical aims. Ampère sought to reduce the current forces to mathematical formulae and he sought experimental evidence to support his very early view that the electrical currents in permanent magnets must circulate around the particles of permanent magnets. Both these points, he felt, were essential to his theory of magnetism as dynamic electricity. He could abandon neither. Finally, there were a whole host of hypotheses to which Ampère was not absolutely committed and which he rather generously threw out for consideration. The most important of these are in the 'Réponse' to van Beck in which Ampère attempted to make his electrodynamic molecule the basis for both physics and chemistry.[8] As we shall see, Faraday's criticisms of Ampère's theories forced him to retreat to his 'hard core' and abandon all else.

In 1820, Faraday was 29 years old. At this point his 'fame', if that is even the proper word, was restricted to London and even to the immediate environs of the Royal Institution. He had shown competence as an analytical chemist, had investigated and published on the passage of gases through capillary tubes,[9] and was just beginning his researches with James Stodart on steel.[10] He had long been interested in electricity and magnetism as general powers of matter but he had never done research of any importance on either subject. In short, he was hardly qualified to be a critic of someone like Ampère whose scientific stature was underlined by his membership of the Académie des Sciences. Faraday knew this. His diffidence was quite obvious in his correspondence at this time. In April 1820 he used the very term in a letter to G. De la Rive.[11] Even after he had shown the keenness of his critical eye in a published account of Ampère's work, he wrote to Ampère, '. . . I cannot help but feel that I am the unworthy gainer and you the loser by a correspondence between us, and that though I receive so much I contribute nothing to it'.[12] This diffidence led to Faraday's insistence that his historical sketch of electromagnetism be published anonymously.[13] This is the only case I know in which Faraday did not publicly declare his authorship.[14]

Faraday's criticisms reflect his awareness of his position. His objections to Ampère's hypotheses or theories were almost always couched in personal terms. He repeatedly stated that it was his limited views, either of mathematics or physics, that stood in the way of his understanding of what Ampère was driving at. I will argue, that this uncertainty about his own competence led Faraday to adopt the position towards theories and experiments which was the basis for his criticism of Ampère. This marked the beginnings of his own career in electrical science.

There is little record of Faraday's reaction to what was happening in France in 1820. News of Oersted's discoveries did not reach the Royal Institution until 1 October, when Humphry Davy burst into the laboratory to repeat what Oersted had done. Not until late in March 1821 did William Hyde Wollaston attempt, in the laboratory of the Royal Institution, to discover if a current-carrying wire could be made to rotate on its own axis.[15] Faraday was not there at the time.[16] In late May, at the London Institution, he observed the effects of a strong permanent magnet upon the electric arc, and carefully noted it in his *Diary*.[17] There are no other signs of particular interest or expertise. However, sometime in the late spring or early summer of 1821 Richard Phillips, one of the editors of the *Annals of Philosophy* and a long time friend, suggested to Faraday that he write an account of what had been done up to that point in the new science of electromagnetism.[18] It was this suggestion that was to start Faraday on his 40-year electromagnetic quest.

2 Faraday's first critique of Ampère

The 'Historical Sketch of Electromagnetism' appeared in three sections in September and October 1821 and in February 1822. The experimental parts were probably written in July, August and September 1821. Some of the last part dealing with electromagnetic theories, was written later.[19] Before we look at this history, we ought to ask what position Faraday took with regard to the relationships between experimental observations, hypotheses and theories, as he confronted the problem for the first time. Unfortunately there is little documentation on this point. About all we have from Faraday is his famous praise of Isaac Watts's *The Improvement of the Mind* in which the reader was warned to be careful in his use of language and cautious about the erection of general theories from 'a few particular observations, appearances, or experiments'.[20] Such advice was particularly good for someone about to make the acquaintance of Ampère who was guilty of both sloppiness of language and premature generalisation. Yet his reading of Watts seems a very slim foundation for Faraday's attitude. It is a commonplace that this kind of empirical caution, or 'Baconianism', was the prevalent attitude at this time in England.[21] There is evidence that the need for empirical caution was forcefully called to Faraday's attention just as he began to work on and write about electromagnetism.

A Baconian philosophy of experiment

In the March issue of the *Annals of Philosophy*, an article appeared attacking the use of hypotheses in the defence of the Franklinian one fluid theory of electricity. The substance need not detain us, but the methodological injunctions are of interest. The anonymous author began by praising the Baconian method:

> It has been repeated so often as almost to require an apology for its introduction, that the Baconian philosophy proceeds by discovering and establishing facts, holding that upon such a foundation alone, can be raised any structure deserving the name of science. The philosophy which has happily been almost exploded by Bacon and his successors, lays its foundations in hypotheses; and the labours of its adherents are spent in ingenious conjectures, or in efforts to bend the various facts discovered, to give those conjectures an apparent truth. A Baconian philosopher gathers his maxims and principles from the united rays of numerous observations and experiments, and as they are received in all the simplicity with which the facts themselves express them, they yield to the mind all that satisfaction and

confidence which spring from the clear perception of truth. On the contrary, an hypothesis is incapable of teaching any truth at all. . . .[22]

And further:

Unfortunately, the worthlessness of hypotheses is not their greatest evil; they invariably tend either to mislead the mind from those conclusions naturally deducible from experiments, or to induce an extravagant regard to some circumstances to the neglect of others equally or more important.[23]

The polemic that followed these introductory remarks well illustrated Watts's injunctions. It probably caught Faraday's attention, for he read the *Annals of Philosophy* closely.[24] But another example struck even closer to home. In the spring, summer and autumn of 1821 — i.e. in precisely those months in which Faraday was repeating the experiments on electromagnetism done by others and writing his account a series of articles appeared by John Herapath in the *Annals of Philosophy*.[25] In the April issue, Herapath began his 'A mathematical inquiry into the causes, laws and principal phaenomena of heat, gases, gravitation, &c.'.[26] Further articles and criticisms from others followed throughout the next year. Faraday had just completed a series of experimental researches on gases[27] and was well able to judge and evaluate both Herapath's methods and his conclusions.

What is striking about Herapath's papers is their formal resemblance to Ampère's early writings on electrodynamics. Like Ampère, Herapath used a few experimental observations as foundations for propositions from which he then mathematically deduced the properties of gases and predicted discoveries. We do not know Faraday's reaction but we do have a short and devastating critique of Herapath's work that appeared in the very same issue of the *Annals of Philosophy* in which the first part of Faraday's 'Sketch' was published. Faraday almost certainly saw it before writing his section on electromagnetic theories. The anonymous author first considers the proper relation between theory, hypothesis and experiment:

In Prop[osition] IX and its cor[ollarie]s which depend upon the last, he asserts in a somewhat positive manner, that MM. Dulong and Petit are mistaken in the result drawn from their experiments; but without entering upon any examination of their reasoning, and solely on the authority of his own theory. Thus even granting the validity of the proof above considered, he is assuming an hypothesis producing a result at variance with experiments (by his own confession) and in consequence rejecting the experiments.[28]

The lesson is clear: experiment regulates theory, not the other way around. It is reflected in the 'Sketch' and later writings of Faraday by his insistence on the circular nature of the electromagnetic 'lines of force', as opposed to Ampère's equally strong advocacy of central electromagnetic forces. Hypotheses cannot be freely used, but must lie within the domain defined by experimental investigation. But what if experiment cannot or has not yet defined such a domain? Here Herapath rushed boldly in to be met by another cold blast of criticism:

But the theorem in question rests upon the existence of a point of absolute cold; and, therefore, we must hesitate in admitting it until we have made up our minds on that much controverted point. Mr. H[erapath] has not proved that any such point exists; and till that is done, it is premature to think of finding an expression to represent it.[29]

This was precisely Faraday's attitude towards Ampère's circular electrical currents, especially those that were assumed to go around the particles of magnets. As Gooding argues in Chapter 6, he had made a similar criticism of fluid theorists supposition of an absolutely neutral electrical standard. Finally, the critic calls attention to an important lacuna in Herapath's theory. It does not offer a mechanism to explain the interaction of gas particles:

I would propose to his further consideration one difficulty attending it. Some atoms, he admits, may be composed of smaller particles; and, therefore, there can be no repulsions or collisions among these particles, yet there is between the 'little individual bodies' formed by them, and the other atoms of the gas; and as they must all be of the same kind, and endued with the same properties, there is a difficulty in conceiving how some of them come to unite, and others to repel one another, which needs some explanation.[30]

We can summarise these criticisms briefly. They will serve as a background for Faraday's treatment of Ampère (and others) in his 'Sketch'.

1. It is not scientifically proper to make up states or entities for which no experimental evidence exists.
2. Hypotheses cannot be freely invented, but must have some experimentally verifiable aspect.
3. Hypotheses must be clear and unambiguous, and they must serve to explain, in a mechanical way, the phenomena for which they are invented.

Faraday's 'historical sketch'

We know Faraday's experimental temper. I should like here to suggest simply that it was reinforced by the controversy over Herapath's theory. Unlike the subject of electromagnetism, in which Faraday was a novice, that of gases was very familiar. The full force of the criticism levelled at Herapath could be appreciated by him. Finally, the fact that the critics ended up disputing the mathematical aspects of the theory undoubtedly reinforced his own suspicions of the trustworthiness of the mathematical way which he thought inevitably anticipates nature.[31] As Faraday remarked to Ampère in September 1822 about the theories of electromagnetism proposed by Ampère, by Berzelius and by Prechtl:

these philosophers I believe and others also have given theories of electromagnetism which they stated would account not only for known facts but even serve to predict such as were not then known and yet when the new facts came (rotation for instance), the theories fell to pieces before them. These instances are sufficient to warn such feeble spirits as myself and will serve as my apology to you for not at once adopting your conclusions. I delay not because I think them hasty or erroneous but because I want some facts to help me on.[32]

Let us now turn to Faraday's assessment of the various experiments and theories of electromagnetism which appeared in the 'Sketch'. We may recall his diffidence as he faced the works of men such as Oersted, Berzelius and Ampère, all established scientists of high rank. He was, he wrote to Stodart at this time, 'but a young man, and without a name, and it probably does not matter much to science what becomes of me'.[33] He had confidence in his own experimental ability and carefully and painstakingly repeated the major experiments that had been done since Oersted's announcement.[34] By and large, the first two parts of the 'Sketch' merely summarised what had been done, although Faraday typically warned his readers early on that,

> There are many arguments in favour of the materiality of electricity, and but a few against it; but still it is only a supposition; and it will be as well to remember, while pursuing the subject of electro-magnetism, that we have no proof of the materiality of electricity, or of the existence of any current through the wire.[35]

This warning should be recalled when we come to his treatment of Ampère's theory.

In the last, and theoretical section, Faraday first examined Oersted's theory. He was here brief to the point of curtness for he wrote, 'I have very little to say on M. Oersted's theory, for I must confess I do not quite understand it'.[36] Nevertheless, he did the best he could with it, and it is worth repeating his account here:

> The theory of M. Oersted, therefore, seems to require that there be two electrical fluids; that they be not either combined or separate, but in the act of combining so as to produce an electric conflict; that they move nevertheless separate from each other, and in opposite spiral directions, through and round the wire; and that they have entirely distinct and different magnetical powers; the one electricity (negative) propelling the north pole of a magnet, but having no action at all on the south pole; the other electricity (positive) propelling the south pole, but having no power over the north pole.[37]

Two things stand out in this description: Faraday's attempt to visualise the complicated mechanical structure Oersted apparently wished to suggest to account for electromagnetism, and the fact that, with all its many flaws, the hypothesis did explain the phenomenon of electromagnetic deviation of a compass needle mechanically. Faraday quickly reviewed and dismissed a number of other schemes, including that proposed by Berzelius, without much discussion.

The bulk of the 'Sketch' he devoted to Ampère's view which, as he willingly stated, was the only one truly deserving 'the title of *A Theory*'.[38] But, he could hardly disguise his impatience with Ampère's work:

> M. Ampere commences by assuming the existence of two electric fluids, according to the theory which is now general, I believe, in France. There appears to be no

doubt about his meaning on this point, for though he uses the term electricity very frequently, and in a way which might be understood, perhaps, as applying equally either to a particular state of a body, or to a particular fluid existing among its particles, yet by the use of the term *electric fluids* in one place, and by the mention of electric currents as currents of matter, it is nearly certain that M. Ampere means to speak of electricity as consisting of two distinct fluids, which, though the one is called positive, and the other negative electricity, are considered as equally positive in their existence, and possessed of equal powers.[39]

Faraday then confessed that he could not follow Ampère's treatment of his idea of the electric current(s) in the voltaic circuit[40]:

M. Ampere, while speaking of the battery and connecting wire, says, it is generally agreed that the battery continues to convey the two electricities in the two directions it did at the moment the connexion was first completed; 'so that a double current results, the one of positive electricity, the other of negative electricity, parting in opposite directions from the points where the electro-motive action exists, and reuniting in that part of the circuit opposed to those points'.[41]

How this confrontation of two separate currents at the mid-point of the circuit gave rise to the observed effect puzzled Faraday completely:

This reunion would, of course, take place in the wire, and one may be allowed to ask, whether the magnetic effects depend on it, as M. Oersted seems to think, who calls it the electric conflict, and also what becomes of the electricities that accumulate in the wire.[42]

But the difficulties did not end here. Ampère made no attempt to use his hypothetical currents to *explain* electromagnetism by their confrontation, and he further confused the issue by suggesting a quite different model which Faraday found equally puzzling:

But, from other parts of M. Ampere's memoirs, a very different idea of the electric currents may be gained; the one electricity is considered as continually circulating in one direction; while the other electricity circulates and moves in a current in the opposite direction, so that the two electricities are passing by each other in opposite directions in the same wire and apparatus.[43]

I have quoted Faraday at some length for two reasons. Because the 'Sketch' was not included in the collected *Experimental Researches* it is not easily available. It also reveals Faraday's distrust of Ampère's unrestrained invention of hypothetical entities and processes. By contrast when stating what happened in a closed voltaic circuit, Faraday tried to describe only the phenomenon rather than offering a counter hypothesis. He believed only the former was required for the foundations of a theory:

Now as it is in this state that the wire is capable of affecting the magnetic needle, it is very important for the exact comprehension of the theory that a clear and precise idea of its state, or of what is assumed to be its state, should be gained, for on it in fact the whole of the theory is founded . . . and we may, therefore, be allowed to expect that a very clear description will first be offered of it. . . . [A]s M.

Ampere has chosen always to refer to the currents in the wire, and in fact, founds his theory upon their existence, it became necessary that *a current* should be described.[44]

But Ampère could not observe, and therefore could not describe an electric current. At the very outset Faraday found Ampère's theory seriously deficient. Despite his failure to give a precise definition of currents Ampère made further use of them. Diplomatically Faraday remarked that it was a bold idea for Ampère to assume the existence of electrical currents in permanent magnets. It was even bolder to propose that they circulated around the molecules of the magnet. Faraday remained sceptical of what was becoming a rather large set of gratuitous assumptions. These assumptions had heuristic value because by means of them Ampère was able to progress from discovery to discovery. Faraday could not accept the theory. Surprisingly in view of his earlier admission about Oersted's theory, he concluded his 'Sketch' by stating that Oersted's theory was marginally better than Ampère's. This was because it did at least attempt to explain electromagnetism.[45]

Ampère probably never read the 'Sketch', and was, therefore, unable to profit from Faraday's criticisms. But this anonymous piece was obviously a milestone for Faraday's work. It is well known that while Faraday was repeating the mapping of the compass needle near a current-carrying wire he noticed that the needle appeared to want to revolve around the magnetic pole.[46] This effect led Faraday to the discovery of electromagnetic rotation. This result made an enormous difference to Faraday's position. The 'Sketch' was anonymous but the rotations paper he signed. This was the paper to which Ampère made his first response. Before looking at this side of the dialogue it would be useful to clarify what the two were arguing about.

3 The dialogue begins

By the middle of 1822, after Ampère's response to the rotations paper had appeared, Ampère had devised five theories that he wanted to be taken seriously. These were in order of appearance[47]:

1. Magnetism is the result of current electricity.
2. Permanent magnets contain co-axial electrical currents or electrical currents around the particles of the magnet which produce the observed magnetic effects.
3. An electrical current is the passage of the two electrical fluids (themselves the products of the decomposition of the luminiferous aether) in opposite directions through a wire.
4. The attractions and repulsions of current carrying wires are the resultants of the central forces acting between small current elements in the wires.
5. These central forces are propagated by the vibrations of the luminiferous aether.

Faraday doubted every one of these points, as he wrote to G. De la Rive on 12 September 1821:

> I think the analogy between the helix & common bar magnet far stronger than before. But yet I am by no means decided that there are currents of electricity in the common magnet. I have no doubt that electricity puts the circles of the helices into the same states as those circles are in that may be conceived in the bar magnet but I am not certain that this state is directly dependent on the electricity, or that it cannot be produced by other agencies and therefore until the presence of Electrical currents be proved in the magnet by other than magnetical effects I shall remain in doubt about Ampere's theory.[48]

Faraday's doubts were based on experiments he recorded in his *Diary*. A week earlier on 5 September, he had made a magnetised needle pass into the centre of a current-carrying helix.[49] This series of experiments, concluding with the entry for 10 September, shows Faraday examining, amongst other things, Ampère's assumed identity of ordinary- and electro-magnetism. So although the paper on rotations was intended primarily to announce his new discovery, he took the opportunity to use his results to challenge Ampère's position. Ampère's central force assumption was the most obvious one to attack and so Faraday concentrated on it. Ampère had written in an early paper: 'Two electric currents attract one another when they move parallel to one another in the same direction; they repel one another when they move parallel to one another in opposite directions'.[50] Faraday's experiments were directed at this point. To simplify, what he accomplished was the mapping of the structure of magnetic action of currents to show how rotational forces could and did produce all the observed phenomena. The new rotational apparatus dramatically illustrated this point.[51] Faraday insisted that *all* the apparent attractions and repulsions, as well as the rotations, could be explained by assuming the circular structure of the force surrounding current carrying wires.[52] This was in direct contradiction to Ampère's theory of central forces.

Although this was the main thrust of Faraday's paper he did not ignore the other aspects of Ampère's work. Faraday opposed his own experimental results to Ampère's claim that magnetism was nothing but electricity in motion which Ampère thought he had proven by imitating permanent magnets with helices. Faraday showed that there are three conditions in which magnets and helices differed. First:

> One pole of a magnet attracts the opposite pole of a magnetic needle in all directions and positions; but when the helix is held alongside the needle nearly parallel to it, and with opposite poles together, so that attraction should take place, and then the helix is moved on so that the pole of the needle gradually comes nearer to the middle of the helix, repulsion generally takes place before the pole gets to the middle of the helix, and in a situation where with the magnet it would be attracted.[53]

Second:

> . . . The poles, or those spots to which the needle points when perpendicular to the ends or sides of a magnet or helix, and where the motive power may be considered

perhaps as most concentrated, are in the helix at the extremity of its axis, and not any distance in from the end; whilst in the most regular magnets they are almost always situate in the axis at some distance in from the end.[54]

Third:

> . . . The similar poles of magnets, though they repel at most distances, yet when brought very near together, attract each other. This power is not strong, but I do not believe it is occasioned by the superior strength of one pole over the other, since the most equal magnets exert it, and since the poles as to their magnetism remain the same, and are able to take up as much, if not more, iron filings when together as when separated, whereas opposite poles, when in contact do not take up so much. With similar helix poles, this attraction does not take place.[55]

Faraday's final, and must subtle, criticism of Ampère's theory of the identity of magnetism and electricity in motion took the form of a simple demonstration. It was a counter proof to Ampère's experiment in which he showed that a helix acted like a magnet. Faraday made a magnet that should have acted like a helix. He took a plate of steel and bent it around until it formed a hollow cylinder. He then magnetised it so that opposite poles were at each end:

> one end was north all round, the other south; but the outside and inside had the same properties, and no pole of a needle would have gone up the axis and down the sides, as with the helix, but would have stopped at the dissimilar pole of the needle. Hence *it is certain, that* the rings of which the cylinder may be supposed to be formed, are not in the same state as those of which the helix was composed.[56]

This proved that the electric currents that Ampère supposed to exist in the permanent magnet could not be concentric.[57]

Throughout this paper, Faraday refrained from giving any hint as to his own theoretical ideas. In the 'Sketch' he had insisted that the current carrying wire ought to be in some kind of a peculiar *state*. He made this point again in discussing the hollow magnet. In his 'Note on new electro-magnetical motions', dated January 1822 he offered the first experimental evidence for this *state*.[58] There he noted that the force of cohesion between the molecules of mercury through which the electricity was passing was apparently lessened by the electrical current. This result obtained with Davy indicated that intermolecular forces were involved in electrical conduction.[59] This effect helped confirm a suspicion about Ampère's theory that was first aroused by his work on electromagnetic rotations. Although Faraday had not used the philosophical terminology, he had earlier used a logical argument to illustrate that Ampère had perpetrated the fallacy of affirming the consequent. 'If A, then B; I observe B; Therefore A'. The accusation was made in the letter to G. De la Rive quoted earlier. The argument explains his affirmation that 'until the presence of Electrical currents be proved in the magnet by other than magnetical effects I shall remain in doubt about Ampere's theory'.[60]

Ampère's reaction

Historians have treated Faraday's work on electromagnetic rotations as an interesting debut which reveals Faraday's experimental skill and promises great things for the future. But it shook up the present when it was published. Ampère was profoundly affected by the discovery of the rotations. He returned to the importance of Faraday's paper time and time again, both in his published and his private writings. It is not difficult to understand why. If Ampère had predicted such rotations, as his theory permitted him to do, this would have made his theory far more acceptable. He had lost ground to Faraday. Some of this was recovered when he showed that a magnet would rotate on its own axis while conducting a current (that had also been predicted by his theory). The fact remains that an astonishing effect had been discovered by someone who was not merely critical of his theory but intent upon substituting a new way of looking at electromagnetism. Faraday's new view was absolutely irreconcilable with Ampère's. He could not let Faraday's paper go by without comment. The French translation of Faraday's paper[61] was followed by extensive notes by Ampère[62] in which he responded to the implicit and explicit criticisms that Faraday had made. These responses narrowed the theoretical options from which Ampère could choose thereafter. They thereby helped to shape the path that his future researches would take.

We should briefly glance at what Ampère had done since the autumn of 1820 when he made his first, brilliant discoveries. To simplify, Ampère followed two paths almost from the beginning of his work in electrodynamics. On one path, he spun ingenious hypotheses on the nature and propagation of the electrical forces that he supposed were the causes of magnetic appearances. He first proposed co-axial currents in magnets. Then, in January 1821, he cautiously adopted Fresnel's suggestion that these currents circulated around the particles of magnets.[63] Also in 1821 he suggested that the attractions and repulsions of current-carrying wires could be accounted for by undulations or polarisations in the luminiferous aether. For these physical, *ad hoc* hypotheses he had little or no experimental evidence. During these months Ampère also attempted to reduce the actions of current elements to mathematical precision. He had derived a formula for such actions as early as the autumn of 1820 but had not been able to make his calculations accord with experiment. The problem, which he did not see clearly for almost a year, lay in his evaluation of the constant, k, in the formula he had arrived at earlier for the electrodynamic force between two current elements. According to Hofmann, Ampère realised by March 1822 that to apply the general form of this force law to his and Faraday's discoveries of rotatory magnetic effects entailed a change in the value of k. Although his commitment to his physical hypotheses reached its strongest point during 1821, much of his experimental work was devoted to discovering a method of establishing the value of k.[64] His 'Réponse à la lettre de M. Van Beck sur une nouvelle expérience électro-magnétique', which appeared in October 1821,[65] adopted definitively the hypothesis of electrodynamic molecules. He used this hypothesis to present a general theory of chemical, magnetic and electrical phenomena.

One other preliminary point is worth stressing before we look at Ampère's notes. Faraday's attack on Ampère's use of *ad hoc* hypotheses and his lack of predictive success hit Ampère at two points where he was already vulnerable. Ampère was a close friend of Fresnel who had recently battled successfully against the opposition of the corpuscularism of the Newtonian–Laplacians. The most vocal of these opponents was J.-B. Biot. His defence of light particles required an ever increasing number of *ad hoc* hypotheses to fit the corpuscular theory to the evidence. Fresnel's victory, in which Ampère had played a small part, was due to four things: his more elegant use of the undulatory theory to explain optical phenomena, the number of hypotheses burdening the corpuscular theory, the decisive character of the relationship between his theory and experiment and finally the changing personal institutional allegiances.[66] Two of these are particularly important. Perhaps with Biot's defeat by Fresnel in mind, Ampère wished to avoid jeopardising his position by inviting further criticisms of his use of physical hypotheses and experiment by Faraday. The mathematical way must have seemed far safer. It was after all Ampère's own territory. Faraday's discoveries and criticisms of Ampère's hypotheses were largely responsible for Ampère's turning away from the physics of electromagnetism to concentrate instead on the mathematical laws of its action.

Ampère's notes to the French translation of Faraday's paper can be divided into two categories[67]: the philosophical and the direct. The former deal with what Ampère felt to be essential in a scientific theory. In the latter Ampère confronted Faraday's criticisms directly and tried to neutralise them by using his own theory to explain the phenomena that according to Faraday did not fit it. The philosophical responses are largely confined to notes two and four. Note two marks Faraday's statement that 'Several important conclusions flow from these facts; such as that there is no attraction between the wire and either pole of a magnet; that the wire ought to revolve round a magnetic pole and a magnetic pole round the wire'.[68] Instead, as Faraday later insisted, the *simple* action is the circular one. Ampère responded:

> The revolution of the conducting wire and of a magnet, one around the other, that M. Faraday considers as the basic fact [fait primitif] throughout this memoir will not permit the phenomena to be analysed mathematically; to do this, it would be necessary to be able to determine precisely the action between each element of the wire and each particle of the magnet.[69]

This, of course, was simply to insist that Faraday should carry out Ampère's programme. Faraday was neither capable nor willing to do this. But there was more:

> The attractions and repulsions of two finite conducting wires, discovered by M. Ampère, are also not simple facts. It seems to us that this name can only be given to the laws of mutual action; which action must be admitted between two points within two ensembles of an infinity of these points, thus providing the phenomena that we observe. It then follows that simple facts cannot be immediately observed, but can only be deduced from observations with the aid of mathematical calculation.[70]

We may note that Ampère was not quite accurate here. He did not yet have the experimental measures with which to determine the constant, k, in his equation. He was therefore unable to use 'le calcul' to determine *his* 'fait primitif'.

Ampère continued his criticism in note four. He responded there to Faraday's bold claim that 'it is evident that the attractions and repulsions of M. Ampere's wires are not simple, but complicated results':[71]

> If, in this passage, M. Faraday means only that the attractions and repulsions of electric currents are complicated facts in that they are the result of an infinite number of actions between all the infinitely small parts of these currents [Faraday had not meant this], he would be in accord with M. Ampère. But, he finds them complicated from another point of view because he takes the rotary action for the basic fact [fait primitif] and nicely shows that these attractions and repulsions can be reduced to it. But, we have just shown, on the contrary, that if the basic fact be taken as the attractions and repulsions between the small parts of the electric currents, following the laws given by M. Ampère, then the circular motions of the conducting wires and of the magnets around one another can be immediately deduced.[72]

Faraday knew that attractions and repulsions of small currents cannot be observed. He also appreciated that Ampère had *not* deduced the rotations from his formula, probably because he was preoccupied by attractions and repulsions. Rather, it had been Faraday who'had shown that rotation was a necessary consequence of the patterns of force indicated by how magnetised needles behaved near a current carrying wire. He might well have asked why Ampère's view should seem more 'simple' or 'primitive' than his own. To preserve an experimental opening for mathematical analysis, Ampère had to make his attractions and repulsions more primitive than Faraday's rotations. However, Ampère replied by appealing first to the equivalence of the two primitive facts. 'The only thing that can be concluded from this is that facts such as those that are here in question can be explained equally well in these two ways, and they cannot serve to resolve the question'. He then pointed out that 'all the actions that produce the phenomena discovered up to now take place between two points along the line joining them, just like the attractions and repulsions admitted by M. Ampère between two small parts of electric currents'. From these attractions and repulsions 'can easily be deduced all electro-magnetic facts, including those with which M. Faraday has just enriched this science'. The superiority of Ampère's theory was now that 'these facts become part of the general laws of physics, and there is no need to admit a rotary action as a simple and primitive fact [fait simple et primitif] for which there is no other example in nature and which it seems difficult to us to consider as such'.[73] Faraday was unimpressed by this argument and continued to see reality in his own novel way. Faraday's 'fait primitif' eventually grew into his lines of force which became the basis for most of his mature researches.

Ampère's annular ring experiment

Ampère's response to Faraday's challenge was hardly convincing. To the three objections on the identity of helices and permanent magnets, Ampère replied only to the second concerning dissimilarities between their poles. Not until later was Ampère able to explain away the anomaly of the location of the magnetic poles in helices and magnets (see below). The hollow magnetic cylinder was another matter. Here Ampère felt confident that he had the answer:

> When one supposes currents in the magnet around its axis, the analogy of the hollow cylinder with the helix ought to be exact; but if one holds that these currents are established around the particles of magnets, as M. Ampère has done in a memoir read to the Institute in January, 1821, in which he announced that this hypothesis seemed more probable to him (*), then the magnetised needle inside the hollow cylinder will always be outside these currents, whereas in the helix, it is inside them. This is what accounts for the differences in action remarked by M. Faraday.[74]

The asterisk refers to another note in which Ampère pointed out that he now had experimental evidence to support his hypothesis of the molecularity of the electrical currents in magnets. In July 1821 he had performed an experiment in which he had hung an annular copper ring, suspended by a very fine thread, inside a spiral of insulated copper wire (Fig. 5.1). The purpose of the

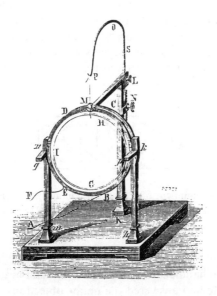

Figure 5.1 Ampère's annular ring. (From Joubert (1885–7), **2**: 213.)

experiment was to determine whether electrical currents could be induced by the current-carrying wires. If the annular ring deviated when a permanent magnet was held near it while a current circulated in the surrounding insulated wires then Ampère would have had to conclude that the currents in permanent magnets were co-axial; if no deviation occurred they would be molecular. There was no deviation and Ampère concluded:

> . . . it thereby results that no electrical current can be excited by influence. This has led the author [Ampère] to believe that, before magnetisation, there are electrical currents around the particles of bodies susceptible of magnetisation, but that they exist in all sorts of directions. Thus, their actions on points outside of these bodies are mutually cancelled and these actions became manifest only when, by magnetisation, specific directions are given to these currents.[75]

This experiment and this explanation of Faraday's hollow magnet were absolutely fundamental for Ampère's future work. The central core of his electromagnetic views was the identity of magnetism and current electricity. The evidence for this identity was his ability to reproduce or explain *all* cases of magnetism by suitably arranged electrical currents. For Ampère, Faraday's cylinder was explicable only if the currents that cause magnetism were molecular.

The July 1821 experiment also permitted Ampère to deal with the problem of the location of the poles in a magnet and in a current carrying helix. In a letter to De la Rive of 12 June 1822, he showed how a simple adjustment of his electrodynamic molecules could remove all difficulties.[76] All that was required was another small *ad hoc* supposition, namely, that the molecules were not all aligned parallel to the magnetic axis, but were 'bent' into curves (presumably by the inter-molecular magnetic forces of the particles themselves) (Fig 5.2). Then the poles of the permanent magnets would not be at their extremities. This explanation could not be derived from co-axial currents.

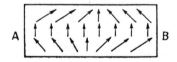

Figure 5.2 Ampère's alignment of his electrodynamic molecules. (From Ampère to De la Rive, 12 June 1822, in *Launay* (1936–43), **2**: 581.)

In the early summer of 1822, Ampère must have been reasonably pleased with the way he had handled the severe attack which Faraday had made in his rotations paper. He had answered the major objections, at least to his own satisfaction. More important still, was the fact that earlier in 1822, he had found the correct value of k.[77] He was, therefore, able to push his calculations along with some despatch. The only cloud was the slowness with which his work was accepted. No doubt this would pass and he would be able at last to enjoy the glory due to him as a *savant* of the first rank. But that summer he was dealt two harsh blows that altered the course of his work. The first came from his Swiss friend, Baron Maurice. In a letter of 5 July, Maurice sent him the criticism of 'une personne qui s'occupe de science' and who remained sceptical of Ampère's theories. The anonymous sceptic said:

I am not yet as satisfied as you are with the developments of Ampère's theory. I would wish with all my heart that the deductions from his principle could be simplified and made more rigorous because this principle is, itself, brilliantly simple when compared to the complicated hypotheses of the English and the Germans. It is not so much the mental gymnastics necessary to envision the actions of the currents which repels me in this theory as it is the great number of purely gratuitous hypotheses, the abuse of the consideration of the infinitely small about which one can say anything that one wants, and the mixing in of certain dynamical ideas whose introduction seems arbitrary and whose influence is not precisely spelled out. It even seems that the author has recently made some modifications to his hypothesis on the disposition of currents in magnetised bars in order to explain certain phenomena made by M. de la Rive. . . . No one can deny that everything that M. Ampère has done has been very ingenious, but I cannot believe that this is going to last very long *just as it is* [*tel quel*] and it will be sad if this theory fails, for all the others, especially those of the Germans, are frightfully complicated.[78]

From Ampère's point of view, Biot had been defeated by Fresnel on similar grounds. How seriously Ampère took this criticism is revealed by the length and detail of the letter he wrote in answer to Maurice.[79] But no matter how he twisted and turned in his answer, he did not successfully dismiss the charge that his theory was burdened with *ad hoc* hypotheses.[80]

This letter might have upset Ampère only mildly, but for another shock. In August 1822 he and A. De le Rive repeated the copper ring experiment using a powerful horseshoe magnet as the detector of any possible induced current. This time it succeeded![81] The results were read to the Académie des Sciences on 16 September. Ampère was unequivocal about the results. The experiment 'consequently leaves no doubt of the production of electrical currents by influence [of currents], unless there might be a little iron in the copper which formed the mobile circuit'.[82] Ampère's report indicates that the copper ring remained 'magnetic' throughout the entire time that the current passed through the coil of wire. Faraday was quite excited about the news,[83] although his *Diary* gives no indication that he repeated the experiment. What is important about this experiment is Ampère's treatment of it. Although he could not deny the evidence of his own eyes — that the ring was moved by the magnet — he did the next best thing. He dismissed it. He never published the report he gave to the Académie, and he disposed of the experiment with the curt remark that 'This fact of the production of electrical currents by influence, although interesting in itself, is, however, independent of the general theory of electrodynamic action'.[84] Ampère later had cause to regret this when Faraday announced his discovery of electromagnetic induction.[85]

4 Conclusion

What can this possibly mean? What has happened to the experiment that Ampère had explained by the existence of molecular currents, *not* induced co-axial currents? After all, he had based his answer to Faraday's second criticism on this explanation. Ampère now found himself in an impossible situation. He had publicly changed his theory in accord with the earlier results of the copper ring experiment and publicly announced that the location of the poles in permanent magnets could *not* be accounted for by assuming induced co-axial currents. Now he had discovered those unwanted currents! As his anonymous critic had made clear another *ad hoc* adjustment would threaten the whole theory. So Ampère swept the whole thing under the rug.[86] He also made a marked change in his scientific direction. This is visible in Ampère's work from the summer of 1822. Gone are the brilliant, but often wild, guesses and hypotheses that he had thrown out with such abandon in his earlier papers. His publications now became austere and mathematical, culminating in the great *Mémoire sur la théorie mathématique des phénomènes électrodynamiques uniquement déduite de l'expérience* which appeared in 1826.[87] It was this work that earned him James Clerk Maxwell's accolade that he was the 'Newton of electricity':

> The whole, theory and experiment, seems as if it had leaped full grown and full armed, from the brain of the 'Newton of electricity'. It is perfect in form, and unassailable in accuracy, and it is summed up in a formula from which all the phenomena may be deduced, and which must always remain the cardinal formula of electro-dynamics.[88]

Some of the credit must go to Faraday who, more than anyone else, pushed Ampère onto his new path.

Notes

1. Oersted (1820a) in Latin and rapidly translated into English, French and German as Oersted (1820b, c, d).
2. Faraday (1821–2, 1821b). This latter was translated into French as Faraday (1821c). Ampère (1821b) commented on this.
3. A.-M. Ampère (1775–1836). The standard biographies remain Launay (1924) and Valson (1885). See also L.P. Williams, 'André-Marie Ampère', *DSB*, **1**: 139–47.
4. Fox, R. (1974).
5. Fresnel (1820), Williams, L.P. (1965), 145–5, Ross (1965).
6. J. Hofmann, 'Electromagnetic induction and Ampère's evaluation of experimental evidence in electrodynamics: 1820–1823', (unpublished), 31ff. See also Caneva (1981).

7. The most striking example of this was Arago's discovery of 'magnetism by rotation' (Arago's wheel). Ampère never tried to *explain* what was happening in terms of his theory. He only sought to *reproduce* the phenomenon by substituting current-carrying spirals for the compass needle or bar magnet. I will be treating this subject in greater detail in a future article.
8. Ampère (1821a).
9. Faraday (1819).
10. Stodart & Faraday (1820, 1822).
11. Faraday to G. De la Rive, 20 April 1820, *Correspondence,* 1: 45.
12. Faraday to Ampère, 3 September 1822, *Correspondence,* 1: 58.
13. Phillips to Faraday, 4 September 1821, *Correspondence,* 1: 49. Faraday (1821–1).
14. See Faraday (1823b), *ERE,* 2: 161 where he admitted authorship.
15. Faraday to Stodart, 8 October 1821, *Correspondence,* 1: 51.
16. See Faraday (1823b), *ERE,* 2: 159 where he says he later came in, helped with their experiments and 'heard Dr. Wollaston's conversation'.
17. Faraday, *Diary,* 21 May 1821, 1: 45–6.
18. Phillips to Faraday, 4 September 1821, *Correspondence,* 1: 49.
19. Faraday (1823b), *ERE,* 2: 161. See also Hartley (1965).
20. Watts, I. (1809), 44, Williams, L.P. (1965), 12–13.
21. See Porter, R.S. (1977), Weindling (1980), Inkster (1981) for the political and social reasons for this caution.
22. 'Observations on a memoir "On the theory of Franklin, according to which electrical phenomena are explained by a single fluid," read at the Royal Institution of the Sciences at Amsterdam, by M. Martin van Marum, Knight of the order of the Belgic Lion, Secretary of the Dutch Scientific Society, Director of the Teylerian Museum, &c, &c.', *Ann. Phil.,* 1821, 17: 181–6, 181.
23. *Ibid.*
24. See Williams, L.P. (1965), 43–4.
25. Herapath also was, apparently, known to Faraday personally; this hardly guarantees that he read the articles. See Phillips to Faraday, 4 September 1821, *Correspondence,* 1: 49.
26. Herapath (1821).
27. Faraday (1821a).
28. 'Remarks upon Mr. Herapath's theory', *Ann. Phil.,* 1821, 18, 223–6, 224.
29. *Ibid.,* 225–6.
30. *Ibid.,* 225.
31. Cantor (this volume) and Gooding (1982b). The issues of the *Annals of Philosophy* during the autumn and winter of 1821 and the spring of 1822 contained a number of anonymous articles, critical of Herapath's mathematical and physical reasoning.
32. Faraday to Ampère, 3 September 1822, *Correspondence,* 1: 58. Compare Faraday to G. De la Rive, 9 October 1822, *Correspondence,* 1: 60.
33. Faraday to Stodart, 8 October 1821, *Correspondence,* 1: 51.
34. Phillips to Faraday, 4 September 1821, *Correspondence,* 1: 49. Phillips apologizes, in this letter, saying, 'I do feel no little regret that I should have been the cause of so much trouble & annoyance to you'.
35. Faraday (1821–2), 196.
36. *Ibid.,* 107.
37. *Ibid.,* 108.
38. *Ibid.,* 111. Faraday's emphasis.
39. *Ibid.* Faraday's emphasis.
40. Ampère realised that he had not been very clear in this exposition. As he wrote to his friend, Roux-Bordier on 21 February 1821, 'Je sais bien que mon mémoire n'est pas rédigé assez cliarement; célà vient de ce que je l'ai ecrit avec une hâte extrème et par

morceaux détachés que j'ai ensuite réunis comme j'ai pu', Launay (1936–43), **2**: 565–7, 566. See also Williams, L.P. (1983), *passim*.

41. Faraday (1821–2), 112.
42. *Ibid.*
43. *Ibid.*
44. *Ibid.* It is worth remarking what Faraday's *own* ideas seem to be. The electric 'current', whatever that may be, throws the wire into a 'state' and it is this 'state' that underlies electromagnetic effects. I suggest that Faraday envisioned an effect of the 'current' on the molecular forces of the wire. See Williams, L.P. (1965) in which I argue that Faraday was using the concept of point force-atoms as early as 1821.
45. Faraday (1821–2), 117.
46. For a full analysis of how Faraday came to notice this see Gooding, Chapter 6.
47. See Blondel (1982), 69–107.
48. Faraday to G. De la Rive, 12 September 1821, *Correspondence,* **1**: 50.
49. Faraday, *Diary*, 5 September 1821, **1**: 53, para 35.
50. Ampère (1820), 76. 'Deux courans électriques s'attirent quand ils se meuvent parallèlement dans le même sens; ils se repoussent quand ils se meuvent parallèlement en sens contraire'.
51. Williams, L.P. (1965), 161ff.
52. Faraday, *Diary*, 4 September 1821, **1**: 51, para 20.
53. Faraday (1821b), *ERE,* **2**: 143.
54. *Ibid.*, 144.
55. *Ibid.*
56. *Ibid.*, 145. My emphasis.
57. *Ibid.*
58. Faraday (1822), *ERE,* **2**: 156–7.
59. Davy, H. (1823).
60. Faraday to G. De la Rive, 12 September 1821, *Correspondence,* **1**: 50.
61. Faraday (1821c).
62. Ampère (1821b).
63. Blondel (1982), 98ff.
64. Hofmann, *op. cit.* (6), 5–7.
65. Ampère (1821a).
66. Fox, R. (1974), Frankel (1976), Caneva (1980), James, F.A.J.L. (1984).
67. Ampère (1821b).
68. Faraday (1821b), *ERE,* **2**: 129.
69. Ampère (1821b), 371. 'L'action révolutive du fil conducteur et d'un aimant l'un autour de l'autre, que M. Faraday considère comme fait primitif dans tout ce Mémoire, ne suffirait pas pour soumettre les phénomènes au calcul; il faudrait qu'il eût déterminé d'une manière précise l'action qui a lieu entre chaque élément du fil et chaque particule de l'aimant'.
70. *Ibid.* 'Les attractions et les répulsions de deux fils conducteurs d'une longueur finie, découvertes par M. Ampère, ne sont pas non plus des faits simples; il nous semble qu'on ne peut donner ce nom qu'aux lois d'action mutuelle; qu'il faut admettre entre deux points pour qu'il en resulte, entre deux assemblages d'une infinité de ces points, les phénomènes qu'ils nous présentent; dès-lors les faits simples ne peuvent être observés immédiatement, mais seulement conclus des observations à l'aide du calcul; . . .'
71. Faraday (1821b), *ERE,* **2**: 132.
72. Ampère (1821b), 373. 'Si M. Faraday, dans ce passage, entendait seulement que les attractions et répulsions des courans électriques sont des faits compliquées en tant qu'ils résultent d'une infinité d'actions entre toutes les parties infiniment petites de ces courans, il serait d'accord avec M. Ampère; mais il le regarde comme compliqués sous un autre point de vue, parce qu'il prend l'action révolutive pour le fait primitif, et montre très bien que ces attractions et répulsions peuvent y être ramenées; mais nous

venons de faire voir qu'en considérant, au contraire, comme fait primitif les attractions et répulsions entre les petites portions de courans électriques, d'après les lois données par M. Ampère, on en déduit immédiatement les mouvemens circulaires des fils conducteurs et des aimans les uns autour des autres'.

73. The previous four quotations are from *Ibid.*, 374 which reads: 'La seule chose qu'on en peut conclure, c'est que les faits qui, comme ceux dont il est ici question, s'expliquent également bien des deux manières, ne peuvent servir à résoudre la question. Nous nous bornerons à remarquer que toutes les actions qui produisent les autres phénomènes découverts jusqu'à ce jour, ont lieu entre deux points suivant la ligne qui les joint, comme les attractions et répulsions admises par M. Ampère entre deux petites portions de courans électriques, et dont on peut déduire si facilement tous les faits électro-magnétiques, y compris ceux dont M. Faraday vient d'enrichir la science; en sorte qu'en adoptant la théorie de M. Ampère, ces faits rentrent dans les lois générales de la physique, et qu'on n'est pas obligé d'admettre comme fait simple et primitif une action révolutive dont la nature n'offre aucun autre exemple, et qu'il nous parait difficile de considerer comme tel'.

74. *Ibid.*, 376. 'Quand on suppose les courans dans l'aimant autour de son axe, l'analogie du cylindre creux, avec l'hélice devrait être complète; mais si l'on admet, comme l'a fait M. Ampère dans un Mémoire lu à l'Institut en Janvier 1821, que ces courans sont établis autour des particules des aimans, hypothèse qu'il annoncait dans ce Mémoire comme lui paraissant la plus probable (*), l'aiguille aimantée dans l'intérieur du cylindre creux se trouve toujours en dehors des courans, tandis que, dans l'hélice, elle leur est intérieure; ce qui doit produire les différences d'action qu'a remarquées M. Faraday'.

75. *Ibid.* '. . . il en résulte que l'on ne peut point exciter de courant électrique par influence; ce qui a porté l'auteur à penser que les courans électriques existent, avant l'aimantation, autour des particules des corps susceptibles de magnétisme, mais qu'ils y existent dans toutes sortes de directions; ce qui fait que leurs actions sur des points situés hors de ces corps se détruisent mutuellement, ces actions ne se manifestant que quand on donne, par l'aimantation, des directions déterminées à ces courans'.

76. Ampère to De la Rive, 12 June 1822, in Launay (1939–43), **2**: 580–2.

77. Hofmann, *op. cit.* (6), 11.

78. Maurice to Ampère, 5 July 1822, in Launay (1936–43), **3**: 924–5. 'Je ne suis pas encore aussi satisfait que vous des développements de la théorie de M. Ampère. Je voudrais de tout mon coeur que les déductions du principe se simplifiassent et devinssent plus rigoureuses, parce que ce principe est lui-même brillant de simplicité à côté des hypothèses compliquées des Anglais et des Allemands. Ce n'est pas tant la contention d'esprit nécessaire pour saisir les actions des courans qui me répugne dans cette théorie que le grand nombre d'hypothèses toutes gratuites, l'abus de la considération des infiniment petits avec lesquels on peut dire tout ce qu'on veut, et le mélange de certaines idées dynamiques dont l'introduction n'est pas suffisamment motivée ni l'influence nettement caracterisée. Il paraît même que l'auteur a fait récemment quelques modifications à son hypothèse sur la disposition des courants dans les barreaux aimantés, afin de pouvoir expliquer certain phénomène observé par M. de La Rive. . . . On ne peut nier que tout ce qu'a fait M. Ampère ne soit très ingénieux, mais j'ai peine à croire que cela tienne longtemps *tel quel*; et il faudra vivement regretter cette théorie si elle tombe; car toutes les autres, celles des Alemands surtout, sont d'une effrayante complication'.

79. Ampère to Maurice, 6 July 1822, in *ibid*, **3**: 925–8.

80. *Ibid.* See particularly p. 927 for Ampère's defence of his 'bent' lines of electrodynamic molecules needed to meet Faraday's objections.

81. De la Rive (1822) presented to the Société de Physique et d'Histoire naturelle de Genève on 4 September 1822 an inadequate and misleading account of his work. Ampère read 'Notice sur quelques expérience nouvelles relatives a l'action mutuelle de deux portions de circuit voltaique et à la production des courants électriques par influence, et sur les

circonstances dens lesquelles l'action électrodynamique doit, d'après la théorie, produire dans un conducteur mobile autour d'un axe fixe un mouvement de rotation continu, ou donner à ce conducteur une direction fixe' on 16 September 1822 to the Académie des Sciences in Paris but it was not then published. It was published from the manuscript for the first time in Joubert (1885–7), **2**: 329–37.

82. *Ibid.*, 334. 'ne laisserait, par conséquent, aucun doute sur la production des courants électriques par influence, si l'on ne pouvait soupçonner la présence d'un peu de fer dans le cuivre dont a été formé le circuit mobile'.

83. Faraday to G. De la Rive, 9 October 1822, *Correspondence*, **1**: 60. Recent research by Mendoza (1985) suggests that it is not self evident that there would have been an effect only when the current and the primary was established or when it was cut off. See also Williams, L.P. (1985).

84. Ampère *op. cit.* (81), 334. 'Ce fait de la production de courants électriques par influence, très intéressant par lui-même, est d'ailleurs indépendant de la théorie générale de l'action électrodynamique'.

85. Thompson (1895), Ampère (1831) (The December 1831 issue of the *Annales* was late; Ampère made this claim in January 1832). For another view of this episode see Ross (1965).

86. It did not stay there for long. In January 1832 Ampère claimed that he had discovered electromagnetic induction in 1822. It is ironic that Ampère passed by a discovery that would have elevated his scientific status to the very first rank as a result of being a prisoner of his own theories. See note 85.

87. Ampère (1827).

88. Maxwell (1892), **2**: 175.

6

'In Nature's School': Faraday as an Experimentalist

David Gooding

We are used to thinking about Faraday as one of the greatest experimentalists who ever lived. The success and influence of his experiments has eclipsed the processes of experimentation, so that we still know very little about the latter. In this essay I want to redress the balance by answering the question 'What was Faraday so good at doing'? The simple answer is that Faraday was good at learning how to do experiments. The simplicity is deceptive. We tend to identify 'experimentation' with 'demonstrations', interpreting experiments through results whose significance we already know through theory. This confines experiment to the traditional roles of supporting or refuting theories against their rivals and of making phenomena and data self-evident. But these uses depend as much upon mastery of the arts of construction and presentation as they do upon actual control of natural processes. As experimentalists are well aware, experiments rarely work at first, or as expected. When they do work, it is often for the wrong reasons. The technical and observational processes that constitute an experiment are reworked until it can be performed by any competent practitioner. Why is this necessary?

At first only one or two people know how to do an experiment and to observe its results. A natural phenomenon is at first identified with its discoverer and a few initiates and would not exist without them. To become accepted as part of scientists' experience that phenomenon must be transferred from the personal realm to the public domain, where it can be reproduced and witnessed by all. To be seen as a natural fact it must be seen to exist independently of any particular person, laboratory or experimental technique.[1] Faraday was good at moving his discoveries from the personal domain of the contingent to the public forum of the demonstrable and self-evident. However, Faraday's public account of his own role was disarmingly modest. He presented his experiments as a process of learning from nature. He wanted his audiences in the great lecture theatre of the Royal Institution to think of themselves as being in 'Nature's school'.[2] Closer examination of the development of his experiments suggests a different image of nature as collaborator rather than instructress. So my question should be reformulated: How did Faraday turn tentative and private results into public, collectively witnessed and self-evidently *natural* facts? And how did he win so much cooperation from nature?

Faraday's records of his experimental work show that he learned a great deal whilst getting his experiments to work. Surprisingly, this process of learning has not been studied. Sometimes his understanding of a phenomenon altered so much that the outcome — the result that signalled the completion of an experiment — differed from what he had anticipated theoretically. In this respect even a confirming experiment may create new problems for a theory.[3] Faraday was an effective experimentalist because he was able to use information acquired in the course of making an experiment work. He used this information to modify and clarify his conception of the experiment and his expectations about its outcome. I call it 'information' to distinguish it from the familiar but misleading ideas of visual observation, the passive recording of data, and learning by trial and error. (For example, numerical results were usually only a means to more important, qualitative judgements.[4]) Moreover, what he learned was not purely visual, verbal or conceptual in character. Nor was it entirely procedural or practical. Faraday was good at combining perceptual, conceptual and practical knowledge to represent and commun- icate new information about nature.[5]

Faraday's experimental practice contrasts with the passive conception of observation with its emphasis on visual perception, its neglect of the extent to which experimenters must intervene in natural processes and its subordination of experiment to theory as a method of gathering evidence whose significance is given from the outset. The active nature of exploratory work is sometimes acknowledged but then dismissed as intellectually uninteresting (typically, as 'trial and error'). Faraday's laboratory notes and his published papers are a remarkably complete record of a major experimentalist who regarded 'all that elevates and enlightens the intellect' as *practical*.[6] They show that the relationship between trials, their outcomes and learning is more interesting and more complex than we realise.

1 Mastery of nature and mastery of culture

Making an experiment work involves solving several distinct but interrelated types of problems. These I call: discrimination, representation, proof, scale and demonstration. Faraday encountered these problems when developing exploratory, open-ended procedures into proven methods of demonstrating the reality of natural phenomena. He was particularly good at discriminating artefacts of his apparatus, practices or theoretical beliefs from information about (or actually due to) the processes under investigation. Scientists often cite the problem of distinguishing signal from noise to illustrate this point. But this analogy implies a greater degree of prior agreement about how to recognise signal and noise than we usually find in experiment at the frontiers. Much of Faraday's time and energy went towards 'proving' his experiments. This involved experimenting to determine whether a tentative discrimination between reality and appearance had been made correctly in exploratory work. Students of scientific method are beginning to appreciate how much goes into successful discrimination and how dependent this is upon effective representations (I discuss representation in some detail in section three).[7]

A related practical problem was to alter the scale of effects, i.e. to make minute effects into 'sensible' phenomena that could be witnessed by lay observers.[8] This was done by magnifying the effect, either optically (e.g., through back-projection of small effects) or causally (e.g., by making the wanted, insensible effect cause a more obvious one). Demonstration experiments make phenomena and processes evident to lay observers. Good demonstrations solve the problems of discrimination, proof and scale. Faraday did this so effectively that he made it difficult for others to realise that most of his experimental work told him more about the investigative techniques he used than about nature. Faraday's most famous experiments were demonstrations in this sense. They made phenomena self-evidently *natural*, seemingly due to natural processes rather than human ingenuity and artefice. But it is these experimental procedures that occupy the several thousand pages of the *Diary* and the *Experimental Researches*.

Faraday's mastery of these practices made them invisible. The very invisibility of enabling techniques is what made the demonstration experiment so effective as a means of disclosing nature directly to lay-observers. Faraday knew that an experimentalist preoccupied by practicalities or encumbered by problems with his apparatus will make his audience very much aware of them as well.[9] His success in the public domain was to make the experiments transparent. An experiment is transparent when the apparatus and procedures appear to contribute nothing to what the experiment shows. Like the preparations and manipulations of a magician, they are unobtrusive, though not necessarily invisible. This is how Faraday persuaded his audiences to perceive the great lecture theatre at the Royal Institution as *Nature's* school — not Faraday's. In nature's school the phenomena displayed are natural facts, free of human ingenuity or artifice.

Mastery of culture appeared as mastery of nature. Faraday had laboured for hours, days and weeks to acquire the skills necessary to produce these effects. He knew that nature cannot be disclosed directly, without preparation or prejudice. His own daily experience confirmed the degree to which scientists construct their perceptions and the self-evidence of those perceptions. Yet he continued to believe that properly conducted experiments do provide perceptual knowledge about nature.[10] He thought practical experience more reliable and less prone to the distortions of intellectual prejudice than observation interpreted through theory.[11]

Faraday's view of exploratory and proving experiments was more sophisticated than that implied by his metaphor of nature as school mistress. Yet this
metaphor does capture Faraday's view of demonstrations. As far as he was
concerned, the large audiences at his lectures at the Royal Institution did not
need to know how much preparation went into the demonstration of nature.
But we need to understand the preparatory work if we are to understand the
force of experiment as an agent of intellectual, technical and social change.

2 The place of experiment

An architectural image may help delineate the place of experiment at the
Royal Institution in the early nineteenth century. Faraday's *Diary* records the
journeys of natural phenomena from their inception as personal, tentative
results to their later objective status as demonstrable, natural facts.[12] These
journeys can be visualised as passages from the laboratory in the basement up
to the lecture theatre on the first floor. This was a passage from a private place
to a public space. As Sophie Forgan has pointed out, the basements of these
houses were private; usually reserved for servants.[13] In her chapter she reminds
us that the upper floors of the Royal Institution where Faraday lived and had
his study, were also private. We can visualise the dissemination and
demonstration of natural phenomena as a public activity sandwiched between
these two layers of privacy. Every public experiment made the journey up the
stairs to the lecture theatre.[14] This reminds us of the uniqueness of the Royal
Institution, which brought extensive resources for producing new knowledge
together with facilities for disseminating it.

But physical proximity often disguised temporal distance. The *Diary* shows
that although a few of Faraday's experiments took only a few hours to reach
maturity, many took weeks to perfect. Others such as the search-coil
experiments, occupied him several times during the four decades of his active
scientific career. To recover an idea of the magnitude of the preparatory work
we can compare the several thousand pages on which Faraday recorded the
invention and conduct of his experiments with the few pages needed to state
the main results of these experiments. This is the difference between the stack,
say, 18 inches high, and one barely an eighth of an inch high. We can make this
comparison because Faraday recorded the lives of many of his experiments, in
writing and with diagrams.[15] But to explain the *difference* in the size of the two
stacks of paper we must rely on things that he could not describe in drawing or
writing. These include the procedures underlying the possibility of observation, the tools and instruments with which observable phenomena were
produced and the tacit skills that enabled him to make it all work.[16] These are
neither tangible nor literary. This may explain why they have been ignored by
historians. Some can be recovered and used to interpret scientific developments of historical and psychological interest. In his chapter Tweney draws
attention to the importance of procedure in Faraday's *Chemical Manipula-*

3. FARADAY'S DIARY

being the record of his researches from 1820 to 1862, which he bequeathed to the Royal Institution saying in his will ". . . these I offer for the Library of the Royal Institution if the Managers should think them worth a place"

Plate 12 Faraday's manuscript *Diary*. Royal Institution.

tion. My prehistory of certain demonstration experiments also emphasises the importance of concrete and procedural aspects of his work, insofar as they can be recovered from the inscriptions and artefacts available.

Faraday's contribution to the development of science and technology consists in the remarkable number and importance of his experimental results. This work can also contribute to our understanding of that development as a learning process. Here his contribution was to record in detail work which actualised mere possibilities, making their reality an irreversible matter of public experience. The ability to make phenomena real epitomises the force of experiment as an agent of change. But Faraday's skill as master of an experimentalist's culture does not fully explain that force. To do that we would have to examine prevailing conceptions of experiment and Faraday's influence on them, particularly his influence on the use of experiment in science education.[17] Here I want to draw attention to the private *beginnings* of experiments, that is, to the truly open-ended experiments that enabled Faraday to make phenomena visible and accessible to others. In these the techniques and instruments are still too opaque to be of use in the lecture theatre.

3 The prehistory of a new phenomenon

Changes in the way scientists perceive the world are often initiated by one or two people. They persuade others, first of the existence of a new phenomenon and then of its importance. This makes the transition from the personal to the public domain important to the history of science.[18] I want to show how Faraday used practical ways of presenting phenomena to translate novel effects into communicable, shareable facts. This was a precondition of his winning the agreement of his contemporaries, both about what they experienced in the course of a new experiment and about the significance of that experience. My examples include some ordinary objects, such as the bottle cork that Faraday is said to have carried about during the early 1820s. The early history of this and other, more complex pieces of apparatus, shows that their invention shaped the construction and the communication of early interpretations of new electromagnetic phenomena.

New magnetic motions: representation and realisation

My first example is the phenomenon of magnetic rotation which Faraday realised in September 1821. I will discuss this in the context of Davy's investigation of the magnetic effects of currents. I want to show how Faraday reached a working prototype in which he got a bit of wire to move around an ordinary magnet. This was an entirely new effect of natural forces. The perfected rotation apparatus performed the important function of communicating a new interpretation of a novel physical action. Its later and more familiar technological applications in motors and dynamos depended on Faraday's ability to demonstrate the reality of continuous rotary motion due to an electric current. Here three points about the interpretation of new results are important. First, when confronted with truly novel possibilities, observers do not know quite how to interpret them. Yet they soon reach agreement about how to see what is new. Second, as studies of analogical inference show, the novel is usually interpreted through the familiar.[19] But complete assimilation of the novel to the familiar would blunt the ability of new information to change existing views. How is complete assimilation avoided? Finally, what Faraday did was often a precondition of what he saw. These last two points need elaboration.

Faraday believed in the possibility of preserving novel aspects of phenomena. Like many of his contemporaries, he recognised that new phenomena are often as difficult to describe as they are to obtain reliably. Observer's confusion may be shortlived but it is nonetheless very real. This is why Ampère, Roget and others emphasised the need for representations and mnemonic devices for the interpretation and exploration of electromagnetic phenomena.[20] Mnemonics were devised and tried in the laboratory, realised as demonstration apparatus and put to use in lecture theatres.[21] Their success as aids to experimentation and demonstration earned them a role as exemplary, textbook representations of new phenomena. Successful representational practices helped fix interpretations. By the time they were published these devices and practices embodied new ways of thinking about the phenomena.

The brevity of the un-practised, pre-conseptual state makes it difficult to recover. It was usually dismissed as an unimportant or undesirable stage, to be got through as quickly as possible. However, as Elspeth Crawford argues Faraday had the extraordinary ability to capture and hold this state of not being sure how to proceed. He used the ability to criticise his own experiments as well as those of others. Here I shall recover the 'pre-articulate' stages that led to established interpretations, by looking at examples of their construction. The first of these is drawn from reports published by Davy and by Faraday in 1821 and 1822.[22] These suggest that one of Faraday's interpretations of electromagnetism emerged from Davy's earlier exploration of the region of the current. When repeating some experiments of Ampère, Davy observed that the magnetised needle set in the positions 1–n, as shown in Fig. 6.1(a).

These were the disconnected results of individual observations. To make them intelligible Davy ordered the outcomes so that successive positions of the needle displayed the structure shown in Fig 6.1(b). The ordering could have been achieved operationally and in real time (by moving the needle around the circumference of an imaginary disc) or pictorially (by recording the observed 'set' of the needle in each case). The result would be the same in either case. It is the device Faraday published in his 1821 review of the spate of experiments occasioned by Oersted's discovery (discussed by Pearce Williams in his chapter). This device is shown in Fig. 6.2(a). It consisted of a cardboard disc

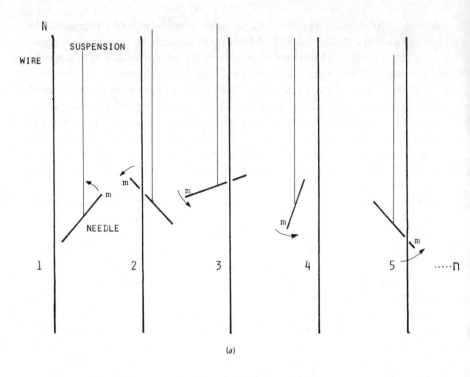

(a)

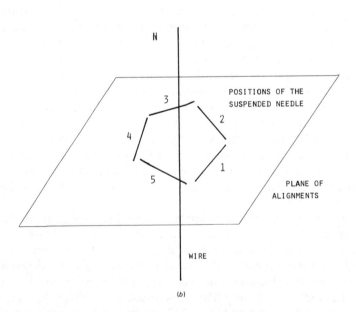

(b)

Figure 6.1 (a) Exploring the region of a current with a magnetised needle. (b) A representation of the positions of the suspended needle.

mounted on an axle. Arrows drawn on the disc represented the direction of the magnetic effect, so that the disc exemplified the circulatory aspect of electromagnetism. This was a model of an interpretation of the outcome of a sequence of operations.

Faraday's drawings of representational devices and images are typical of those published by many others at this time. These were part of the attempt to

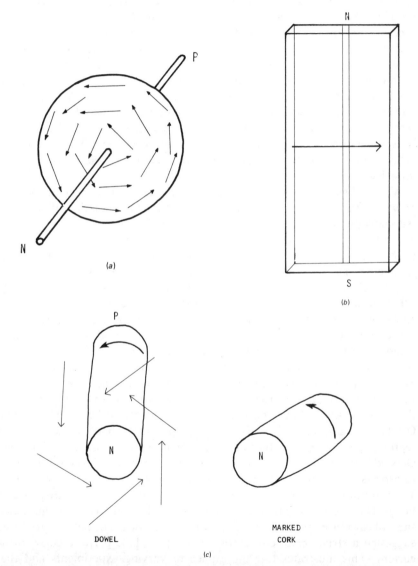

Figure 6.2 (*a*) Davy's disc device. (From Faraday (1821–2), plate, Figure 11.) (*b*) Faraday's glass box. (From Faraday (1821–2), plate, Figure 3.) (*c*) Faraday's marked dowel. (From Faraday (1821–2), plate, Figure 6 & 7.)

discern structure and order in the confusion engendered by Oersted's discovery. They conveyed likely relationships between electric wires and magnetised needles. Faraday made a glass box on which he drew a line and an arrow, as shown in Fig. 6.2(b). This was made to help would-be observers remember one of the (by then) favoured ways of interpreting the interaction of currents and magnetised sensors. In the autumn of 1821 Davy and Faraday were still electromagnetic novices. Even when practised in observation, Faraday needed such devices to orient perception in new or unfamiliar experimental arrangements, and to show lay observers what to look for. Another version of this mnemonic consisted of a wooden dowel on which he drew an arrow to represent the 'circumferential' or 'circuital' aspect of one form of electromagnetic interaction. This is now in the Faraday Museum at the Royal Institution. But it is a relatively refined version. We know the prototype only by anecdote. Faraday carried an ordinary bottle cork about with him, marked as shown in Fig. 6.2(c). By sticking a pin into this he could convey the direction of the magnetic action of the current thus represented. (This shows that sometimes anecdote can usefully complement other historical sources.)

What did such artefacts have to do with perceiving new phenomena? My answer to this question shows how important the manipulation of artefacts, especially the crude prototypes, can be to our understanding of experiment as a learning process. By realising aspects of an effect visually or operationally, these objects and images made them concrete, objects of public experience. Arranging the operations and their outcomes in this way resolved the perceptual uncertainties created by the announcement of Oersted's discovery. When devices such as Faraday's cork or Davy's disc successfully conveyed precisely that aspect of a phenomenon intended by its inventor, this success 'bootstrapped' them into a more interpretative role.[23] In this new role others could use it to examine the phenomena further.

If images and artefacts enable observers to translate their personal experience into a social and public form then we should find other examples in which observational practices — what observers *did* — helped to shape how they came to *think* about new phenomena. Many would-be observers found Oersted's description of his discovery opaque. Davy had to find a way of reproducing it in a form that he could communicate more effectively than Oersted had. Davy's disc was meant to solve this problem. It owed something to aspects of electromagnetic phenomena besides the one so far described. When repeating Ampère and Arago's observation that a wire attracts iron filings, Davy made an important modification. He sprinkled iron filings on a sheet of card through which a vertical wire was passed. The pattern produced suggested a structure of concentric circles in a plane perpendicular to the current. This illustrates the importance of varying experiments and that variation often includes exploring possibilities inherent in an arrangement, not suggested by theory.[24]

We do not know which experiment came first. Perhaps the trial with the iron filings was informed by those with the needle (described in Fig. 6.1). It is plausible to suppose that the image embodied in Davy's disc provided an interpretation of the needle positions and the filing patterns. This integrated these two different pieces of information, drawing attention to alignments and away from motions (which would otherwise be interpreted in terms of traditional pondermotive forces). But if we had evidence that the iron filing experiments preceded those with the needle, then I would suggest that the image of concentric rings provided an interpretation that structured Davy's investigations with the magnetised needle. Either reconstruction is compatible with my view of exploratory observation in which learning is more important than proof. I shall use this view to interpret my second example, for which there is both textual and artefactual evidence.

Davy's disc and Faraday's cork were constructs, not natural phenomena. They were made to solve the problem of communicating about a concrete, perceptual world. This problem arose first in the local context of the laboratory. But they had to convey their interpretations to a wider audience. This they did by expressing the result as, for example, the circle made up of needle alignments or of filings. This image became fixed as an interpretation of the whole domain of interventions and outcomes. One of the most important of these outcomes was that a wire can be made to circulate around a magnet and the magnet about a fixed wire. Faraday demonstrated these in September 1821. It is possible that Faraday was looking for an effect suggested by W.H. Wollaston's theory of rotating currents.[25] But in that case his discovery was inadvertent; the result, perhaps, of a fortunate bit of manipulation. This would suit the naïve 'trial and error' view that exploratory experiments are

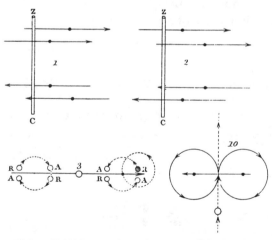

Figure 6.3   Faraday's pictorial summary of how a magnetised needle behaves near a very strong current. The wire is vertical and the needles are suspended at the point indicated by a dark spot. Faraday's 'Figure 3' is a summary of 1 and 2 (see the text). (From *ERE*, **2**, plate 2.)

worthwhile only when they address the predictions of a theory. Faraday's laboratory record shows a different sequence of events, and this suggests that he had different aims. In particular, it suggests that he was more interested in resolving a tension between two observations than in proving an interpretation of one of them. Faraday wanted to reconcile two anomalous aspects of electromagnetism. One concerned attraction and repulsion, namely, the fact that whether a needle is attracted or repelled seems to depend simply on position. Fig. 6.3 shows his diagram of this, published in 1821.[26] The problem was to interpret this fact in a way that made it compatible with the other main anomaly of structure. As represented by Davy's disc and circles of filings, this was that no known force exhibited structure in the way electromagnetism did.

SEPT. 3RD, 1821.

Electromagnetic expts. with Hare's Calorimotor. To be remembered that this is a single series? ELECTRO-MAGNETISM.

1. Position of the expt. wire A*.
2. Positions at first ascertained were as follows

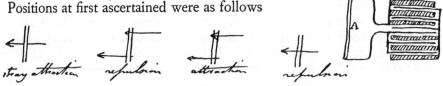

3. On examining these more minutely found that each pole had 4 positions, 2 of attraction and 2 of repulsion, thus

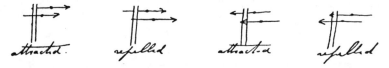

4. Or looking from above down on to sections of the wire

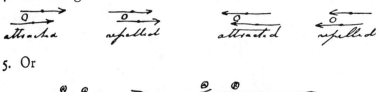

5. Or

Figure 6.4 The sequence of operations that lead to the result in Figure 6.3, as recorded in Faraday's *Diary*, 3 September 1821, **1**, p. 49.

'Sept. 3rd, 1821'

During his experiments on 3 September 1821 Faraday was using these two interpretations simultaneously. By the end of the day he had resolved the tension in favour of one of them.[27] How did he do this? Faraday's record is reproduced in Fig. 6.4. He first recorded that the experimental wire was positioned vertically rather than horizontally. This reflects that fact that the magnetised needle was used analogously to the pith ball of an electroscope, i.e. as a hand-held sensing device. It could be moved more freely round a verticle wire. In the early experiments the needle was suspended on a thread, sometimes by one end and sometimes at its mid-point. Faraday then recorded the tendencies of the needle to approach or recede from the wire. He represented these as properties of position, not as the effects of pondermotive forces. Next he recorded a 'more minute' observation of the behaviour of the needle from above and from the side. This behaviour could be interpreted in terms of each pole of the needle having two positions of attraction and two of repulsion. This brought out the first of the two anomalies mentioned earlier. Finally he gave a pictorial summary which compressed all of the preceding results into a single pair of diagrams, shown in Fig. 6.5.

Up to the end of paragraph five there is an unresolved tension between the two interpretations. One is based on the conventional pondermotive forces while the other uses Davy's disc or circles. The next development apparently resolves the tension. This is a verbal statement in pagraph six: 'These [effects] indicate motions in circles round each pole . . .'. The verbal description is accompanied by a diagram of the apparent motions. Faraday had imagined, but had not yet tried to produce these motions. He now had an interpretation which could be expressed both pictorially and verbally: 'Hence the wire moves

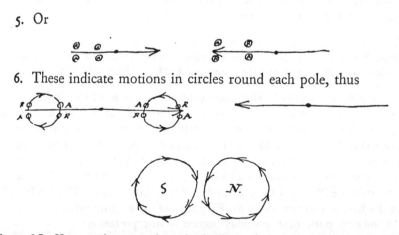

Figure 6.5 How motion near the poles becomes circles around each pole. From Faraday's *Diary*, 3 September 1821, **1**, p.49–50.

in opposite circles round each pole and/or the poles move in opposite circles round the wire'.

This last statement is a prediction. It states a consequence of Faraday's interpretation of the behaviour of the needles. But his verbal description of these in paragraph six is literally false. With the arrangement drawn here, he could not 'indicate motions in circles round each pole'. The effects depicted in the diagram are the successive positions of needles obtained in a *sequence* of operations. A needle does not approach or recede from a wire if, as shown in the diagram, the two are in the same plane. Faraday's important inference from the temporal sequence to spatial structure tacitly transforms that sequence into a spatial arrangement. As with Davy's disc, a set of interventions is expressed by a single image. But the image of a circle only applies if one makes a mental transformation, so that needle (or magnet) and wire are in the same vertical plane. This transformation — imagining that it is the *wire* which describes circles instead of the needle — probably had a practical objective, to solve a problem of representation. Faraday needed to record and describe in two dimensions an interpretation of something that was supposed to happen in three dimensions.

How did Faraday try to 'establish the motion of the wire'? First he placed a piece of wire so that

> its lower end dipped into a little basin of mercury in the water and its upper entered into a little inverted cup containing a globule of mercury.

Then, magnets 'of different powers' were 'brought perpendicularly to this wire'. However, they 'did not make it revolve as Dr Wollaston expected, but thrust it from side to side'.[28] Faraday now realised that the wire would move bodily, not on its axis. Further exploration showed that the wire tends to move in either direction along a line perpendicular to the axis of the approaching magnet. This led him to make an important variation:

> The wire [was] then bent into a crank form, thus [Fig. 6.6(a)], and by repeated applications of the poles of the magnets the following motions were ascertained, looking from above down on the circle described by the bent part of the wire . . . .

He brought the magnet towards the 'centre of motion' of the crank, i.e., its axis.[29] The crank swung around so as to strike the magnet. By moving the magnet quickly out of the way and reinserting it the other way round he got the crank to keep moving. He recorded this motion in the *Diary* as a ring, shown in Fig. 6.6(a). The ring represents a circle described by a point on the rotating crank. The rotation was produced by 'repeated applications of the poles' at points indicated by the letters 'N' and 'S' around the rings in Fig. 6.6(b). This was the first electric motor, with Faraday acting as commutator!

In the next paragraph Faraday turned to interpretation:

> The effort of the wire is always to pass off at a right angle from the pole, indeed to go in a circle round it; so when either pole was brought up to the wire perpendicular to it and to the radius of the circle it described, there was neither

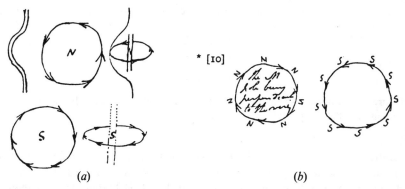

Figure 6.6 (*a*) Faraday's rotating crank. From Faraday's *Diary*, 3 September 1821, **1**, p. 50. (*b*) Chasing the crank with a North or South magnetic pole. From Faraday's *Diary*, 3 September 1821, **1**, p. 50.

attraction nor repulsion, but the moment the pole varied in the slightest manner either in or out the wire moved one way or the other.

There were certain positions of unstable equilibrium but not the attractions and repulsions required by Ampère's analysis.[30] Faraday then established that the action occurs if the magnet is outside the plane of the circle shown in Fig. 6.6(b). This result was important because it showed that the magnet was not interacting with the current construed as a three dimensional entity confined to the axis of the wire. This ruled out Wollaston's hypothesis and any theory that took electricity to be something inside the wire, whether Ampèrian current elements or imponderable fluids. Faraday later made much of these implications, but he did not dwell on them here.[31] He went on to make an important inference:

> From the motion above a single magnet pole in the centre of one of the circles should make the wire continually turn round.

From the several distinct sets of manipulations just described, Faraday had learned how to construct a rotation apparatus:

> Arranged a magnet needle in a glass tube with mercury about it and by a cork, water, etc. supported a connecting wire so that the upper end should go into the silver cup and its mercury and the lower move in the channel of mercury round the pole of the needle. The battery arranged with the wire as before. In this way got the revolution of the wire round the pole of the magnet.

It is possible to explain his inference in the following way. Faraday knew that a wire crank would try to rotate, as it were, around the *pole* of the magnet. The motion could not be continuous because the pole had to be close to the *axis* of the crank (not outside the circles in Fig. 6.6(a)). This meant that the crank collided with the magnet. One solution was to move the magnet out of the way and reverse it as the crank went by. Faraday's rotation device realised another

Figure 6.7   Faraday's sketch of his first rotation device. From Faraday's *Diary*, 3 September 1821, **1**, p. 50.

solution: to straighten the wire but keep the magnetic pole 'inside' the axis of motion of the wire by placing both in the same axis. Faraday's first quick sketch of the rotation device is shown in Fig. 6.7. The circles he drew now represented the actual path of the end of the wire dipped into the mercury. He had now realised the circles he had invented earlier in the day (at paragraph six), when he imagined that the magnet and the wire are in the same vertical plane.

The passage from what could be imagined to what could be realised was not direct, nor was it guided by purely theoretical considerations. The sequence of operations in paragraphs 7–13 is a fine example of Faraday's practical intelligence. It shows that his interpretations had to undergo considerable experimental clarification so that Faraday could learn the material conditions necessary to realise the effect. Only then could experiment be brought directly to bear on the prediction of paragraph six. We find this throughout the *Diary*, for example in his later experiments on the magneto-optical effect. There Faraday learnt the unspecified conditions by modifying his apparatus and its arrangements. Learning to do experiments involves doing, not simply deriving.[32]

4 The rhetoric of experiment

Although the rotations were not private in the epistemological sense, the effect was still personal, i.e. peculiar to Faraday. No one else had seen it; nor could they see it without instruction from him. His concluding entry for the day read: 'Very satisfactory, but make a more sensible apparatus'. Faraday intended to make the effect more visible, accessible and self-evident.[33] This shows how quickly he turned to the problem of demonstrating circular motion.

Most people familiar with this episode will think of the apparatus published in 1822, shown in Fig. 6.8. This demonstrated both the rotation of the wire around the fixed vertical magnet and the 'converse' effect, rotation of a pivoted magnet around a fixed vertical wire. This made both forms of rotation apparent to lay observers. However, Faraday made another device for his scientific colleagues. This was a pocket-sized rotation apparatus, which by mid-November he was sending to several scientific friends (Fig. 6.9). Though less spectacular, this device was important in winning acceptance of the fact

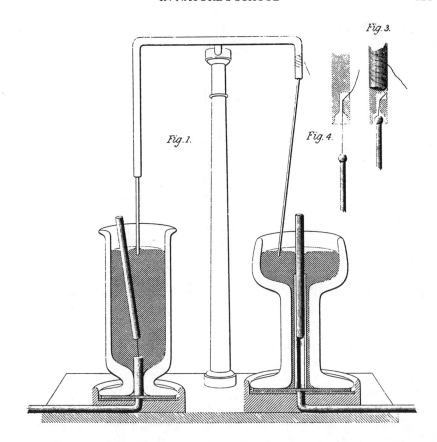

Figure 6.8 The rotation apparatus developed for demonstrations. This version shows, on the left, that a magnet can be made to rotate about a wire as well. From *ERE*, **2**, plate 4.

and also recognition of his role as discoverer. It illustrates Faraday's recognition of the rhetoric of experiment; to make a phenomenon real he had to make it accessible.

Access is often made more easy by practical means than by verbal communication. He made it easy for others to reproduce the effect by sending them the device. This also shows how aware he was of the possibility of failure. It reduced the risk by making it unnecessary for others to acquire all of the practical skills and tacit knowledge that Faraday had so labouriously built up.[34] The 'pocket' rotation apparatus embodied much that Faraday had learned about electromagnetic experiments. It symbolises a rather neglected factor in Faraday's success as an experimentalist: his ability to identify and avoid pitfalls so as to make sure that experiments by others would reproduce his own results. That others should see for themselves was important to Faraday's epistemology and to his ambitions as an experimentalist.

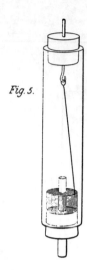

Figure 6.9 The 'pocket' rotation apparatus that Faraday sent to fellow scientists. From *ERE*, **2**, plate 4.

The preceding discussion makes clear that I doubt that a desire to test theoretical views (whether Wollaston's, Barlow's, Ampère's or Davy's) led Faraday to deduce the rotation effect. Nor do I think that he stumbled upon it by trial and error. The structure of the entries in his notebook suggests that Faraday was exploring new possibilities. A striking feature of paragraphs 1–6 is that each numbered entry (with its accompanying drawing) incorporates information contained in the preceding entry. Each interprets some aspect of the previous trial (or entry) in the light of what Faraday had just done with the needle. From paragraphs 7–13 the correspondence between what he did and what he recorded is not as direct. Yet each trial incorporated information learnt in the previous ones, as shown by the modifications made to the form and arrangement of the wire and by his use of the magnet. This process was not one of testing a single, unchanging hypothesis or model. Rather, up to paragraph 13, the end of the 'first day', his interpretatons changed and developed as each trial added new information. This is a nice illustration of the active character of observation. By looking closely at his modifications of an apparatus we have come to understand the emergence of an interpretation and Faraday's realisation of it. This shows the closeness of the interaction of thought, action and belief.

Faraday's method of active exploration made variations of a property with *position* all-important. This method was one source of his later field physics, devised to explain these variations. Like an explorer of geographical territory, Faraday occupied the very space filled by the forces he was investigating. This approach contrasted strongly with Ampère's emphasis on null-experiments, made with balances designed to measure forces between stationary or semiconstrained conductors and sensors. Faraday's approach was typical of other members of the London electromagnetic network of the 1820s.[35] But he pursued it further than anyone else. We will now see that by 1836 Faraday occupied that physical space with his person as well as with his instruments.

5 Mapping the electrostatic lines

Faraday scholars acknowledge the importance of patterns such as Davy's iron filings or Chladni's acoustical figures to his concept of magnetic lines. Yet his search for pattern in the work on electrostatics has escaped their notice. Between 1834 and 1836 he made several attempts to obtain more direct evidence of the existence of electrostatic lines. He hoped such evidence would come from their structuring effects on, for example, lycopodium powder sprinkled on an electrolyte.[36] Though he could not observe electrostatic lines directly, he was keen to construct maps of them. These experiments show that the method of active intervention contributed to what was later named as a 'field' conception of electricity. They also show that he varied the method of investigation to obtain even more direct perceptual access to lines of induction.

By 1836 he had developed methods of correlating electrostatic intensity to position. These methods generated maps of lines and surfaces of equal intensity.[37] One method used a traditional indicator of intensity, the gold leaf electroscope. By moving it about in a copper boiler and noting the amount of deflection of its leaves (Fig. 6.10(a)), Faraday built up this picture of surfaces

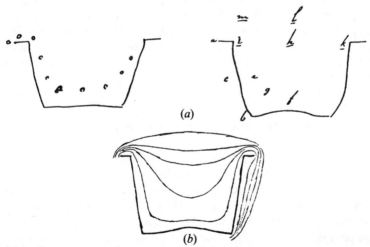

Figure 6.10 (a) Mapping the electrostatic field: positions and degrees of intensity as indicated by a gold-leaf electroscope. (From Faraday's *Diary*, 8 December 1835, **2**, p. 413–4. (b) Lines of constant deflection of the leaves of the electroscope. (From Faraday's *Diary*, 8 December 1835, **2**, p. 414.)

of constant deflection (Fig. 6.10(b)). Another method reminds us how much Faraday depended on senses other than vision. He moved the end of a wire connected to an electrostatic generator around an earthed copper boiler. Variation of the pitch of the sound of the discharge indicated a change in the intensity of the electricity being discharged. These techniques allowed Faraday to draw his first pictures of equal intensity. The lines reproduced in Fig. 6.10(b) are not lines of induction.[38]

Faraday now sought a method of observing the lines themselves. The observational techniques he employed varied in sophistication, but all used stroboscopic observation of a diffused form of electrostatic discharge called the electric brush. Most were adapted from methods developed by Charles Wheatstone in experiments on the velocity of electrostatic discharge. These are described by Bowers in Chapter 8. The simplest method comprised moving the fingers in front of the eye. But this required much practice. The most elaborate used Wheatstone's revolving mirror device. All showed that the brush consisted of many filaments or 'striations' (Fig. 6.11(a)).[39] The filaments changed form as the two terminal points were moved about. This indicated to Faraday that though variable in form, the brush remained constant in structure (Fig. 6.11(b)). As he pointed out in the published report, because the finger method required much practice it was less likely to disclose the structure than observation via Wheatstone's mirror. Once again he preferred to rely on the results of technical ingenuity rather than the variable skills of would-be observers.

Technical means of augmenting and structuring ordinary vision reassured Faraday about the ability of experiment to win new information about nature. His confidence in the use of such perception enhancing techniques was probably reinforced by his well-known distrust of the use of theoretical constructs to order experience. As he argued in 1850, theoretical inferences should not 'go far beyond or at all events not aside from the results of experiment'.[40] My next examples illustrate how this affected Faraday's interpretations of null-results.

6 The pursuit and capture of charge: Faraday's cage

Faraday's *Diary* shows that during 1836 and 1837 he was working out the implications of observational possibilities for a conception of electric charge. This series of experiments culminated in the construction of the famous Faraday cage, an apparatus so large that he could place himself inside it along with his instruments. Why was Faraday so keen to occupy this territory and capture charge?

It is plausible to suppose that his attempts to isolate electricity of one kind were attempts to prove or to falsify fluid theories of electricity. He presented these experiments in this light himself in October 1837. By then he probably did see them as simple refutations of fluid hypotheses. But this interpretation

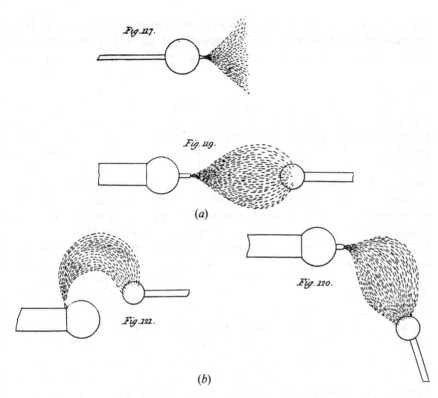

Figure 6.11 (a) An engraving of the luminous lines of discharge ('striations') in the electric brush. (From *ERE*, 1, plate 8). (b) Other forms of the electric brush in which its structure is shown to remain the same. (From *ERE*, 1, plate 8.)

overlooks developments which made it possible for Faraday to bring experiment to bear upon hypotheses in such a direct manner.

During 1835 he repeated and varied experiments with metal buckets and boilers which were part of the established repertoire of electrostatic demonstrations.[41] He may have thought it possible to capture or isolate electricity of one kind, independently of its opposite. By January 1836 he realised that an isolated charge (an inherently positive or negative state) cannot be detected without begging important physical questions. This brought out an implication of certain observational practices which was to transform his understanding of the experiments. It became explicit in a thought-experiment in which Faraday discussed the electrical observations that could be made by mites occupying a globe surrounded by a larger conducting sphere. He argued that they could determine the electrical state of their globe only as a relative quantity. As we shall see this expressed succinctly what Faraday had learnt about electrostatic phenomena during the preceding year. But the thought-experiment altered the physical interpretaton of procedures with devices that appear to contain electricity of one kind or to exclude it altogether. This necessitated a reinterpretation of the meaning of established demonstration experiments such as the ice-pail experiment. By October 1837 Faraday was ready to alter the physical meaning of a whole tradition of experimentation in electrostatics.

Whereas the spectacular effects of other experiments quickly made their way upstairs to the lecture theatre, these two experiments were not presented to the public. The cage was so large that it had to be built in the lecture theatre. Its effects could not be safely demonstrated to a large audience. Faraday's report of it appeared in the *Philosophical Transactions*. The thought experiment remained unpublished. Perhaps Faraday felt that it was unworthy; perhaps he did not recognise its importance to the development of his new understanding of electrostatic phenomena. He later turned it into a demonstration with a white mouse in place of the mites in a lecture in 1843 on the ice-pail expeiment.[42] The events show that some experiments were confined to the basement of the Royal Institution for many years. However, even on that occasion not everything went upstairs to the lecture theatre. The limitations of the observability of electricity had further implications for Faraday's views of electricity and matter. He did not announce these until the following spring.[43]

Two points about these experiments deserve emphasis. First, though he appeared to be repeating well-known experiments on induction, Faraday actually varied them in ways which contributed directly to the radical reinterpretation of inductive phenomena he had made by the spring of 1836. Varying the experiments involved exploring new observational possibilities. These were inherent in or suggested by the available instruments and techniques (as we saw in the 1821 experiments). This elicited new information about the behaviour of static electricity. Here was another instance of learning through doing. Although the learning involved the refinement and augmentation of observational techniques, the effect here was quite different. The 1821 rotation experiments helped Faraday *develop* the image of electromagnetic circles as a demonstrable and interpretable fact. By contrast this work *undermined* the conceptions that informed his initial experimental approach to electrostatic phenomena. This created a need for a new one. There is a similar process in Faraday's work on diamagnetism, in which some of the conceptions that informed his investigations were refined and transformed between 1845 and 1849.[44] The second point is that the development of new conceptions requires the reinterpretation of familiar experiments and the learning of new observational practices. As Kuhn has argued, new physical concepts are usually acquired in this way.[45] This is why Faraday was keen to appropriate the existing domain of electrostatic experiments.

Why did Faraday build the cage?

When examining variations in the electric intensity in the region of large electrified containers Faraday found, as expected, that the electrometer showed indications of charge unless the container was completely covered. He had surmised in December 1835 that electrical effects within these bowls, buckets and boilers must be caused by induction.[46] This was not consistent with the mathematical theory of electrostatics because the properties of inverse square forces required that there be no induction within a closed conductor. But Faraday regarded this mathematical answer as irrelevant to his problem. As an experimentalist he had to see what an electroscope does inside a completely closed conductor. Metals conduct but they are opaque, glass is transparent but does not conduct. So he had to build a conducting container large enough to allow an observer to get inside with the electrometer. But this container would have to allow an audience to see the electrometer too.[47]

Solving these practical problems of observation and demonstration was one of Faraday's main reasons for building the cage. Made of strips of metallic foil supported by wire on a wooden frame it was in effect a transparent conducting container. The cage was a 12 foot cube. As Faraday made clear in the published account, he meant to occupy the same space as the electrostatic forces: 'I went into the cube and lived in it' with 'lighted candles, electrometers and all other tests of electrical states'.[48] Making the container larger had important advantages. It reduced the disturbing effects of making observations. For example, a small observation hole in the large cage did not sensibly affect the electrometer, whereas the same size hole in a small boiler would have done. This change of scale also 'magnified' the effects so that lay observers could not fail to see them. The needs of demonstration reversed the usual order: the cage began in the lecture theatre, ended up in the laboratory with the small parrot cage, and returned to the lecture theatre in 1843.

Faraday did not expect to find charge inside the cage. Some assume that he did not actually find charge there.[49] But he did, in two sorts of circumstance. The leaves of an electrometer indicated charge when placed near gaps between the metallic foil strips comprising the cage.[50] The second circumstance was when anything was brought into the cage. Faraday seems to have been surprised by this. His habitual attention to detail led him to concentrate on it. The resulting investigation had a striking effect on his understanding of what he was doing. This is recorded in his *Diary* entries for 15 and 16 January 1836. First he noticed that

> On opening the cube door, then wherever the electrometer was placed within, the introduction of the hand, the head, or a wire made the distant leaves diverge positive. . . .
> Leaving the electrometer inside and closing all up, if a wire or other discharging agent were put opposite the outside away from the leaders [supplying the charge], then the electrometer opened within.[51]

It is typical of Faraday that he should treat this unexpected effect as a new source of information. He now had to decide whether it was due to his procedures and equipment or due to nature. The attempt to explain the conditions of the appearance of charge inside the cage led him to articulate a new concept of electrostatic induction.

Of mites and measurement: a thought-experiment

The established methods of detecting charge had been developed during the eighteenth century. They were understood in terms of fluid theories of electricity. Such theories postulate the conservation of charge, understood as the indestructibility of a quantity of electricity. But Faraday was concerned with a less obvious presupposition, that there is a 'natural', 'unexcited' or wholly neutral state. Such a state is logically entailed by the fact that positive and negative states (or fluids) are defined by reference to a neutral state.[52] Faraday realised its significance during the course of experimentation with the cage. The realisation that his own use of this method implicitly supposed a 'natural standard' meant one of two things. Either the attempt to detect a state of total exclusion of electricity was futile (because a natural standard *cannot* be experimentally determined) or the fluid theoretical approach is correct (in which case it *can* be). He now showed by a thought-experiment that the natural standard is neither necessary nor demonstrable. The thought-experiment assimilates into his thinking the *practical* fact that charge appeared inside the cage only when there is the possibility of a physical connection to the outside (i.e. an opening in the cage). In this respect it is typical of all fundamental experiments:

> But then, what is natural standard and what is Pos[itive], what is Neg[ative]? (— the inside of a metallic vessel). There is no doubt that mites living on the outside of a highly charged globe in air but free from the induction of extraneous bodies or else subject only to a constant regular induction, could not tell that by any effects amongst themselves, and that all their electrometers and machine[s], etc., would have the same relations, etc. on the highly charged surface of [their globe] as ours [on the surface of a larger globe enclosing theirs] . . . .[53]

He argued that the 'laws of action discovered on the inner surface of [the inner globe] would be the same as those applying at the outer surface of [the outer globe]'.[54] The positive or negative identity of the electrical state of those surfaces would make no difference.

This calls into question the physical meaning of two of the most widely used electrical concepts, 'positive' and 'negative'. Faraday asked: 'what then is pos[itive] and neg[ative]', and again, what 'especially is [*sic*] *inherent positive and negative* states?' Faraday answered that there are no such things. He had endeavoured '. . . to obtain some proof of the bodily charge of air in this cube'.[55] However,

> If anything from without connected with the earth was introduced into the cube through the doorway then [the candle] flame, the gold leaf, the electrometer, the hand and all these things were very strongly affected in relation to it, they being Positive and Negative.[56]

These results gave new physical significance to the familiar buckets and boilers. According to Faraday these should no longer be construed as containing or capturing a quantity of electrical 'matter'. Nor should the mathematical explanation of the electrostatic properties of a closed spherical conductor be accepted as a physical explanation. Closed conductors could only exclude electrical influence. This influence could be excluded only by excluding observational access as well! The theorists would keep their fluids only by putting the ontological construal of one of their fundamental postulates beyond the reach of experiment.

Faraday's question, what are inherent positive and negative states? marked the beginning of an important change in experimental strategy. This is similar to the change that had occurred at the end of his first set of observations of the interaction of the wire and magnetised needle in September 1821 (cf. Fig. 6.5). His critique exposed observational weaknesses of the fluid theories. It also brought out the importance of the (now unlikely) possibility of detecting the existence of electricity of one kind. Here at last Faraday behaved as a Popperian might expect. He made the cage experiments of January 1836 into an attempt to capture or contain electricity, for example, by bodily charging all the air inside the cage. Faraday found that he could not charge anything 'bodily'. Any indication of one charge inside he found to be related — operationally — to indications of the opposite charge outside. Faraday had made the practical fact into a practical impossibility. By November of the following year when he read the eleventh series to the Royal Society he had made the impracticable into a natural impossibility: 'The conclusion I have come to is, that non-conductors, as well as conductors, have never yet had an absolute and independent charge of one electricity communicated to them, and that to all appearances such a state of matter is impossible'. He believed that such appearances were 'the consequences of a natural impossibility' not yet understood.[57] These results confirmed his own emerging view of the relational nature of charge. They also provided evidence against the fluid-theorist's assumption that charge can exist in insulators in a 'coerced', 'latent' or otherwise undetectable state. The relational conception made it possible for him to develop a physical interpretation of what the cage experiments showed to be an observational necessity.

The thought-experiment had exposed the physical and epistemological implications of the practicalities of observing electrostatic phenomena. Einstein used a similar thought-experiment in one of his arguments for special relativity, namely that metric concepts must be fully operationalisable.[58] Faraday's argument for the relativity of metrics (his electrical mites) does the same job as Einstein's requirement that metrics do not oblige us to assume anything that is in principle unobservable. Faraday's thought-experiment also anticipated his arguments of 1844 and 1846 about the inherent properties of the ultimate constituents of matter. A premise of these arguments restricts scientists' knowledge of matter to their perceptual knowledge of its properties. This made the relational character of perceptual knowledge of qualities the basis for his whole conception of properties. It banished innate properties, so that inertia joined electricity, magnetism and gravitation as properties which an atom possesses because it is (or is observable as) part of a larger physical system.

This took the argument further than his contemporaries wished or dared.[59] Electrical properties detected by the imaginary mites on Faraday's globe or by Faraday's instruments inside his cage exist because these things are part of larger systems: the outer globe and the fabric of the largest room of the Royal Institution. That room and its inhabitants are ultimately part of the largest system of all, the universe. Constructing his cage in the Royal Institution enabled Faraday to bring the espistemological structure of the universe into the lecture theatre. Although no audience was present on the 15th and 16th, no doubt he believed that *he* was in nature's school.

During 1836 these experiments became demonstrations. They now addressed and tested a clear point of disagreement between Faraday and his contemporaries and predecessors. As this use of experiment is widely discussed I shall draw attention to another role.[60] Experiment does more than support (or falsify) the predictions of rival theories, even when it is embedded in the set of predictions generated by one of those theories.[61] Developing and performing these cage experiments in 1836 focused his thinking on the larger problem of the physical meaning of the principle of the conservation of charge.[62]

Faraday put this in his eleventh series, published in November 1837. But the physical implications of his ambitious experimental and epistemological points were not accepted. Faraday gave a more succinct account in a Friday evening discourse at the Royal Institution on 20 January 1843.[63] Much of this dealt with the implications of his views of static induction for the interpretation of atmospheric electricity. But he also translated the thought-experiment into a real experiment by substituting white mice for the 'mites' that occupied his imaginary electrified sphere 7 years earlier. To demonstrate that conservation does not entail fluids or the materiality of electricity he returned to the oldest and most basic form of this experiment, the bucket experiment. He showed that no matter how close the charged ball C goes towards the bottom of the innermost pail, the total quantity of electricity of a system of concentric pails (as shown in Fig. 6.12(a)) is constant. Further, as more buckets are added the deflection of the electrometer remains unaltered. It is not affected, whether one or several of the buckets are removed at once.

> Again, consider the charged carrier C in the centre of the system, the divergence of the electrometer measures its inductive influence; this divergence remains the same whether 1 [in Fig. 6.12(b)] be there alone, or whether all four vessels be there; whether these be separate as to insulation, or whether 2, 3 and 4 be connected so as to represent a very thick metallic vessel, or whether all four vessels be connected.[64]

A likely contemporary response would be that electric fluid is 'latent' in the insulating matter enclosed by the system of conductors. He anticipated this

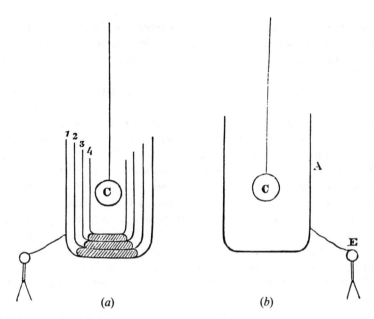

Figure 6.12 (*a* and *b*) The ice pail experiments. (From *ERE*, **2**, 281 and 280, respectively.)

with another thought-experiment. This extends the actual experiment into an imagined, microscopic domain. It typifies the geometrical mode of thinking that Maxwell recognised in Faraday's work.[65] Suppose, he argued, that the number of conductors and insulating layers is multiplied indefinitely. Varying the internal structure of the system in this way would make no difference to the amount of inductive action contained in the whole system. By incorporating real experiment into this sort of argument, Faraday transcended the limitations of actual experiments, making it appear that he could show experimentally that his new interpretation was not affected by considerations of scale, such as the atomicity or continuity of matter.[66]

7 Conclusion

Faraday's success as a discoverer and demonstrator reinforced confidence in the connection between doing experiments and learning about nature. He came to symbolise the educative possibilities of experiment and its role in building empirical foundations for scientific theory. When we look closely at the preparatory work, however, we find that this does not conform to popular notions of experiment. These notions have obscured interesting and important aspects of experimentation as a learning process. Two of these are that experiments are transparent and invariant. An experiment is transparent when the equipment and techniques have been mastered so that they appear to contribute nothing to the outcome. Phenomena stand in their own right, as manifestations of natural processes rather than of human invention. In Faraday's own phrase, the school we are in is Nature's school. There was a tension between this public objectification of phenomena and Faraday's personal experience of the extent to which scientists' perceptions were constructed. Another dubious property attributed to experiments is invariance. Many of those who have studied Faraday's experiments treat them as having identities fixed by their theoretical and pedagogical significance or by the technological implications of their outcomes. This has made Faraday's experiments appear, on the whole, less exploratory and adaptive and more theory-led than they usually were. To interpret all of Faraday's experiments through his theories is like identifying a person by a single accomplishment (or misdemeanour), or by attitudes he or she holds at a certain age. Such a portrait is like a caricature: there is an element of truth in it, but it also misleads in two ways. It implicitly precludes the possibility that methods of observing and exploring a phenomenal domain contribute to scientist's conceptualisations of that domain, and it obscures the different stages and purposes of their experiments.

Faraday's work suggests that we should identify at least three stages in the life of an experiment. These correspond to changes in the epistemological status of the phenomena or information it produces.[67] The first is the invention of strategies for discovery and the representation of new information. This takes place in the private context of the laboratory. The second stage is the development of strategies of proof or disproof, in which procedures, their rationales, and the interpretation of results are tried. Finally, the experiment is perfected as a demonstration, in which otherwise unobservable, recondite effects are made manifest to lay observers. Experiments, like experimentalists, have biographies. Until they mature into demonstrations their lives may be varied and unpredictable. In this essay I have tried to bring out the concrete and structural aspects of specific stages rather than attempt full biographies of experiments. However, the time-span over which Faraday conducted some of his investigations, and his extensive documentation of them, invites such an approach as well.[68]

Notes

I would like to thank Dr Frank James for his helpful discussion of this paper, especially of the 1821 rotation experiments. My treatment of these experiments has also benefited from discussion with Jane Leigh, Susan Perrett, Prof Ronald King and Mr Bill Coates. I am particularly grateful to Mr Coates for providing experimental demonstrations for the version of this paper presented to the 'Faraday Rediscovered' Symposium.

1. Latour (1983). On replication and competence see Collins (1985).
2. Faraday used this expression in the sixth lecture of the Christmas lectures for juveniles for 1851–2 and 1856–7, 'On attractive forces' RI MS F4 J12, p. 17.
3. Examples are Faraday's discoveries of electromagnetic induction in 1831 and of the magneto-optic effect in 1845. For his response to their anomalous character see Gooding (1980a, 1981, 1985a).

4. Faraday's scientific style was concretising rather than abstractive (Caneva (1978)). Faraday often obtained data in a quantitative form but he rarely analysed it. His distrust of mathematical manipulations led him to neglect important avenues of inquiry such as quantitative experimental proofs of conservation. See Gooding (1980a, 1982b).
5. Other approaches to the interaction of thought, talk and action can be found in Tweney (this volume), Harrison (1978) and Gooding (1986).
6. For the importance of practice in manipulation see Tyndall (1894), 39–40 and Faraday (1827), especially i–vi, 590.
7. Hacking (1983); A. Franklin, 'The epistemology of experiment' (unpublished).
8. A lay observer is anyone not yet familiar with the observational practices generally necessary to produce and see a phenomenon. Most scientists are lay observers with respect to new phenomena. New results are established by small groups of experimentalists and their wider acceptance of those results depends on judgements of their competence as observers. For examples see Collins (1975, 1981) and Gooding (1986).
9. For a contemporary view of the abilities of London science lecturers in the 1830s see 'Henry's European diary', 8 April 1837, in Henry (1972–9), 3: 246ff, 253ff; 11 April 1837, ibid., 268ff; 18 April 1837, ibid., 282ff; 22 April 1837, ibid., 307–8; 24 April 1837, ibid., 314–5. A recent discussion is Hays (1983).
10. See Cantor (this volume) and Crawford (this volume). Notwithstanding the differences between the personal, private character of work at the frontiers and the rhetorical style of public demonstrations, both sorts of experimentation were motivated by the conviction that phenomena had to be witnessed personally. See Faraday to Becker 25 October 1860, Correspondence, 2: 749 'I was never able to make a fact my own without seeing it'.
11. Others such as Peter Barlow, shared these views. See Barlow (1820), 109–10, discussed by Gooding (1985b).
12. Of course their significance could still change. An example, Faraday's electro-chemical laws, is discussed by Guralnick (1979).
13. S. Forgan, 'Context, Image and Function: A preliminary enquiry into the architecture of scientific societies' (unpublished).
14. With the exception of large-scale experiments like the Faraday cage (which had to be built in the lecture theatre, the largest room in the Royal Institution) or those he had to conduct out of doors, all Faraday's experiments began in the basement. Unlike contemporaries such as John Herschel, Faraday rarely made trials in public situations. For Herschel's and Faraday's approaches to experiment see Gooding (1985a).
15. Plate 12 shows the manuscript Diary. Together the printed versions and his published papers contain over 5000 pages (not allowing for repetition of Diary entries in the Experimental Researches). Faraday's results could be summarised in, say, ten printed pages.
16. The Diary does not convey a realistic impression of the time devoted to laborious processes such as winding coils on the iron cores used in his 1831 induction experiments. A recent reconstruction of these coils by Jane Leigh and Susan Perrett suggests that, after a satisfactory method had been worked out, it would have taken two people at least 10 hours.
17. The image of Faraday as discoverer was seen through the more familiar image of Faraday as demonstrator. This perception conflated two quite different stages of an experiment, corresponding to two different uses of experiments: exploratory and demonstrative. The conflation was a potent model for science education, in which the latter use is seen as means to the former. It was reinforced by public perception of the Royal Institution as a place of detached, disinterested research, an image created largely by Tyndall (1894) and by Faraday's physician, Bence Jones (1862). Of course the raw materials for this image were very good.
18. Kuhn (1962), 142 pointed out over twenty years ago, 'any new interpretation of nature, whether a discovery or a theory, emerges first in the mind of one or a few individuals. It is they who first learn to see science and the world differently'.

134 FARADAY REDISCOVERED

19. Nersessian (1984b), part 3 argues that analogies provide a temporary mode of representing unknown (unobservable) processes. She argues that analogies function both at a concrete level (enabling scientists to describe the novel in terms of the familiar) and at an abstract level (at which the novel is taken to be identical with the familiar). Another approach to this problem is Caneva (1981), based on Lakatos's (1976) discussion of problem solving strategies in mathematics.
20. See Heilbron (1981), 202–3. This problem is illustrated by R. King's point (made in his demonstration lecture 'Faraday's critical experiments in the discovery of electro-magnetic induction' (unpublished) read to the 'Faraday Rediscovered' Symposium) that the annular ring experiment Ampère made with August de la Rive, was not properly reported by the latter. He failed to state the correct orientations of currents, magnets, etc. For accounts of this experiment see Williams (this volume) and Ross (1965).
21. See, for example, Ampère (1820–2), Barlow (1820, 1822), Faraday (1821–2), Brewster (1820–1), Brande (1820), Cumming (1822, 1827), Roget (1826, 1827), Watkins (1828), Moll (1821, 1821–2), Sturgeon (1850). 'Ampère's electromagnetic telegraph', Edinb. Phil. J., 1820–1, 4: 435. 'Experiments of M. Yelin on electro-magnetism', Edinb. Phil. J., 1821. 5: 391–2. 'New electro-magnetic apparatus', Edinb. Phil. J., 1821–2, 6: 178–9.
22. Davy, H. (1821a and b), Faraday (1821–2).
23. For different approaches to the 'bootstrapping' of hypotheses and classifications see Glymour (1980) and Barnes (1983).
24. These examples illustrate a contrast between cognitive views of experimentation and the more traditional classical philosophical views. On the former, variation is an exploratory form of play and is essential to experiment as a cognitive process. Philosophical reconstructions ignore this pre-linguistic and pre-logical aspect of experiment, writing it out of the history as science as irrational, and therefore irrelevant. For a critical discussion of these issues see Nickles (1983 and 1985).
25. See Brande (1820).
26. Faraday (1821b).
27. Faraday, Diary, 3 September 1821, 1: 49–50.
28. Ibid. Compare the published account Faraday (1821b), ERE, 2: 128–9.
29. Ibid., 128 and plate 2, Figure 2.
30. Ibid., 129. Faraday (1821–2) and Williams (this volume).
31. Faraday (1821b), ERE, 2: 130.
32. Even when there has been a clear theoretical prediction, variation of the sort described here often fills in details which no theoretician has anticipated. See Faraday to Phillips, 29 November 1831, Correspondence, 1: 122.
33. Sensible here meant visible, not sensitive (see Kendall (1954), 77).
34. On tacit knowledge see Polanyi (1964) and on its communication see Collins (1974).
35. The network, described in Gooding (1985b), included Peter Barlow, S.H. Christie, John Herschel, James Marsh, W.H. Pepys, William Sturgeon and others.
36. Faraday (1838b), 1350; (1838c), 1605.
37. Faraday, Diary, 5–8 December 1835, 2, 2691–2720.
38. Others such as William Thomson later defined them mathematically, in terms of equipotential surfaces. See Wise (1979a & b).
39. Faraday (1838b), 1427–1431.
40. Faraday (1850), 2641.
41. For these see Priestley (1767), Tytler (1797) and Heilbron (1982).
42. 'Lecture on electricity at the Royal Institution, Albemarle Street', Reper. Pat. Inv., 1843, 1: 165–84.
43. Faraday (1844).
44. Gooding (1981, 1982a).
45. Kuhn (1970), 174–210 (This is the 'Postscript') and (1974).
46. Faraday, Diary, 22 December 1835, 2, 2768ff especially 2741.

47. *Ibid.*, 15 and 16 January 1836, **2**, 2808ff.
48. Faraday (1838a), 1174.
49. Williams, L.P. (1965), 290.
50. Faraday, *Diary*, 15 January 1836, **2**, 2840. '. . . it was very beautiful to observe how the gold leaves fell again as the wire came opposite the different leaders . . .'.
51. *Ibid.*, 2839.
52. Faraday (1838a), 1175–8. In practice this is the grounded or earthed state of the apparatus.
53. Faraday, *Diary*, 15 January 1836, *2*, 2842; cf *ibid.*, 3 November 1835, **2**, 2549.
54. *Ibid.*, 15 January 1836, **2**, 2842.
55. *Ibid.*, 2843.
56. *Ibid.*, 2859.
57. Faraday (1838a), 1174, 1177 and (1843), *ERE*, **2**: 283.
58. Einstein (1905), translated into English in Lorentz *et al.* (1923), 37–65, 37–43.
59. Faraday (1846c), Airy (1846), Maxwell (1892), **2**: 177.
60. Popper (1959), Harding (1976), Pinch (1985a & b).
61. In Gooding (1982a) I showed this for the magnetic experiments Faraday began in 1845.
62. Gooding (1980a), 22–3. Faraday worked this out in Faraday (1838b) and (1838c), 1617ff especially 1634–45.
63. 'Lecture', *op. cit.* (42).
64. Faraday (1843), *ERE*, **2**: 282.
65. Maxwell (1892), **1**: ix–x; **2**: 28, 176, 187–8. In his first paper on Faraday Maxwell explained that the methods he used to develop mathematical ideas necessary to study electric phenomena were suggested by Faraday's reasoning processes; Maxwell (1855–6) in Maxwell (1890), **1**: 155–229, 157.
66. 'Lecture', *op. cit.* (42), Faraday (1843), *ERE*, **2**: 283. Cf Faraday (1844), *ERE*, **2**: 286–7.
67. See Pinch (1985a) for a contemporary example.
68. Gruber (1974).

Plate 13 Michael Faraday with apparatus. William Walker. Royal Institution, K.M. Reynolds scrapbook. Photograph c.1890s, reproducing cabinet studio portrait taken 18 May 1863.

7

'The Optical Mode of Investigation': Light and Matter in Faraday's Natural Philosophy

Frank A.J.L. James

'Light and electricity are two great and searching investigators of the molecular structure of bodies'.[1] So wrote Michael Faraday in his letter of 25 January 1844 to Richard Taylor, an editor of the *Philosophical Magazine*, entitled 'A Speculation touching Electric Conduction and the Nature of Matter'. This was based on a Discourse he had given to the Royal Institution on 19 January. In this essay I shall examine how Faraday's attitude towards the use of light in his experimental investigations changed from being purely operational to having a marked theoretical significance for his work on the nature of matter. I do not offer a comprehensive, detailed analysis of Faraday's optical work. This essay illustrates the role of experiment and theory in the development of Faraday's natural philosophy.

Faraday is not primarily noted as an optical investigator. As other essays in this volume show, he was primarily concerned with the study of electrical and magnetic phenomena. He is rightly perceived by historians as dominating nineteenth-century electrical science. From an historiographical point of view this has been doubly disadvantageous. The single-minded study of Faraday's work has, until recently, tended to obscure the often valuable contributions of contemporary electrical researchers. This distortion of historians' perceptions has made it impossible to contextualise properly his work within the development of nineteenth-century science. This is a point to which I shall return. With optics this problem of context does not exist because, although Faraday made important experimental and theoretical contributions to optics, he was one among many. In optics no individual has the same dominating influence as Faraday has in electricity. So historians of optics have not concentrated their efforts on any single individual. Studies have been made of most of the important contributors to nineteenth-century optics. We know far more about Faraday's optical contemporaries than we know about his electrical contemporaries.

1 Physical optics in the nineteenth century

Before I discuss Faraday's use of light I will say a little about the theory of light in the nineteenth century. In mid-century all but a few scientists held that light was a transverse undulation in an all-pervading luminiferous aether. This theory had been formulated during the first quarter of the nineteenth century, essentially by Augustin Fresnel.[2] Thomas Young in the first decade of the nineteenth century had proposed a non-mathematical undulatory theory of light and had discovered a version of the principle of the interference of light.[3] In the end Young's theory did not have much influence; he shifted his theoretical views noticeably and his work was subjected to considerable criticism, notably by Henry Brougham.[4] But after Fresnel's theory became established Young's work was held up, especially in England, as the precursor to Fresnel's, for example, by William Whewell.[5]

Fresnel's theory and its subsequent elaborations was an intensely analytical mathematical theory. It possessed a remarkably accurate descriptive ability. For example, it described precisely the phenomena of diffraction and double refraction.[6] The theory also had considerable predictive power. S.-D. Poisson predicted that a bright spot of light would occur in the centre of the diffraction pattern of a small round diffractor. D.F.J. Arago verified the existence of this phenomenon experimentally.[7] William Rowan Hamilton predicted the existence of the phenomenon of conical refraction which he verified with Humphrey Lloyd.[8] These explanatory and predictive aspects of the theory led many scientists, including Fresnel and Young, to conclude that the theory was a true mathematical and physical representation of optical phenomena[9] and that other phenomena, yet to be explained, would in due course be reconciled with it.[10]

Despite these successes there was a serious problem with what I have elsewhere called the 'physical interpretation' of the theory.[11] The use of light to study the nature or structure of matter had been a continuing theme in optical studies from the concluding queries in Newton's *Opticks* onwards.[12] For this use it was essential to know how light and matter interacted. In the particulate theory there was no problem; the study of light was the study of matter emitted by a body.[13] But with the undulatory theory one was studying matter mediated by the aether whose structure was deduced from the explanation of optical phenomena. In addition Fresnel's aether had to be an elastic solid to transmit transverse light waves. Despite these problems the orthodoxy in Britain by the 1830s favoured the undulatory theory.[14] David Brewster's opposition to the theory and his frequent, though ever less effective, sorties against it stand out because he was the only prominent British scientist who did this.[15] His attacks may have forced others such as John Herschel, who initially held a decidedly ambivalent view towards optical theory, into whole-hearted support for the undulatory theory.[16]

In 1833 Brewster objected to the way in which some scientists assumed that the undulatory theory was a physical representation of all optical phenomena, simply because it had accurately described some phenomena and predicted others.[17] As evidence he pointed out that the absorption of light had yet to be explained according to the theory and argued that the absorption of light could not be explained according to the theory. This vitiated the claims of those who argued that the theory was a physical representation of optical phenomena, initiating a controversy which I have described elsewhere.[18] Absorption phenomena were later shown to be compatible with the undulatory theory. This was not done by analytical mathematical methods but by *ad hoc* assumptions and analogical arguments. But there were many optical phenomena (such as dispersion) which despite the immense efforts of scientists, were still beyond the reach of the undulatory theory.

Faraday's views on the undulatory theory of light in the 1830s are not clear. Although his main research was on electricity, he tentatively adopted a wave model to explore analogies between electrical, thermal and magnetic phenomena.[19] He knew of Fresnel's qualitative account of the undulatory theory which he recommended for its clarity of style.[20] In his first experimental use of light Faraday seemed unconcerned with the theoretical problems of the undulatory theory. The supporters of the theory argued that it must necessarily explain all optical phenomena. But until this had been achieved, Faraday thought, experimental methods would have to be used.

2 Electricity and light

Faraday's first sustained use of light was his investigation in the 1830s, into the transmission of electricity by sparks. This work is of interest for two reasons. First, although Faraday did not achieve his goal of developing a notion of specific capacity in gases, this work was later widely acknowledged as laying the theoretical foundations for the study of spark spectra.[21] Second this work does reveal Faraday's initial experimental approach towards light. His work arose out of Charles Wheatstone's work on the nature and velocity of electricity discussed by Brian Bowers in his chapter. In 1834 Wheatstone published the results of spark experiments in which he passed electricity through a circuit of wire half a mile long in which he placed three spark gaps at equal distances along the wire.[22] He observed, using his rotating mirror, that the middle spark was sensibly retarded compared with the other two sparks which flashed simultaneously.

Although Wheatstone did not pursue these researches, by November 1835, Faraday had realised the importance of Wheatstone's work to his theory of electricity: 'The retardation of the middle spark in Wheatstone's three sparks is probably a connecting link between conduction and induction. [I] must consider it in relation to induction in metals'.[23] Faraday's *Diary* reveals that this was one of his main research interests by late 1835 and during 1836.[24] Faraday found when he removed one of the wires connecting the electrodes in Wheatstone's circuit and replaced it by water, glass or some such bad conducting substance, the retardation of the middle spark increased.[25] He conceived of a gradual increase of tension in these substances which was discharged by the spark. Though he did not explicitly say so, Faraday thought that Wheatstone's hypothesis that electricity was transmitted across the gap by ponderable matter (originating from the electrodes) might be correct.[26] He recorded in his *Diary* early in his investigation that it might 'have reference to the nature of the substance of which the points are made'.[27] But he did not examine differences in the spectra of the sparks caused by different electrode materials. Instead he pursued the differences caused by sparking electrodes in different gases and found that each gas produced its own characteristic colour. Although he did not perform detailed chemical analyses as Wheatstone had, Faraday considered the colour of the light to be peculiar to each gas: 'the characters of the electric spark in *different gases* vary'.[28] Faraday disagreed with Wheatstone's contention that the medium in which the spark was exploded had no effect on its light, but did not deny Wheatstone's assertion that spark spectra depended on the chemical nature of the electrodes.

In his theoretical consideration of the nature of the spark Faraday sought to include spark phenomena within his theory of electricity. The passage of electricity along a wire was he thought 'an action of contiguous particles consisting in a species of polarity'.[29] Since there existed this specific relationship between the particles of a conductor and the electricity which it carried, then there must also be a 'specific relation of the particles [of the spark] and the electric forces'.[30] This was shown by the colour of the spark in different gases. He concluded that:

> the ultimate effect is exactly as if a metallic wire had been put into the place of the discharging particles; and it does not seem impossible that the principle of action in both cases, may, hereafter, prove to be the same.[31]

The spark depended on the matter transmitting electricity in the gap. Faraday cautiously assigned the cause of the colour differences to the characteristic relationship between electricity and the gas in which it was sparked, but he did not clarify where he thought the origin of the matter in the gap lay. To some extent this was not important for Faraday since, whatever matter was involved, he could include spark phenomena fully within his theory of induction.

According to Faraday, electricity and matter must exhibit characteristic relationships for each type of matter. Faraday had shown that the light produced by the interaction of electricity and gaseous substances was characteristic of the matter. But equally it must also apply to the metals which transmitted electricity. It was this relationship that was later employed by scientists such as Masson and Ångström, in their work on spark spectra. They specifically acknowledged this work of Faraday's as laying the theoretical foundation for their studies, as it guaranteed, for them, that each chemical element would have a uniquely characteristic spark spectrum.[32] On this basis these and other scientists were able to continue the exploration of the nature of the spark. Faraday does not appear to have taken any interest in this work, presumably because he thought that spectral methods were not sufficiently experimentally developed as a sure method of analysing the chemical composition of incandescent materials.

Apart from this work one has to look very hard in the *Diary* to find Faraday using light before 1845. The only other important mention that I have found occurs on 2 and 6 May 1833 when he sought to discover the effect of passing polarised light through an electrolyte.[33] He found no evidence of an effect though he did publish the nil results.[34] The study of light played a small role in his researches; even his spark work was directed towards electrical ends. Faraday simply used light for experimental purposes. This does not imply he had reservations about its nature which he kept to himself. It shows that Faraday had other things to do. If we consider the vast amount of electrical research work, his chemical consultancy work, his lecturing and administration then we see that his time was fully occupied. If Faraday did have reservations about light then evidence should exist in his manuscripts.

3 Faraday and theories of matter

Why did Faraday in his 1844 'Speculation' place light — which he had not much studied — and electricity — which he had extensively studied — on an equal footing in investigating the molecular structure of matter? Even in the 'Speculation' he was somewhat sparing with his use of light. In it Faraday rebutted a rather simplified version of Dalton's atomic hypothesis.[35] It is not clear why Faraday chose to attack chemical atomism at this time. Almost exactly a year earlier on 20 January 1843 Faraday had given a discourse 'On some phenomena of Electro-static induction'. The notes for this discourse contain a brief paragraph that neatly summarise his *reductio ad absurdum* argument against chemical atomism of the following January:

Influence of this on theory — on my published results — matter and space query their nature — why space *not a conductor* judging by insulators and why it *is a conductor* judging by metals — dont know much of matter or space or particles & atoms — our province is to determine a power or force & determine its laws — that is all.[36]

None of the available reports of the discourse indicate that Faraday mentioned atomism in 1843.[37] This may reflect the fact that such attacks on chemical atomism were not unusual and that Faraday had not, as yet, contributed anything new to this subject. At the 1837 British Association meeting in Liverpool he had supported an attack on chemical atomism mounted by, among others, Whewell, Hamilton and Robert Kane.[38] I commend for the consideration of historians who would seek an explanation of Faraday's views on matter in terms of his religious belief that here we have two Anglicans, one Roman Catholic and a dissenter taking similar positions regarding chemical atomism.

The point is that the argument of Faraday's 'Speculation' was not controversial for physicists. What did attract the attention of his contemporaries was that Faraday had speculated at all. The *Literary Gazette* report of the discourse shows this: 'Curiosity was alive to the "speculations" of our far-famed experimental philosopher. He appeared himself to feel his novel position'.[39] After a quarter of a century of careful experimental discoveries it came as something of a surprise to discover that Faraday was also a speculative theoretician. Although we do not know why Faraday should choose this particular moment to attack Daltonian atoms, it does seem that he was responding to something quite specific. The *Literary Gazette* report commented: 'Mr Faraday's great object as we understood it, was to excite a watchfulness in the present times, when the word atom is so freely used'.[40] Such use could have occurred in a variety of contexts: scientific, literary or philosophical. Who was using the word atom so freely is a question that would repay further study. As an example of the strength of what the *Athenaeum* report called the 'popular'[41] notion of atomism let us consider the rightly anonymous 'Epigram on the "Matter"' with which the *Literary Gazette* concluded its report of this discourse:

> Great Faraday, a few days back,
> The laws of Matter did attack
>   With wonderous hardihood.
> In vain our notions he uproots;
> When Faraday the subject moots
>   *The matter's always good!*[42]

The writer's belief in the popular notion of atomism had survived Faraday's criticism: 'In vain our notions he uproots'. Faraday, for this writer, had not made a convincing case against Daltonian atoms. If this indicates the strength of the popular notions of atomism then there is little wonder that he chose to criticise such a popular version. This explains the structure of Faraday's argument against Daltonian atomism. He knew he had to use an argument which would be widely understood and appreciated. As he also knew that physicists had little time for Daltonian atoms, there was no need to construct sophisticated arguments for them.

'The atoms of Boscovich'

It was one thing to show that chemical atomism was untenable but quite another to propose an adequate alternative. No one at the 1837 British Association had proposed an alternative. Faraday did not wish to dispense with atoms as he well knew they were valuable for dealing with chemical problems.[43] His private memorandum of 19 February 1844 entitled 'Matter' shows that he wished to keep the notion of chemical elements.[44] If material atoms could not sustain such notions then the alternative, immaterial atoms, would naturally present itself.

Many historians have pointed out that Faraday was probably aware of various theories of immaterial atoms propounded during the eighteenth century.[45] Faraday was probably not much influenced by such theories. We can see this by an examination of his attitude towards Boscovichean atomism. In his 'Speculation' Faraday suggested that:

> the atoms of Boscovich appear to me to have a great advantage over the more usual notion. His atoms, if I understand aright, are mere centres of forces or powers, not particles of matter.[46]

None of the three reports of the discourse on which the 'Speculation' was based, mention Boscovich; two mentioned centres of force,[47] and the third in the *Chemical Gazette*, mentioned neither, and indeed played down Faraday's attack on Daltonian atomism.[48] The important point about Faraday's atoms is not their provenance,[49] but Faraday's purpose in writing his 'Speculation'. This was a semiotic exercise. He wanted to make it abundantly clear that he did not believe in the existence of Daltonian atoms. They could not explain the phenomena on which he had experimented. By mentioning Boscovich he sent clear signals to the rest of the scientific community of his continued rejection of Daltonian atomism. Faraday mentioned Boscovich only once more when pointing out that his centre of force atoms were not Boscovichean but merely 'like' those of Boscovich.[50] These references to Boscovich contrast with seven uses of the phrase centres of force or of power and with the many other uses of 'centres'. One final piece of evidence I will offer for this merely semiotic use of Boscovich comes from his memorandum on 'Matter' (written less than a month afterwards).[51] In this he does not once mention Boscovich. Instead he concentrated on the implications of his centre of force atoms. Had Faraday been secretly committed to Boscovichean atomism then it would be apparent in his private writings.

4 The experimental implications of atomism

Faraday needed a programme of experiments to explore and demonstrate the superiority of his hypothesis of centre of force atoms. His electrical work had already led him this far but he needed to investigate other phenomena or risk the charges of inadequacy that he had levelled at Daltonian atoms. There are hints in the 'Speculation' of the course his research might go. For example, Faraday assigned optical, magnetic and other properties to the atmosphere of forces surrounding the centre.[52] He also believed that his centre of force atoms had implications for 'the theory of light and the supposed aether'.[53] Faraday must have given much thought to the experimental implications of his atomic hypothesis. He was well aware that many scientists had used light to investigate the nature of matter so this would have seemed an appropriate moment to use light for this present purpose. This is why he placed light and electricity on an equal footing in the quotation which opened this essay.

His thoughts on the nature of matter raised problems about the aether. This is supported by his memorandum on 'Matter' of 19 February 1844. In this Faraday mentioned an observation, that he attributed to Brewster, whereby light is reflected before it touches the reflector.[54] This meant that the light is reflected not at the apparent material surface of the body but by some power beyond it. This power interacts with the light ray. The implication was that reflected light did not behave as it should according to the undulatory theory and that light waves did not interact with matter as the theory supposed.

A consequence of Faraday's centre of force atomism is the structural similarity that atoms of different elements must have to one another. They would differ only in the types of forces that surrounded them. It was possible that some atoms might not possess certain types of force, but Faraday believed that some forces (e.g. magnetism) were universal. This meant that they had yet to be experimentally detected. From 1844 through to August 1845 Faraday made few entries in his *Diary*. Most were entirely concerned with chemical topics. However in May 1845 Faraday tried to obtain magnetic effects from a wide range of materials.[55] He found that in addition to iron and nickel, cobalt was also magnetic.[56] He repeated experiments that he had first published in 1836, when it had occurred to him that since metals are demagnetised when heated, perhaps they could be magnetised when cooled.[57] In May 1845 he cooled about forty materials to $-166°F$ to see if they became magnetic, but none did.[58] He reported these negative results in a note to the *Philosophical Magazine* on 7 June.[59] Faraday was obviously seeking to extend magnetism beyond the three materials known to possess it. This result which did not support his hypothesis was perplexing.

Magnetism, light and matter

Faraday then went off to the British Association meeting in Cambridge which was held from 18 to 25 June where he met William Thomson just then coming of age.[60] On 23 June[61] Thomson read a paper on statical electricity.[62] Faraday may not have been present but the experimental queries with which Thomson closed his paper were very similar to the experimental queries with which he closed his first letter to Faraday of 6 August.[63] In both Thomson wondered what effect a transparent dielectric would have on polarised light. Faraday, after returning from four weeks in France on 2 August,[64] wrote to Thomson on 8 August.[65] He referred him to his 'negative result' of 1833,[66] but added that he 'purpose[d] resuming this subject hereafter'.[67]

On 30 August 1845 Faraday returned to the study of the relationship between light and electricity under the title 'Polarized light and Electrolytes'.[68]

He first passed polarised light through a solution of sulphate of soda and other solutions undergoing electrolysis[69] but there was no change in the polarised light. This confirmed the results of his 1833 experiments.[70] But Faraday extended this line of research to solid materials such as the silicate borate of lead glass that he had made in the late 1820s.[71] On 5 September he wrote 'all these experiments are *nil*'.[72] What happened next was the result of Faraday marrying together his June attempt to extend the phenomenon of magnetism, with this unsuccessful use of light to examine electrolysis. When Faraday returned to his laboratory eight days later, instead of passing light through electrolytes he placed various transparent media in lines of magnetic force. He then passed polarised light through them.[73]

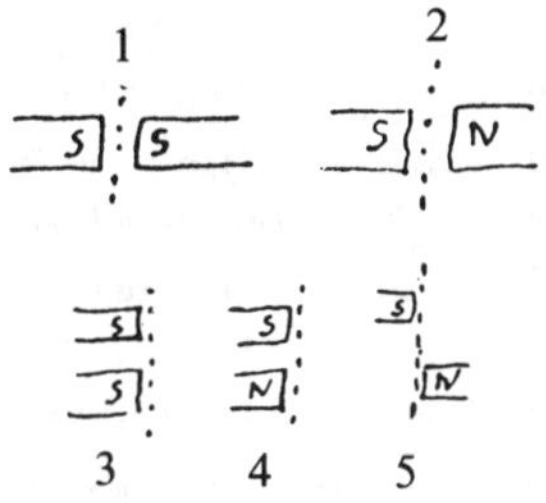

Figure 7.1 The positions of Faraday's electromagnets for exploring the relationship of light and magnetism. (From Faraday's *Diary*, 13 September 1845, **4**, 7499.)

In what seems to have been an initial control experiment Faraday used air to see if there was any effect.[74] He arranged the electromagnets in five possible ways (Fig. 7.1) and then examined the state of polarisation of the light in each position with a Nicol prism. No effect was apparent in any position. Faraday now knew that any effect he might produce would be caused by whatever he changed in the arrangement — i.e. not to air or to the electromagnets being in different positions. With flint glass, rock crystal and calcareous spar he obtained no effects.[75] Next he tried the piece of lead glass that he had previously tried with electricity.[76] With positions 1–3 he found no effect. But with position 4 he discovered that the state of polarisation of light had been altered after passing through the glass in the magnetic lines of force. 'Thus [he wrote] magnetic force and light were proved to have relation to each other. This fact will most likely prove exceedingly fertile and of great value in the investigation of both conditions of natural force'.[77] This was the magneto-optical effect that we now term the Faraday effect. His discovery was important both for the study of light and for the study of magnetism:[78]

the great power manifested by particular phenomena in particular forms is here further identified by its direct relation in the form of light to its forms of Electricity and Magnetism.[79]

In this experiment Faraday had observed that the ray of light passing through the glass had to some degree been depolarised. He then set about exploring the conditions under which the phenomenon could be found. He determined experimentally that 'when the *polarized ray* passes *parallel* to the lines of *magnetic induction*, or rather to the *direction of the magnetic curves*, that the glass manifests its power of affecting the ray'.[80] During the day he varied the media and the source of the magnetic lines.[81] With his large ringed electromagnet he saw the effect 'better than in any former case'.[82] He ended the entries for that day with 'Have got enough for the day'.[83]

Faraday had shown that light can be used to demonstrate that magnetic phenomena occurred in substances other than iron, nickel and cobalt. He believed that the heavy glass was in a 'magnetised state'.[84] Materials formerly thought to be unaffected by magnetism were in fact susceptible. He used light as a probe in his investigation of the nature of magnetism and of matter. Had he been interested only in the magneto-optical effect as such he would not have tried to detect the effect in other materials. (These experiments did not presuppose a detailed theory of light or aether.) To extend the effect he needed to get a stronger magnet.[85] When he recommenced experiment 5 days later on 18 September he had obtained a large electromagnet from Woolwich.[86] He made explicit that his purpose was to use light to examine magnetism when he noted that the electro-magnets took time to reach their full intensity: 'In this way the effect is one by which an optical examination of the Electromagnet can be made'.[87] With his strong electro-magnet Faraday re-examined the various media in which he had earlier failed to detect the effect to see if he could now do so.[88] Having established that the phenomenon was not restricted to the heavy glass Faraday then returned to the phenomenon in heavy glass which he now called a 'dimagnetic'.[89] In this series of experiments Faraday moved the glass to different positions relative to the electro-magnets. Using the state of polarisation of the light he examined the places where the lines of magnetic force did or did not have an effect. 'This shews what I had anticipated and was sure must happen'[90]: the magneto-optical effect could be used to map the lines of magnetic force. Using electro-magnets and polarised light the lines of force emanating from the iron could be made apparent:

> It seems impossible to suppose that the electric current is the sole cause and *source* of this power. There must be an immense store in the iron before hand, which the electric current does not generate but merely direct. Shall perhaps be able to penetrate a little into this point by the optical mode of investigation.[91]

Faraday had not observed the effect with electricity; he reasoned now that electricity did not have sufficient strength to render the phenomenon visible. He later confirmed: 'that it is *the magnetic lines* only that are effectual'.[92]

Within a week Faraday was at the beginning of the path which would lead to the fulfilment of his goal, that of making magnetism a force universal to all matter. On 22 September he established, using a sensitive magnetometer, that there was no magnetism inherent to the glass and so confirmed that the effect was caused solely by the electro-magnet.[93] He continued to extend the effect but could not obtain it in gases.[94] On 26 September he came to the conclusion that the 'magnetic force does not act on the ray of light directly (as witness non action in air, etc.), but through the mediation of the special matters'.[95] Magnetism affected the behaviour of polarised light by influencing the matter through which the light was passing. He immediately realised that this was 'a new magnetic force or mode of action on matter'.[96] This aspect of Faraday's work eclipsed the discovery that had initiated the sequence of experiments which he termed 'the *first* true relation of Magnetism and light'.[97]

The limitations of light

During a transitional period of a month or so he worked on both the magneto-optical effect and on the new magnetic action on matter. But Faraday now faced a new problem. Using light he could demonstrate that magnetism affected a wide variety of materials. He could not use light to extend the effect to optically opaque substances. Moreover he would have to start making detailed assumptions concerning the nature of light and its interaction with matter. His 1844 'Speculation' and memorandum on 'Matter' show he had some reservations about this. As he emphasised in the published paper his results vindicated his more restricted approach to the problem of matter:

> Recognizing or perceiving *matter* only by its powers, and knowing nothing of any imaginary nucleus, abstract from the idea of these powers, the phenomena described in this paper much strengthen my inclination to trust in the views I have on a former occasion advanced in reference to its nature.[98]

Universal magnetism would add another force belonging to centre of force atoms. He had shown that magnetic effects occurred in many other substances. In his published paper he said that opaque bodies such as 'wood, stone and metal'[99] must also be magnetic in the general sense. This confidence was due to the fact that by this time he had established a direct experimental link between magnetism and matter that did not use light.[100]

On 6 October he tried to align the glass by means of magnetic lines of force.[101] This change of method indicates the importance to Faraday of non optical means of demonstrating the universality of magnetism. He tried to detect this by floating a glass bar in water and seeing if there was any movement when he brought a magnet near. There was not. Faraday did not return to this until the beginning of November.[102] On the fourth[103] instead of floating the glass in water he suspended it by a silk string in a glass tube placed between magnetic poles:

> I found I *could* affect it by the Magnetic forces and give it position; thus touching dimagnetics by magnetic curves and observing a property quite independent of light, by which also we may probably trace these forces into opaque and other bodies, as the metals, etc.[104]

Three days later Faraday found the effect with a rock crystal that had not previously shown the magneto-optical effect: 'So though I could not find the effect by the optical test because of crystallization, it easily appears here and probably will do so with all crystals'.[105] Faraday's drive to establish magnetism as a universal force, akin in this respect to gravitation, led him to concentrate on diamagnetism once he found that he could produce the phenomenon without light.[106]

5 Faraday and aether theory

Faraday had made an important optical discovery by experimental means without considering the analytical mathematical theory of light or of the aether. This was a rare event after Fresnel. His discovery of the magneto-optical effect was widely and quickly acclaimed.[107] The discovery of the magneto-optical effect provided him, in two ways, with the opportunity to elaborate his earlier discussion of the aether. First Faraday now had empirical grounds for his hypothesis of centre of force atoms. He could turn to the task of working out the implications of this hypothesis for the aether, confident that these implications would be equally well founded. Second, his discovery of the magneto-optical effect would qualify him in the eyes of the scientific community as someone able to comment on the theory of light. Faraday knew that he would have to trespass on intellectual territory that had for 20 years been the strict preserve of scientists who had a mastery of analytical mathematical methods. His discovery gave him the confidence to point out problems with the aether, though not with the undulatory nature of light.

   Until this time very little had been done to prove the existence of the elastic solid aether required to transmit transverse light waves. Optical work had been mainly directed towards reconciling optical phenomena such as the absorption and dispersion of light with the theory.[108] Young's and Fresnel's argument concerning the existence of the aether were repeated by scientists such as Whewell and Airy who forcefully defended the undulatory theory and the physical existence of the aether against attacks made by Brewster without developing any new approaches.[109] Although Brewster did not support the particulate theory of light, as his enemies supposed, and in the late 1840s he regarded himself as an optical 'rienist'[110] (i.e. agnostic), he became an isolated figure. But at the same 1845 British Association meeting when Faraday and Thomson met, James Challis[111] and G.G. Stokes[112] initiated a debate on the problem of explaining stellar aberration according to the undulatory theory.[113] From mid-1845 until March 1846 Challis and Stokes fought out the issue in six papers in the *Philosophical Magazine*.[114] This debate was mathematical in content, but it must have confirmed Faraday's suspicions of mathematics,[115] because it was quite clear that the central issues were the nature of the aether and its interaction with ponderable matter.

   Faraday's situation in early 1846 was that he had made a fundamental optical discovery which raised in his own mind serious questions about the aether. It was clear that there was no consensus, even between mathematicians, about the physical constitution of the aether. Faraday must have known of the scientific and institutional marginalisation that had happened to Brewster for his repeated attacks on the undulatory theory. Although neither had questioned the existence of the aether the Challis–Stokes debate indicated that the nature of the aether was a legitimate subject for discussion.

'Thoughts on ray-vibrations'

Faraday's enduring interest for historians partly is that there is something mysterious about him. He often went to great lengths to avoid situations which he believed might arouse controversy. Faraday believed that only experiments provided firm knowledge of the world. Theories and hypotheses were human constructs and as such quite fallible. But equally he knew they were important to his colleagues and he went to great lengths to avoid hurting their theoretical sensibilities. Yet in the case of his criticism of the aether, he went to quite extraordinary lengths. He even initiated a myth whose creation has yet to be fully described. When Faraday rejected Daltonian atoms in his 1844 'Speculation', he knew that he had the majority of physical scientists on his side. But when he chose to criticise the aether in 1846 he knew that he would not have their support. This is clear from the events surrounding its presentation and from its content.

The basic myth, of which there are many embroidered versions, is that on 10 April 1846 Wheatstone was due to deliver a discourse.[116] He and Faraday were waiting around outside the lecture theatre for the clock to strike when Wheatstone panicked and fled down the stairs. Faraday stepped into the breach and gave Wheatstone's discourse, followed by his impromptu 'Thoughts on Ray-vibrations'. What did happen? On 3 April the electro-metallurgist James Napier was due to give the discourse but was prevented from doing so for reasons that are not clear.[117] John Barlow, the Secretary of the Royal Institution, asked Faraday to fill the gap.[118] Faraday consented and chose for his topic 'Wheatstone's Electro-Magnetic Chronoscope'.[119] Faraday was maintaining their partnership in which he gave discourses with material provided by Wheatstone. Wheatstone had been working on this topic in 1845.[120] We do not know when Napier indicated that he could not provide his discourse. But on 28 March Faraday was advertised as the lecturer for the following Friday.[121] He had at least a week's notice to prepare the lecture.[122] However, at the end of the letter in which he reported the lecture to the *Philosophical Magazine* he wrote:

> I do not think I should have allowed these notions to have escaped from me, had I not been led unawares, and without previous consideration, by the circumstances of the Evening on which I had to appear suddenly and occupy the place of another.[123]

Unless Faraday had a very peculiar definition of the word 'suddenly' this is remarkably disingenuous![124]

Plate 14 John Barlow. Franz Hanfstaengl. Royal Institution, Faraday Album, I:39. Salted paper print.

One more curious event relating to this Discourse should be mentioned. The previous week's Discourse was given by Lyon Playfair on the specific gravity of bodies. Playfair concluded this presentation with an attack on chemical atomism and suggested that he had 'to deal only with centres of force, according to the views of Prof. Faraday'.[125] This was a fortunate occurrence. After he had discussed Wheatstone's chronoscope, Faraday used Playfair's remarks as a lead in to his 'Thoughts'.[126]

Faraday asked what properties would be allocated to the nuclei of ponderable matter and what to the nuclei of aether particles. If the nuclei exist then their properties of '*ponderability* and *gravitation*'[127] were due to a force super added to them. But if the aether particles were without this force, which is the case according to the aether theory, then they are more material 'in the abstract sense, than the matter of this our globe'.[128] This is because proportionately aether particles have more nucleus and less force. But they also have infinite elasticity which is as important as gravity is to ponderable particles. The aether nuclei are infinitely small and the elasticity infinitely intense. This is a centres of force conception.[129] Here Faraday was trying to end the distinction between ponderable matter and aether by showing that the particles of each differed only in the number of forces each has. Faraday no doubt thought that if he could show that this distinction was unnecessary then it became easier to imagine how forces acted between particles. The *reductio ad absurdum* structure of this argument is reminiscent of his argument on chemical atomism in his 1844 'Speculation', though somewhat less aggressive and caricatured.

His criticism he wrote, 'endeavours to dismiss the aether, but not the vibrations'.[130] Faraday was proposing a solution to the problem of the 'physical interpretation' of the undulatory theory. This had been largely ignored by its proponents in their enthusiasm for a theory which embraced an expanding domain of optical phenomena.[131] Because Faraday thought that physicists had neglected this problem he was pointing out another, in addition to the one raised by the Challis–Stokes debate.

What would replace the aether? Faraday argued that if particles were connected by lines of force then, disturbances would propagate between them as vibrations in the lines not in the luminiferous aether.[132] Faraday proposed the existence of lines of force spread throughout space transmitting through the centres of force: 'there are lines of gravitating force, those of electro-static induction, those of magnetic action, and others partaking of a dynamic character might be perhaps included'.[133] The experimental work begun in 1845 had established magnetism as a universal force and had allowed Faraday to extend his speculative reach to the aether.

6 Light and matter: Stokes's work on fluorescence

Yet Faraday did not reject the aether permanently. He used theories that best promoted his experimental work. This is why he brought back the aether for his work on gold films and solutions of the mid-1850s. By the early 1850s Faraday had become acquainted with Stokes.[134] Their correspondence shows that they met fairly frequently when Stokes was in London. Stokes, one of the most eminent of nineteenth-century mathematicians, had a rare combination of mathematical and experimental skill. In April 1851 he discovered experimentally that ultra-violet light, when passed through a solution of sulphate of quinine, changed its wavelength and became blue. He explained this phenomenon, which he later called fluorescence, in qualitative thermodynamic terms.[135] Stokes had realised that fluorescence could be used to observe the extension of the ultra-violet spectrum. He first carried this out in the Royal Institution with Faraday in January 1853.

On 6 November 1852 Stokes was invited by Barlow, at Wheatstone's suggestion, to give a Friday Evening Discourse at the Royal Institution on fluorescence.[136] He gave this on 18 February 1853.[137] The surviving correspondence shows that Stokes was keen to include as many clear experimental demonstrations as possible. He knew that to make fluorescence visible to a large audience would be a difficult task.[138] Faraday picked up this point in his first mention of Stokes's work on 14 December 1852. He experimented with different light sources to discover which was the best to show the phenomenon of fluorescence.[139] He found that burning sulphur in oxygen produced a very strong fluorescence in sulphate of quinine.[140] Stokes also wanted a revolving mirror with which to measure the duration of fluorescent phenomena.[141] Stokes was apparently using his forthcoming discourse as a means of acquiring access to the instrumentation that was available at the Royal Institution but not in Cambridge. Stokes's first visit to Faraday's laboratory was probably on Monday 10 January 1853.[142] He went at least once more before his discourse.[143] In the course of these investigations Stokes used the electrical apparatus at the Royal Institution. He discovered an invisible (ultra-violet) spectrum six or eight times longer than the visible spectrum.[144]

The transmission of light through gold

Faraday was occupied with other research at the time but early in 1856 he returned to Stokes's work on fluorescence. The main motivation behind Faraday's work was, as he wrote in his *Diary* on 21 April 1856, his:

> ancient query, whether it is possible by any means to alter a ray by change of its number of vibrations or otherwise, so as to convert one ray into another.[145]

I have not been able to locate this 'ancient query'. Faraday was quite clear that he was looking for a phenomenon quite distinct from absorption i.e., 'without an effect like that of Stokes'.[146] In Stokes's experiments, the wavelength of ultra-violet light had changed after passing through a solution of sulphate of quinine. I think that this showed Faraday that it should be possible to answer his ancient query. Faraday thought that he could achieve this with 'particles so small in relation the vibration dimension and yet so eminent in their power on light as is shown by their reflexion effect'.[147] Within these defining factors his choice of gold as a material with which to conduct these experiments seems fairly obvious.

Faraday asked Warren de la Rue for some gold. On 28 or 29 January 1856 he went to De la Rue's private laboratory and looked at the effect that beaten gold leaf had on light.[148] At first Faraday used beaten gold leaf, but this produced too many stray effects to be satisfactory and he decided to deposit a gold film on glass by chemical means.[149] He calculated that the wavelength of visible light was between 5 and 7 times that of the accepted thickness of gold leaf which in turn was much thicker than the gold deposits on glass that he had made[150] — a point he later made explicit.[151] He had found that optical phenomena, such as reflection or absorption, still occurred with these materials even though their dimensions were smaller than the wavelength of light.[152]

How light could be affected by something smaller than its wavelength had not been explained by the undulatory theory of light. Faraday thought that since the vibrations of light were so large compared with the particles of gold films, 'they [the phenomena] ought to change much with particles and films of these dimensions'.[153] This was something of a puzzle for he found that ultra-violet light[154] of much shorter wavelength than ordinary light, was unaffected when passed through gold films. Light that should be affected by transmission through gold was not, while visible light was so affected. He was now faced with the problem that:

> If particles not having continuity can reflect light as a continuous surface will it not shew that several separated particles may act at once and therefore at a distance on a ray of light — and then must not the particles be likened rather to centres of force than to solid atoms?[155]

Once again Faraday was using light to explore the structure of matter. The inferences that he drew at this point were similar to those of ten years earlier. He went on to find that pressure applied to a gold film changed its optical properties: 'Has the pressure converted the layer of atoms into a continuous layer by expansion and welding, and is that all the difference? I rather think it is'.[156] Despite much effort he did not find the phenomena he was seeking. On 21 April he described the experiments on gold as a 'long and as yet nearly fruitless set of experiments'.[157]

Yet Faraday persisted. He must have been strongly motivated to learn more about the structure of matter. On 13 June he gave a discourse on the silvering of mirrors and on this gold work.[158] He did not disclose the theoretical problems behind the work. Although Faraday had explicitly used the undulatory theory of light throughout this research, in this discourse, he had used it simply in the form of waves without considering the aether. This was not surprising given his 1846 views on the aether. After about 5 months of effort and with little to show for it, Faraday still adhered to this position and was still concerned to use light as a tool to examine the structure of matter. Thus on 1 July he noted in his *Diary* a consideration concerning the relation of the lateral and axial wavelengths of light in comparison with the dimension of the gold particles when under pressure.[159] He believed that because he had more control over the structure of matter when under pressure, he could reduce the possibility of random effects. On 4 July he speculated on the shape of particles of compressed matter, but again in terms of the wavelengths of light. Yet he had returned to 'particles'[160] which were composed of 'atoms'.[161]

Faraday supposed that the 'particles' affected the light by a joint action of their inner and outer parts.[162] When following out in the ensuing months this idea he suggested that the 'pressed gold shews the true characters of the metal and the other forms of gold'.[163] He found experimentally that the 'two surfaces [of gold] (for it is nothing like structure) seem to act separately on a light undulation'.[164] He suggested on 22 October that 'the most probable'[165] cause of transmission and reflection of light by this thin layer of gold was 'the effect of the joint action of the inside and outside of particles at the same instant upon an ether undulation'.[166]

This was the first time Faraday had mentioned the aether in connection with this research. It is not clear from the context whether this should be read as a serious reference to the aether or as meaning simply the wavelength of light. But it does indicate that Faraday's thoughts were turning towards considering how the aether might interact with the gold particles. Three days later on 25 October he explicitly considered the interaction of the aether with the gold:

> However minute the vibration of an ether molecule, it must have a sensible relation to the ether wave and therefore a distinct relation to the very minute molecules of gold, and may well be reached by them in their action.[167]

Bearing in mind what Faraday had said about the aether ten years earlier, this is a most extraordinary statement. Yet he put it in his Royal Society Bakerian lecture on the subject which he was writing at the end of October.[168] He wrote: 'that it seems probable the particles [of gold] might come into effective relations to the much smaller vibrations of the ether particles'.[169] Faraday was prepared to make his return to aether theory public.

The introduction to his Bakerian lecture explained why his position had changed. He begins by calling the undulatory theory 'That wonderful production of the human mind'.[170] He regarded the theories as human constructs and therefore fallible, as human things invariably are. This theory should account for the physical idea of forces acting at a distance. 'Admitting for the time the existence of the ether, I have often struggled to perceive how far that medium might account for or might mingle in with such actions generally'.[171] This is a reference to his various private and public speculations of the 1840s. He was concerned 'to what extent experimental trials might be devised which, with their results and consequences, might contradict, confirm, enlarge, or modify the idea we form of it'.[172]

7 Conclusion

This statement holds the key to Faraday's theoretical beliefs and his ability to change them: experiment was supreme. But to understand how it impinged on theoretical considerations it is necessary to characterise Faraday's commitment to experimentation. First, Faraday performed experiments in areas which he knew to be theoretically interesting. This is not to say either that the theory directed his experiments or that he was committed to a particular theory. Second, when he proposed theories Faraday made these strictly conditional on experimental results. These could and sometimes did oblige him to change his mind.

This contextual picture of Faraday is rather different from the image of Faraday presented by those who see him as heir to various eighteenth-century natural philosophers. The evidence indicates that Faraday was working within the nineteenth-century framework of science. Increasingly he responded to nineteenth-century formulations of problems such as the nature of atoms and of the aether. Yet historians have claimed that as regards matter and aether, the questions he dealt with were those asked by eighteenth-century natural philosophers.[173] I have shown that Faraday's arguments were directed to primarily nineteenth-century problems. Since this explains the course of Faraday's work, I see no reason to invoke eighteenth-century antecedents in the absence of clear textual evidence. It is unlikely that Faraday's interests would have been served by answering eighteenth-century questions — that is not a viable strategy for obtaining the support of one's contemporaries. Faraday was well aware of the differences between the audiences that he was addressing. He made changes to the content and to the language of the 'Speculation' and the 'Thoughts'. We know this by comparing versions of these lectures as private documents, as discourses to the special audience of the Royal Institution, and as challenges to the wider scientific community.[174]

We do not have a number of Faradays. We have a variety of schools of thought that developed from his writings. This is not unusual in the history of science. We have only to think of the Newton of the *Principia* and of the *Opticks*. Even the same writings can lead to different traditions. For example, Faraday the field theorist and Faraday the experimentalist, to name but two. This sort of retrospective identification leads to historiographical problems. In the case of Faraday and light I have argued that for some problems, especially in matter theory, Faraday used the 'optical mode of investigation'. What others made of his work was their business, though it makes work for historians.

Notes

I am very grateful to Dr David Gooding for the long discussions of which this paper is but one product; I also thank Dr Geoffrey Cantor for many useful comments. I thank the archivists of the following institutions for permission to work on various manuscripts in their care: The Royal Institution, The Institution of Electrical Engineers, The University Library Cambridge, The Royal Society and University College London.

1. Faraday (1844), 137.
2. Augustin Jean Fresnel (1788–1827). For studies of Fresnel see Silliman (1974) and Frankel (1976).
3. Thomas Young (1773–1829). The best life of Young remains Peacock (1855). For his

work on interference see Young (1802) in Young (1855), **1**: 170–78. For a discussion of this work see Latchford (1974).

4. For a discussion of these points see Cantor (1970 and 1971). Henry Peter Brougham (1778–1868). See [Brougham] (1804) for an example of his criticism.
5. Whewell (1837), **2**: 390–462, especially p. 442.
6. For diffraction see Fresnel (1821–2) in Fresnel (1866–70), **1**: 247–382. For double refraction see Fresnel (1827) in Fresnel (1866–70), **2**: 479–596. Translated into English (by A.W. Hobson) as Fresnel (1852).
7. Arago (1819) in Fresnel (1866–70), **1**: 229–37. This was Arago's report on Fresnel's paper for the Académie des Sciences' diffraction prize commission of which he was a member. On p. 236 he reported Poission's prediction and his own experimental verification.
8. Lloyd (1833) where he reported Hamilton's prediction and his own experimental verification of conical refraction. Hamilton made this prediction by considering mathematically how a ray of light obeying Fresnel's equations would behave on entering various crystals. For details see Graves (1882–9), **1**: 623–38 and Hankins (1980), Chapter 6.
9. For Fresnel's statement of this position see Fresnel (1852), 262. For Young see Young (1824) in Young (1855), **1**: 412–17, 416–17.
10. Fresnel (1827–9), **27**: 161.
11. James, F.A.J.L. (1984).
12. Newton (1730). See for example queries 20, 29, 30 and 31.
13. For statements of this position see Priestley (1767), xiii. Biot (1816), **2**: 148–9. Brewster (1832), 321.
14. Cantor (1983), chapter 6 and Cantor (1975). See also Crosland and Smith (1978) especially pp. 30–48.
15. David Brewster (1781–1868). For discussion of his work see Morse (1972). See also Olson (1975), especially pp. 177–88.
16. Herschel (1831), art. 291, where he wrote 'it is by no means impossible that the Newtonian theory of light, if cultivated with equal diligence with the Huyghenian, might lead to an equally plausible explanation of phenomena now regarded as beyond its reach'. In Herschel (1833) he announced his full commitment to the undulatory theory.
17. Brewster (1833).
18. James, F.A.J.L. (1983c).
19. Gooding (1980a), 20–2, (1980b), 95–7; Brush (1970).
20. Faraday to Mitscherlich, 4 August 1830, *Correspondence,* **1**: 101. Fresnel (1822) in Fresnel (1866–70), **2**: 3–146 translated into English as Fresnel (1827–9).
21. See James, F.A.J.L. (1983b).
22. Wheatstone (1834), 587.
23. Faraday, *Diary*, 3 November 1835, **2**, 2554.
24. He published some of his results in Faraday (1838b).
25. *Ibid.,* 1329–30.
26. Wheatstone (1861b), 201.
27. Faraday, *Diary*, 5 January 1836, **2**, 2799.
28. Faraday (1838b), 1421. Faraday's emphasis.
29. Faraday (1838a), 1165.
30. Faraday (1838b), 1421.
31. *Ibid.,* 1406.
32. For a discussion of this see James, F.A.J.L. (1983b). For some specific acknowledgements see Masson (1851), art. 159. Ångström, (1854); translated into English (by John Tyndall, see p. 202 of Tyndall (1895)) as Ångström (1855), 330.
33. Faraday, *Diary*, 2 and 6 May 1833, **2**: 482–504. Faraday had, on 10 September 1822, previously tried this experiment, *Diary*, **1**, 71. For a discussion of this early work see Gooding (1985a).

34. Faraday (1834b), 951–5.
35. In the letter to Taylor, Faraday (1844) does not refer specifically to Dalton. However, in 'Royal Institution', *Lit. Gaz.*, (27 January 1844), 60–1, (which is a report of the Discourse), Faraday apparently mentioned Dalton specifically and linked his atoms with those of Hooke and Wollaston (p. 61).
36. M. Faraday, 'On some phenomena of electro-static induction', RI MS F4 G13.
37. 'Royal Institution', *Lit. Gaz.*, (28 January 1843), 55–6. 'Meeting of the Royal Institution', *Chem. Gaz.*, 1843, **1**: 194–5. 'Lecture on electricity at the Royal Institution, Albemarle Street', *Reper. Pat. Inv.*, 1843, **1**: 165–84. (This is apparently a verbatim account).
38. 'Seventh Meeting of the British Association for the Advancement of Science', *Athenaeum*, (7 October 1837), 743–55, 747. Faraday's anti-Daltonism certainly stretched back to January 1834. In (1834a), 869 he wrote that he found it 'very difficult to form a clear idea of their nature'. Later that year he visited Hamilton in Dublin who reported to his sister that Faraday held 'almost as anti-material a view as myself' (Hamilton to Sister Sydney, 30 June 1834, Graves (1882–9), **2**: 95–6).
39. 'Royal Institution', *op. cit.* (35), 60–1.
40. *Ibid.*, 61.
41. 'Royal Institution', *Athenaeum*, (27 January 1844), 90.
42. 'Royal Institution', *op. cit.* (35), 61.
43. Faraday (1844), 141.
44. M. Faraday, 'Matter', IEE MS. Published in Levere (1968), 105–7, 107.
45. Williams, L.P. (1965), 78, 87–9 and 295–6 suggested that Faraday was not only aware of, but actively and secretly used the theory of point atomism proposed in Boscovich (1763); translated into English as Boscovich (1922). Heimann (1971) proposed that Faraday got his matter ideas from 'a native British tradition of natural philosophy' (p. 253) in particular from Priestley (1777). These suggestions proliferate because as Heimann pointed out 'Faraday did not indicate his sources' (p. 247).
46. Faraday (1844), 140.
47. 'Royal Institution', *op. cit.* (35) and 'Royal Institution', *op. cit.* (41).
48. 'Meeting of the Royal Institution', *Chem. Gaz.*, 1844, **2**: 81–2.
49. See Spencer (1967). This adversely criticises the thesis espoused in Williams, L.P. (1965) that Faraday was a convinced and secret Boscovichean from an early point in his scientific life. Heimann (1971) does likewise, but replaces Boscovich with eighteenth century British natural philosophers. Gooding (1978) argues strongly against both Williams and Heimann and for a rational interpretation of Faraday based on the texts. In support of Gooding's position I add that Heimann's argument also implies that Faraday held a secret philosophical commitment, though Heimann does not stress this in the way Williams does with Boscovich and Faraday.
50. Faraday (1844), 141.
51. Faraday, *op. cit.* (44).
52. Faraday (1844), 141.
53. *Ibid.*, 144.
54. Faraday, *op. cit.* (44), 106.
55. Faraday, *Diary*, 17, 22, 28 May 1845, **4**, 7401–18.
56. *Ibid.*, 7410.
57. Faraday (1836).
58. Faraday, *Diary*, 17 May 1845, **4**, 7401.
59. Faraday (1845).
60. William Thomson, later Lord Kelvin (1824–1907). Faraday was definitely at the British Association on 24 and 25 June, see 'Fifteenth meeting of the British Association for the Advancement of Science', *Athenaeum*, (28 June 1845), 639–44, 639 and *ibid.*, (26 July 1845), 746–8, 746 repectively. What they talked about is unknown but Faraday sent Avogadro (1844) to Thomson for comment. See Thomson to Faraday, 6 August 1845, *Correspondence*, **1**: 310.

61. 'Fifteenth meeting of the British Association for the Advancement of Science', *Athenaeum*, (12 July 1845), 697–702, 699.
62. Thomson, W. (1845).
63. Thomson to Faraday, 6 August 1845, *Correspondence*, **1**: 310.
64. Bence Jones (1870a), **2**: 214–25.
65. Faraday to Thomson, 8 August 1845, *Correspondence*, **1**: 311.
66. Faraday (1834b), 951–5. Thomson added a footnote to Thomson, W. (1845), 12, saying that this had been Faraday's result.
67. Faraday to Thomson, 8 August 1845, *Correspondence*, **1**: 311. Thomson later tried to visit Faraday at the Royal Institution, but he was out. See Thomson to Faraday, 25 August 1845, IEE MS, Faraday to Thomson, 25 August 1845, ULC add MS 7342, F30.
68. Faraday, *Diary*, 30 August 1845, **4**, 7434.
69. *Ibid.*, 7437–44.
70. *Ibid.*, 1 September 1845, **4**, 7471.
71. *Ibid.*, 5 September 1845, **4**, 7485.
72. *Ibid.*, 7497. Faraday's emphasis.
73. See Tyndall (1894), 94 where he wrote 'while once sauntering with him through the Crystal Palace, at Sydenham, I asked him what directed his attention to the magnetization of light. It was his theoretic notions'.
74. Faraday, *Diary*, 13 September 1845, **4**, 7499.
75. *Ibid.*, 7500–3.
76. *Ibid.*, 5 September 1845, **4**, 7485.
77. *Ibid.*, 13 September 1845, **4**, 7504.
78. See Knudsen (1976).
79. Faraday, *Diary*, 20 October 1845, **4**, 7872.
80. *Ibid.*, 13 September 1845, **4**, 7510.
81. *Ibid.*, 7520–36. This is an example of learning to improve an effect by varying an experiment; see Gooding (this volume).
82. Faraday, *Diary*, 13 September 1845, **4**, 7532.
83. *Ibid.*, 7536.
84. *Ibid.*, 7510.
85. *Ibid.*, 7512.
86. *Ibid.*, 18 September 1845, **4**, 7538.
87. *Ibid.*, 7541.
88. *Ibid.*, 7553–67. With some he did — or at least thought he did — with others not. He also found that magnetism circularly polarised the light passing through the glass (*Ibid.*, 7550).
89. *Ibid.*, 7576.
90. *Ibid.*, 7585.
91. *Ibid.*, 7600. Faraday's emphasis.
92. *Ibid.*, 3 October 1845, **4**, 7739. Faraday's emphasis.
93. *Ibid.*, 22 September 1845, **4**, 7656.
94. *Ibid.*, 26 September 1845, **4**, 7670.
95. *Ibid.*, 7693.
96. *Ibid.*, 7694.
97. *Ibid.*, 7695.
98. Faraday (1846a), 2225. He specifically referred to his 1844 'Speculation' in a footnote to this passage.
99. *Ibid.*, 2226.
100. Faraday was able to make alterations in proof at least until 15 December by which time he had discovered diamagnetism. See *ibid.* note to title of paper. For an example of an alteration Faraday in the manuscript version used 'dimagnetism', RSMS PT 30.1, but presumably changed this at proof stage after his correspondence with Whewell about a name for the phenomenon. Faraday to Whewell, 8 December 1845, *Correspondence*, **1**:

320 and Whewell to Faraday, c10 December 1845, *Correspondence*, **1**: 321, where Whewell suggested diamagnetism instead of dimagnetism.

101. Faraday, *Diary*, 6 October 1845, **4**: 7742–3.

102. During the middle of October Faraday returned to experiment on light and electricity. On the eleventh he built a long helix round a glass tube (*ibid.*, 7744), in which he placed different substances. He tried air first but with no success (*ibid.*, 7747). Water did produce an effect (*ibid.*, 7750) as did sulphate of soda. He wrote 'so the helix is a good thing, and in the case of the polarised ray may truly be said to be electrified' (*ibid.*, 7752). Although he did not obtain the effect in air his expectation of success was increased by his next discovery which he took at first to be due to phosphorescence (*ibid.*, 7775). Further analysis on 13 October showed this to be heating effects in water forming a lens (*ibid.*, 7787). Faraday thought this could be used to detect very small effects, bringing success within his reach (*ibid.*, 7788).

103. On the previous day he made the first public announcement of his discoveries to the Managers and Members of the Royal Institution. RI MM 3 November 1845, **9**: 357 and RI MS GM **5**: 288, were reported in 'Our weekly gossip', *Athenaeum* (8 November 1845), 1080 and 'Electricity, magnetism, and light', *Lit. Gaz.* (8 November 1845), 737 respectively. (The *Lit. Gaz.* reported the wrong date.)

104. Faraday, *Diary*, 4 November 1845, **4**, 7902.

105. *Ibid.*, 7 November 1845, **4**, 7934.

106. The development of this discovery has been discussed by Gooding (1981 and 1982b), Knudsen (1976) and Williams, L.P. (1965), 408–64.

107. This phenomenon had been sought more than twenty years earlier by Herschel and others but with no success. Gooding (1985a) shows that this earlier effort contributed to the rapid dissemination of Faraday's work in the scientific community. For details of its subsequent development see Spencer (1970).

108. Cantor (1983), 166–72.

109. Whewell (1833), xv–xvii. Airy (1833). Both of these were a response to Brewster (1833).

110. Brewster to Brougham, 21 February 1849, UCL, Brougham papers, 26, 638.

111. James Challis (1803–1882), Plumian Professor of Astronomy at Cambridge.

112. George Gabriel Stokes (1819–1903), then a fellow of Pembroke College, Cambridge.

113. Challis (1845a). Stokes (1845a).

114. Stokes (1845b). Challis (1845b). Stokes (1846a and b). Challis (1846a and b). This debate continued after these papers but this need not concern us. See Wilson (1972) for an account of the entire debate.

115. For Faraday's views of mathematics see Gooding (1982b), 246–8 and Cantor (this volume).

116. The reason for the date of 10 April, which was Good Friday that year, was that at the beginning of Faraday (1846c) he referred to 'the last Friday-evening meeting' (p. 345) which as the 'Thoughts' were dated 15 April 1846, have led most historians, Bowers excepted, to assume a date of 10 April.

117. 'Royal Institution', *Lit. Gaz.* (11 April 1846), 340–1, reported Faraday's discourse on pp. 340–1 in which Faraday made it clear that it was Napier who had been due to lecture (p. 340). James Napier (1810–1884). For accounts of his life see *Proc. Chem. Soc.*, 1885, **47**: 333–4 and Tatlock (1886–7). He had already given one discourse 'The practice of Electro-Metallurgy' on 2 May 1845, and would give another 'On Dyeing' on 3 March 1848 (RI lecturers index). Although he spent most of his life in Scotland he worked in London for the electroplating company Elkington and Mason from 1842 until 1849.

118. 'Royal Institution', *op. cit.* (117), 340.

119. *Ibid.* Bence Jones (1870a), **2**: 227 is quite clear that it was Faraday who was scheduled to give this discourse.

120. Wheatstone (1845).

121. 'Meetings for the Ensuing Week', *Athenaeum* (28 March 1846), 326.

122. As is evident from his manuscript notes for the lecture, RI MS F4 G23.
123. Faraday (1846c), 349–50. In this Faraday expanded on his remarks which had been reported in 'Royal Institution', *op. cit.* (117) 4 days earlier.
124. Despite the number of improbabilities contained in the usual account and its clear mythic character this story was completely accepted by Williams, L.P. (1965), 331 and 380 and (1967). Bowers (1975b), 22 while pointing out some of the problems of the story, in the end substantially accepted it. The earliest reference that I have found to this myth is Thompson (1898), 197. Martin (1934) 122–3, expanded the story. One of the more recent accounts, Goldman, M. (1983), 90, states (without references) that Wheatstone left because he had heard that 'Joseph Crabtree a notorious and inveterate heckler of lecturers was present'.
125. Lyon Playfair, 'On the Bulks of bodies, and the nature of the difference between unlike forms of the same body, such as diamond, graphite and coke', reported in 'Royal Institution', *op. cit.* (117), 340.
126. *Ibid.*
127. Faraday (1846c), 347. Faraday's emphasis.
128. *Ibid.*
129. *Ibid.*
130. *Ibid.*, 348.
131. Airy and Whewell, who had been among the severest critics of Brewster, took different positions in regard to Faraday's work. Airy (1846) was critical (but gently so compared to the treatment he had given Brewster). Whewell on the other hand wrote that he was looking forward to more speculations. Whewell to Faraday, 7 August 1846, *Correspondence*, 1: 343.
132. Faraday (1846c), 348.
133. *Ibid.*, 347.
134. Stokes by now had become Lucasian Professor of Mathematics at Cambridge. This chair was not well paid and he took on a teaching job at the Royal School of Mines in nearby Jermyn Street. Larmor (1907), 1: 9.
135. Stokes (1852). For an account of Stokes's work on fluorescence see James, F.A.J.L. (1983a).
136. Barlow to Stokes, 6 November [1852], ULC Add MS 7656, B124. Wilson (1976) misdates this letter.
137. Stokes (1853).
138. Stokes to Faraday, 26 November 1852, IEE MS. This is supported by Barlow to Stokes, 12 November [1852] and 22 November 1852, ULC Add MS 7656, B121–2 respectively.
139. Faraday, *Diary*, 14 December 1852, 7, 13011–23.
140. *Ibid.*, 13015. Stokes to Faraday, 7 January 1853, *Correspondence*, 2: 509.
141. *Ibid.* This was an idea that he had suggested in Stokes (1852), art 224, but seems not to have done anything about until the chance of his discourse. It appears that he may have carried out this experiment see Wheatstone to Faraday, 26 January 1853, *Correspondence*, 2: 512.
142. Stokes to Faraday, 7 January 1853, *Correspondence*, 2: 509.
143. Stokes to Faraday, 14 February 1853, *Correspondence*, 2: 515.
144. Stokes (1853), 264. Stokes spent a considerable amount of time in the ensuing years working on this discovery. He published his results in Stokes (1862).
145. Faraday, *Diary*, 21 April 1856, 7, 14722.
146. *Ibid.*
147. *Ibid.*
148. *Ibid.* 2 February 1857, 7, 14243. Faraday says that he visited De la Rue 'Last Tuesday Evening (28 Jany)'. That Tuesday was 29 January.
149. *Ibid.*, 14255.
150. *Ibid.*, 14273.
151. *Ibid.*, 7 February 1856, 7, 14332.

152. *Ibid.*
153. *Ibid.*
154. Which he idiosyncratically called Stokes's rays on two occasions, *ibid.*, 16 May 1853, **6**, 13055 and 29 September 1856, **7**, 15057.
155. *Ibid.*, 13 February 1856, **7**, 14407.
156. *Ibid.*, 11 March 1856, **7**, 14529b.
157. *Ibid.*, 21 April 1856, **7**, 14722.
158. Faraday (1856)., The gold part is on pp. 310–12.
159. Faraday, *Diary*, 1 July 1856, **7**, 14834.
160. *Ibid.*, 4 July 1856, **7**, 14849.
161. *Ibid.*
162. *Ibid.*
163. *Ibid.*, 22 October 1856, **7**, 15186.
164. *Ibid.*, 20 October 1856, **7**. 15165.
165. *Ibid.*, 22 October 1856, **7**, 15186.
166. *Ibid.*
167. *Ibid.*, 25 October 1856, **7**, 15243a.
168. Faraday (1857).
169. *Ibid.*, 146.
170. *Ibid.*, 145.
171. *Ibid.*
172. *Ibid.*
173. Williams, L.P. (1965), Harman (1982).
174. For another example of the relationship of private and public science see Rudwick (1982).

Plate 15 Charles Wheatstone. Unknown. Institution of Electrical Engineers. Reproduced from a slide.

8

Faraday, Wheatstone and Electrical Engineering

Brian Bowers

Electrical engineering rests on a foundation of scientific research. One of the most important parts of that foundation was the electrical and magnetic discoveries made by Michael Faraday. These provided the scientific basis for devices fundamental to electrical engineering such as the electric motor, transformer and the generator. But electrical engineering did not emerge from its scientific basis by some natural and inevitable process. It required the intervention of scientists who could see the practical engineering possibilities that might arise from scientific research.

In the 1830s it is impossible to make any distinction between people whom we would now call pure scientists and those whom we would call applied. There then existed a sort of sliding scale between pure and applied science where at different times we can find the same individual at different points on the scale. In the work of both Faraday and Charles Wheatstone,[1] we have excellent examples of people who at different times were on different parts of the scale. While it is fair to say that Faraday tended to remain nearer the pure end, Sophie Forgan in her chapter shows that Faraday was involved closely with a number of applied scientific projects. It is also fair to say that Wheatstone tended to remain near the applied end, but I shall discuss both his pure and applied research to illustrate that distinctions between pure and applied scientists cannot be imposed on the science and technology of the 1830s.

What makes the relationship of Faraday and Wheatstone especially interesting is that at times each quite clearly affected the course of research (pure or applied) being done by the other. Their relationship worked at three interconnected levels. First Faraday was in large part responsible for demonstrating Wheatstone's discoveries to the educated public. Second on a number of occasions they jointly undertook pieces of research. Finally Wheatstone made practical applications of discoveries made by Faraday.

There is a problem with exploring their interaction. Because they worked closely together, rather than by correspondence, evidence concerning their collaboration is rather scarce.[2] The work discussed below is what has been documented, sometimes by others, but it is clear from passing alusions that their collaboration was much more extensive.

1 Wheatstone

Wheatstone was by all accounts lucid and eloquent in private conversation, but he was intensely shy and this made him a poor public speaker.[3] At first sight he seems an unsuitable candidate for the post of Professor of Experimental Philosophy at King's College, London, to which he was appointed in 1834. How he was appointed is not clear. There was no advertisement, no application and no interview board. It seems that his services were sought and he agreed to take the post. It was not a full-time appointment and Wheatstone continued to run, with his brother William, the family musical business they had inherited from their uncle.[4]

Wheatstone was born in Gloucester in 1802. In 1806 the family moved to London. His father set up in business as a manufacturer of musical instruments and taught the flute and flageolet. Among his pupils was Princess Charlotte (1796–1817), daughter of the Prince of Wales (later George IV). His uncle was already in business in London, selling music, and Wheatstone was apprenticed to him. But he did not take to the business and preferred to study how the instruments worked. He was particularly intrigued by the transmission of sound through solid rods and stretched wires. This interest led to a public exhibition in 1821 at his father's shop, of Wheatstone's 'Enchanted Lyre' or 'Acoucryptophone'.[5] Visitors saw this device in the form of large ancient lyre suspended from the ceiling and surrounded, but not touched, by a velvet covered hoop supported on the floor by three rods. The lyre was suspended by a brass wire which passed through the ceiling. This was connected with the sound boards of instruments in the room above, where unseen players performed on the harp, piano and dulcimer. Regular concerts were given. The music critics were impressed and urged music lovers to hear the quality of the music produced.[6] A later exhibition opened in March or April 1822. Wheatstone was able to charge the public five shillings per head for an hour's orchestral concert.[7]

Contemporary press accounts of the Enchanted Lyre make it clear that Wheatstone had other practical ends in view. He envisaged concerts being transmitted to one's house. He even had the idea that parliamentary debates might be transmitted and heard at once, 'instead of being read the next day only'.[8] This concern of Wheatstone's with the transmission of messages over long distances was to be a recurring theme in his life.

2 Faraday and Wheatstone: the lecture context

In May 1823 Hans Christian Oersted came to London. How he met Wheatstone is not clear; perhaps he went to one of Wheatstone's concerts as a 'tourist attraction'. However they met, Oersted put Wheatstone in touch with D.F.J. Arago in Paris.[9] Arago gave an account of Wheatstone's experiments on sound at a meeting of the Académie des Sciences on 30 June 1823.[10] Since Oersted introduced Arago and Wheatstone, it is at least possible that he also introduced him to Faraday. On the other hand Faraday was fond of music so he might have met Wheatstone at one of his concerts.

Wheatstone's initial acoustical work provided the Royal Institution with many interesting Friday Evening Discourses. The physics of music and the working of musical instruments has always been an excellent subject for discourses. The experiments of Wheatstone must have seemed to Faraday an obvious source material. Wheatstone's shyness was a problem, but the solution was easy. Faraday gave the discourse with material supplied by Wheatstone.[11] This initiated a series of 'joint' discourses which extended for over 20 years and included the famous 1846 discourse, discussed by Frank James in Chapter 7, in which Faraday gave his 'Thoughts on Ray-vibrations'.[12]

The first of these joint discourses was on 15 February 1828; the subject was resonance.[13] It was illustrated by experiments on Javenese musical instruments lent by Lady Raffles from the collection recently brought to Britain by Stamford Raffles. Several other joint discourses also dealt with the resonance of solid bodies and of columns of air in pipes and other cavities. On 5 March 1830 the discourse was 'On the transmission of musical sounds through solid conductors'.[14] In this Wheatstone observed that if a conducting substance could be obtained with perfectly uniform density and elasticity then it would be as easy to transmit sound from London to Aberdeen as from one room to the next.[15] He said that experiments by Perrolle had shown that sound was transmitted better in conductors in which it travelled faster.[16] This led him to think about the speed of transmission of sound. At that time Wheatstone thought that progress in the transmission of sound over long distances would probably come from making an artificial voice, which would shout louder. He worked on talking machines for a while but without success.[17] But Wheatstone was still concerned with the idea of transmitting messages over long distances.

3 Work on the nature, velocity and transmission of electricity[18]

In Wheatstone's early electrical work there is no indication that he had in mind the practical purposes so evident in his acoustical work. It is reasonable to suppose that contact with Faraday inspired Wheatstone to turn his attention to electrical phenomena. Faraday first mentioned Wheatstone's new interest in electricity in a discourse on 11 June 1830.[19] He pointed out that the persistence of vision meant that a body could be in motion, yet be perceived motionless. For example, a piece of lighted charcoal whirled around at the end of a string appeared to trace a bright circle. Motion could cause an apparently continuous light. Similarly perhaps one could expose the motion of a spark by somehow rendering the imperceptible motion of its light perceptible. Wheatstone suggested this idea could be used to determine the velocity of the spark. He envisaged deviations from the vibrations of an already vibrating string placed between two electrodes through which a spark passed. From this deviation, Wheatstone contended, he would be able to calculate the velocity of the spark.[20]

In a discourse at the Royal Institution on 1 March 1833, again delivered by Faraday, Wheatstone outlined his motives for studying the spark[21]: 'The object is to ascertain whether the time occupied by the passage of the electric spark is appreciable; if it be, *then the existence of an electric fluid, or of two fluids, and the direction of the passage may be determined*'.[22] By then Wheatstone had abandoned his original method of measuring the velocity of the spark. He now thought he could measure the velocity of electricity crossing between two electrodes by observing a spark with a revolving mirror. He hoped to deflect the image of the spark in the mirror sufficiently to observe its journey across the gap. Perhaps he expected to see the spark emerge from one electrode if electricity was a single fluid, but from both electrodes if it was composed of two fluids.

The following year, 1834, Wheatstone published the results of spark experiments in which he passed electricity through a circuit of wire half a mile long placing three spark gaps at equal distances along the wire.[23] He argued that the order in which the sparks flashed in the revolving mirror would indicate whether the electricity was flowing from one pole of the battery or from both.[24] If the sparks flashed one after the other along the wire then electricity would be a single fluid flowing from one pole of the battery to the other. When he conducted this experiment he observed that the middle spark was sensibly retarded compared with the other two sparks which flashed simultaneously. He concluded that the electricity must have reached these two spark gaps simultaneously. After passing across the first two spark gaps the electricity from both would proceed to the middle spark gap to cause the spark there. He concluded that electricity was composed of two fluids flowing round the circuit. He calculated that the speed his apparatus could measure was 288 000 miles per second. Although he was careful to say that this figure was an estimate, it was widely quoted in the ensuing years as the velocity of electricity. At this point Wheatstone was as interested in the nature of electricity as in its velocity.[25] This work, especially on the behaviour of the sparks, greatly interested Faraday and contributed much to his research on induction. It is discussed by James in Chapter 7.

But how was electricity propagated across the spark gap? In 1835

Wheatstone read a paper which dealt with this question to the Dublin meeting of the British Association.[26] He had prismatically analysed the spark produced when mercury was placed on one electrode. He observed 'a few definite lines of light, separated by very wide dark intervals from each other, some of great brightness'.[27] He repeated this experiment with fluid zinc, cadmium, bismuth, tin and lead (all of which have a fairly low melting point). He found that they possessed spectra similar to that produced when using mercury, but with their lines in different positions. He concluded that 'the appearances [of the spectra] are so different that by this mode of examination, the metals may be readily distinguished from each other'.[28]

Wheatstone also found that the spark spectrum of mercury was the same in the ordinary atmosphere as in a vacuum (presumably the vacuum was not total), in carbon dioxide, or in oxygen. He concluded that the medium in which the spark was exploded 'had no influence on the nature of the light'.[29] When he examined the mercury spark under water, in alcohol and in oil, its spectrum remained the same. Further, some black powder which had been precipitated in these liquids 'proved to be pure mercury, in a very finely-divided state'.[30] He therefore argued that the spark was not a 'consequence of combustion',[31] i.e. the mercury had not oxidised.

Using these results Wheatstone rejected the spark theories proposed by J.-B. Biot,[32] by Humphry Davy[33] and Faraday's unpublished notion of 1834 that in the mercury spark at least some of the mercury underwent combustion.[34] Instead, said Wheatstone, this work supported Ambrogio Fusinieri's theory.[35] He had suggested, in 1827, that when the electric spark passed from one electrode to another it carried some of the ponderable matter of the electrodes with it. This matter transmitted the electricity.[36]

4 The electric telegraph

Wheatstone did not pursue these researches as he thought that the speed of electricity might make it possible to realise his long-held dream of transmitting messages over long distances, by using electricity instead of sound. The potential applications tempted him away, for a time, from pure research. To pursue his idea, Wheatstone applied electrical knowledge derived from the work of Faraday and others.

Wheatstone designed a circuit with which he could transmit a deflection of a needle through long wires to produce a corresponding deflection at the other end. By the mid-1830s he had read Georg Simon Ohm's 'Die Galvanische kette mathematisch Bearbeitet'.[37] He understood that for a telegraph instrument to work satisfactorily it had to have an impedance at least comparable with the impedance of the wires connecting it. Wheatstone therefore made his receiving instruments with many turns of fine wire in their coils. At the same time William Fothergill Cooke was also working on the problem of making a practical electric telegraph.[38] His instruments had coils

of thick wire and relatively low impedance so that most of the signalling
energy was dissipated in the wires connecting the transmitter and receiver.
Cooke had made instruments which worked across a room, but which failed
when even 1 mile separated them.[39] In seeking a solution to his scientific
problem Cooke consulted several leading men of science, including Faraday.
They could not tell him how to make the instruments work through long
wires.[40] Eventually he was directed to Wheatstone whom he met in February
1837.[41] In that year they patented the first practical electric telegraph, the first
engineering application of electricity.[42] This is not the place to describe the
stormy relationship between Cooke and Wheatstone, which led within a few
years to the dissolution of the partnership.[43]

Wheatstone had done nothing towards commercial exploitation of the
telegraph. However, Cooke had explored the commercial possibilities and
recognised — rightly — that the newly developing railway system provided the
most promising application for rapid communication using the telegraph.[44]
Their first commercial installation was in 1838, along the new Great Western
Railway from Paddington to West Drayton.[45]

Generators and electric motors

In developing a practical telegraph many technical problems had to be
overcome. The first telegraphs were battery powered. But batteries were
heavy, expensive and required changing. Electromagnetic induction, discovered by Faraday in the autumn of 1831, offered the prospect of an electric
current not dependent on batteries. The first electromagnetic generator
('magneto') was Pixii's machine of 1832.[46] Later in the decade a variety of
similar machines were made, the best known probably being those of Clarke
and of Saxton.[47] Cooke and Wheatstone tried unsuccessfully to use a magneto
in their early experiments. In a letter to his mother of 4 July 1837 Cooke wrote
'we mean to try whether a machine called "Electro-magnetic" cannot be made
to supersede the galvanic battery'.[48] At that stage it could not, but within a few
years, Wheatstone was using magnetos in his telegraphs.[49]

He also played a part in the evolution of the magneto into the practical
generator. He was one of the independent inventors of the self-excited
generator in 1866. He described his machine to the Royal Society at the same
meeting at which William Siemens described a similar machine.[50] Wheatstone
and Siemens subsequently corresponded about their machines, discussing
how to get the greatest electrical output.[51]

Another problem with the telegraph was to devise a machine that would
indicate letters and numbers. Many thousands of Wheatstone's 'ABC'
telegraphs were made, so-called because the needle pointed towards the
appropriate letter. They had a small 'electromagnetic engine' — electric motor
— in the receiver. But Wheatstone wanted to make and develop better electric
motors and he worked on several. One was conventional (possibly a student
project); three others he called 'eccentric'.[52] He also made a linear motor,
whose stator survives.[53] This needed a higher current than he could have

readily obtained, but it is possible that the Royal Institution's great battery was used to operate it.

Wheatstone envisaged the day when electric motors would have uses other than in the telegraph. For example in a Royal Society paper on electric measurements in 1843 Wheatstone described the rheostat (a word he invented) and added that if ever electromagnetic engines became a useful source of power the rheostat could be used for controlling their velocity.[54]

However, not all such work on engines led to success. In 1840 W.H. Fox Talbot patented a series of ideas for making an electric motor, including one which he called the 'electrolytic gas engine'.[55] This looked somewhat like a single-cylinder steam beam engine. A vertical cylinder contained a piston linked by a crank to a flywheel, but there were no steam pipes. Instead four wires entered the cylinder, two at the base and two higher up. The cylinder contained a little acidulated water and the two lower wires were part of a circuit for electrolysing the water to yield hydrogen and oxygen. A piece of platinum wire linked the upper two wires. A commutator on the axis of the flywheel controlled the connections between the four wires and a battery. Talbot's idea was that the liquid should first be partially electrolysed, then the gases made to recombine by making the platinum red hot. The resultant explosion would drive the piston up, the flywheel would continue moving so that the piston went down again, and the commutator would connect to start the process again. Wheatstone arranged for the manufacture (by W.T. Henley) and testing of the machines.[56] The whole idea sounds rather dangerous. Talbot and Wheatstone were both concerned for the latter's safety:

> I have foreseen the liability to explosion from the cause you mentioned and had requested the workman to furnish the model with a safety valve, but as I found the expense would be thereby augmented I resolved for the present to do without it. I intend to keep at a respectful distance during the experiment and to use one of my telegraphic connectors so that I may break the circuit from a distance before I have occasion to approach the instrument.[57]

No results are recorded and presumably the trials failed although another machine was made.

5 Electrical researches with Faraday

Wheatstone maintained an interest in pure research on electricity. In the late 1830s he worked on the problem of the 'identity of electricities'. During the 1830s much electrical research was devoted to demonstrating that electricity from any source, chemical, frictional, magnetic, thermal, animal, was essentially the same. Faraday had shown that each kind of electricity could produce the same effects — giving shocks, electrolysing water, making sparks etc.[58] In this connection Wheatstone and Faraday were involved together in experiments on thermoelectricity and on electricity from electric fishes. In the latter case, unfortunately, entries in Faraday's *Diary* from October to December 1838 do not give any detail about the precise nature of their collaboration.[59]

However, of their collaboration on thermoelectricity we do have some considerable detail. This indicates the general nature of their cooperation. Thermoelectricity is produced when a circuit contains two metals at different temperatures. The electromotive force produced at the junction between the metals is very small — much less than that given by most chemical cells. The question was whether this electricity was the same as other electricities. Electricity from a chemical cell can easily be made to produce a spark when the circuit is broken. The essential condition is that the circuit should have sufficient self-inductance. Joseph Henry in America had demonstrated this by including in the circuit a coil of wire wound on an iron core.[60] The iron core is magnetised by the current flowing in the circuit. If the circuit is broken the iron demagnetises, but as it does so there is a change in the magnetic field linking it with the coil. This change induces an electromotive force in the coil which can easily be high enough to produce a visible spark at the break in the circuit. Could thermoelectricity be made to yield a spark in this way?

Wheatstone's thermoelectric experiments took place in April 1837, while Henry and another American A.D. Bache were visiting London. Henry and Wheatstone both gave accounts of the experiments. The experiment is difficult to carry out successfully; indeed it is surprising that they managed to see the result they described. The experiment was first carried out at King's College by Wheatstone, Daniell, Henry and Bache on 22 April. Daniell had made a coil according to Henry's description but it did not work. Before they could start work on thermoelectricity, Henry had to make the coil work, which he did with some difficulty.[61] Henry described the experiment in his diary:

> Mr Wheatstone however informed me a few evenings since that he had seen in an Italian Journal an account that the spark had been obtained from thermoelectricity by means of a spiral. Dr Daniell thought it would be impossible to obtain it with the means at command. I however prepared the apparatus, made the attempt by holding a hot poker to one side of the pile and ice to the other; the pile, the coil and a small movable piece of wire forming the circuit to be broken by drawing out the end of the movable wire from the mercury cup. The hot and cold was managed by Prof Wheatstone; the parts of the apparatus was held by Prof Daniell; I managed the wires. All ready. No effect. Again — no effect and again the same result. The other gentlemen now withdrew to another room to inspect some letters. I made a new arrangement of the apparatus, adjusted every part more carefully, called the others, again got all prepared. Prof Wheatstone as before applying the ice and Prof Daniell the poker. 1st attempt no effect perceived. The second a small spark each time I broke the connection. This was seen by all in succession. Bache arrived just before our first attempt & had gone into another room to inspect the letters above alluded to. He requested to be called if the experiment succeeded. The noise we made on the occasion call[ed] him fourth. He afterwards made much sport with our enthusiasm. Prof Daniell flourishing the poker Wheatstone with the ice and I jumping as he said in extacy. The experiment is however an interesting one and not the less so that we are the first mortals who have witnessed it in England.[62]

Wheatstone's account of the same experiment described the coil sufficiently well for me to reconstruct the experiment.[63] According to his account the coil consisted of a spiral of copper ribbon fifty feet in length and $1\frac{1}{2}$ inches wide, and wires being well insulated by brown paper and silk. A coil which *may* be the original is preserved in the Science Museum, having come from from King's College. The dimensions of this coil are as given in Wheatstone's paper. It has additionally five metallic cups for making connections with the aid of a little mercury, fixed at each end and at three points throughout the length:

> Two stout wires formed the communication between the poles of the pile and the spiral, and the contact was broken, when required, in a mercury cup between one extremity of the spiral and one of these wires. Whenever the contact was thus broken a small but distinct spark was seen, which was visible even in daylight.[64]

When using a thermopile similar to that described by Wheatstone I could not see any spark with the apparatus which I reconstructed according to this description. However, a small radio tuned to the medium wave, placed close to the coil produced a distinct click each time the circuit was broken.

Henry, Bache, Wheatstone and Daniell repeated this experiment 2 days later on 24 April when Faraday was present.[65] He also saw the spark. From both Henry's and Wheatstone's accounts of this second set of experiments it is clear that the apparatus had been modified. However, neither account states precisely what these modifications were. New thermopiles were used, possibly with a higher output voltage. But an aside in Henry's account indicates a more significant difference. This concerns a discussion with Faraday on whether thermoelectricity could produce magnetism. Faraday thought it could but Henry doubted it.[66] They appear to have been comparing the effectiveness of coils with or without a soft iron core in producing sparks from the electricity from a chemical cell. It is reasonable to ask whether a soft iron core was used with the coil in the thermoelectric experiment. Wheatstone did not mention one — but he could hardly have overlooked its relevance. A later account of the same experiment indicates that soft iron was used:

> Faraday, Wheatstone, Daniell and he had met to try to evolve the electric spark from the thermopile. Each in turn attempted it and failed. Then came Henry's turn. He succeeded: calling in the aid of his discovery the effect of a long interpolar wire wrapped around a piece of soft iron. Faraday became as wild as a boy, and, jumping up, shouted: 'Hurrah for the Yankee experiment'.[67]

When I connected a coil of wire wound on a soft iron core — an inductance — in series with my copy of Henry's coil and the thermopile it was fairly easy to produce sparks as described. This is presumably what happened.

6 Conclusion

In the electrical researches of Faraday and of Wheatstone, both the work they did separately and the work they did together, we see of the study of curious phenomena transformed into having practical applications. Faraday is entitled to the high regard in which he is held by electrical engineers. They have always looked on him as the founding father of their profession. The highest honour awarded by the Institution of Electrical Engineers is the Faraday Medal, and its most prestigious annual event is the Faraday Lecture. But Wheatstone, who explored the practical possibilities of the work of Faraday and others to the solution of engineering problems, was an essential link between Faraday and electrical engineering.

Notes

I thank Irene McCabe for her help and Bill Coates for practical assistance with demonstrations. I also thank Lenore Symons of the Institution of Electrical Engineers and the National Trust at Lacock Abbey for permission to work on manuscripts in their care.

1. Charles Wheatstone (1802–1875). For an account of his life and work see Bowers (1975a) which was published (with fewer references) as Bowers (1975b).
2. For the closeness of their collaboration see Grabham (1931) and 'Impressions of Faraday — Resources and Dexterity — Dr Grabham's memories', *The Times* (21 September 1931), 9. Both of these are somewhat unreliable, since they were written 70–80 years after the events described.
3. For his shyness and poor public speaking see 'Memoirs of deceased members: Charles Wheatstone', *Proc. Inst. Civ. Eng.*, 1877, **47**: 283–90, especially 286. For his private eloquence see Copleston (1851), 169 and Greville (1885), **1**: 79.
4. Also called Charles (d. 1823). See Bowers (1975b), 4–8.
5. 'Musical intelligence — The enchanted lyre', *Repos. Arts*, 1821, **12**: 173–5.
6. 'Intelligence, literary, scientific etc', *Repos. Arts*, 1822, **13**: 245–7, 246; 'Mr Wheatstone's diaphonicon', *Repos Arts*, 1822, **13**: 298.
7. 'Musical intelligence', *op. cit.*[(5)], 175.
8. *Ibid.*
9. Wheatstone (1823a), 313–4 and 316. See also Wheatstone (1823b), 85–6.
10. 'Séance du lundi 30 juin', *Ann. Chim. Phys.*, 1823, **23**: 312–3, 312. Wheatstone (1823a).
11. See Jeffries (1960), entries 156, (156), 160, 164, 167, 173, 176, 177, 211, 350, 447.
12. Faraday (1846c).
13. 'Proceedings of the Royal Institution', *Quart. J. Sci.*, 1828, **3**: 173. Wheatstone (1828).
14. 'Proceedings of the Royal Institution', *Quart. J. Sci.*, 1830, **7**: 190. Wheatstone (1831).
15. *Ibid.*, 238.
16. *Ibid.*, 244. Perrolle (1799).
17. Wheatstone (1837b).
18. This section is informed by James, F.A.J.L. (1983b), 137–8. See also Bowers (1975b), Chapter 5.
19. 'Royal Institution', *Athenaeum* (19 June 1830), 378–9.
20. *Ibid.*, 379.
21. 'Mr Faraday on some of Mr Wheatstone's experiments on Electrical Light', *Athenaeum* (9 March 1833), 155. 'Mr Faraday on the velocity and nature of the electric discharge', *Lit. Gaz.* (9 March 1833), 152.
22. *Ibid.* Report's emphasis.
23. Wheatstone (1834), 587.
24. *Ibid.*, 590.
25. *Ibid.*, 589. Whittaker (1962), 228 suggests that this high velocity was due to the way in which Wheatstone wound the wire causing cross-induction between different parts of the wire.
26. Wheatstone (1835). This was an abstract of the paper which Wheatstone read to the

Association. William Crookes reprinted this abstract in Wheatstone (1861a) adding that he would print, for the first time, the full text of Wheatstone's paper, without alteration (*ibid.*). This Crookes did as Wheatstone (1861b). The points which Wheatstone made in this full paper are the same which occur in the abstract, although they are made at considerably greater length. It seems reasonable to suppose that the paper Wheatstone published in the *Chemical News* was the same as that read to the 1835 British Association.

27. *Ibid.*, 198.
28. Wheatstone (1835).
29. Wheatstone (1861b), 200.
30. *Ibid.*
31. *Ibid.*
32. *Ibid.*, 201. Biot (1805a) translated into English as Biot (1805b).
33. Wheatstone (1861b), 201. Davy, H. (1822).
34. Wheatstone (1861b), 200. This is found in Faraday, *Diary*, 2 December 1834, **2**, 2193. Presumably, since Faraday did not publish this notion, he must have told Wheatstone of it.
35. Ambrogio Fusinieri (1773–1853) was a Venetian physicist.
36. Wheatstone (1861b), 201. Fusinieri (1827) translated into English as Fusinieri (1844).
37. Ohm (1827), this was not translated into English until Ohm (1841).
38. Cooke to his mother, 5 April 1836, IEE MS, printed in Cooke (1895), letter 1.
39. Cooke to his mother, 5 April 1836, *ibid.*, letter 14.
40. *Ibid.*
41. *Ibid.*
42. English patent 7390/1837.
43. Fahie (1884), Hubbard (1965).
44. Cooke to his mother, 21 July 1836, IEE MS, printed in Cooke (1895), letter 5.
45. Cooke to his mother, 3 April 1838, *ibid.*, letter 38.
46. Hatchette (1832a and b). For a fuller description of early electro-magnetic generators see Bowers (1982), chapter 6.
47. Clarke (1836, 1837), Saxton (1836).
48. Cooke to his mother, 4 July 1837, IEE MS, printed in Cooke (1895), letter 25.
49. English patent 9022/1841. See also the objects in the Science Museum, London.
50. Wheatstone (1867), Siemens (1867).
51. For details see Bowers (1982).
52. English patent 8345/1840. Daniell (1843), 574–81.
53. Bowers (1982), 262.
54. Wheatstone (1843).
55. English patent 8650/1840.
56. Wheatstone to Talbot, 15 December 1840, LA MS 40–89.
57. Wheatstone to Talbot, 15 March 1841, LA MS 41–12.
58. Faraday (1833a).
59. Faraday, *Diary*, 22 October 1838, **3**, 5054 and 3–22 December 1838, **3**, 5068–71.
60. Henry (1835).
61. 'Henry's European diary', 22 April 1837, in Henry (1972–9), **3**: 304–11, 305.
62. *Ibid.*, 306–7. For the Italian memoir see Wheatstone (1837a). Here he reported the work of the Florentine physicist Vincenzio Antinoni and the Sienase physicist Saint-Linari which appeared in *L'Indictore Sanese* (13 December 1836).
63. Wheatstone (1837a).
64. *Ibid.*, 416.
65. 'Henry's European diary', 26 April 1837, in Henry (1972–9), **3**: 315–20. This describes events of two days earlier.
66. *Ibid.*, 316–7.
67. Mayer (1880), 506. Presumably Mayer learnt this story from Henry.

Plate 16 Michael Faraday holding a bar magnet. Maull and Polyblank. National Portrait Gallery. Published October 1857 as No. 18 in the series *Photographic portraits of living celebrities*, Albumen print from collodion negative.

9

Faraday's Field Concept

Nancy J. Nersessian

'When did Faraday have his field concept?' is a controversial issue in the Faraday literature, and one which is usually seen as an *historical* issue. However, before one can hope to answer the question of *when*, one must determine *what* his field concept was, and such a determination is a philosophical issue as well as an historical one. When I first set out to formulate what others say his concept was, I was surprised to find how difficult this is to do, especially as the protagonists are fairly explicit about when he had it. My contention is that this difficulty arises because there are actually three related questions involved in the problem of what Faraday's field concept was:

1. What was Faraday's conception?
2. What is required for a concept to be a 'field' concept?
3. What does it mean to say that someone 'has' a concept, i.e. what general form does the representation of a concept take?

In determining 'when' someone has a particular concept, these three questions need to be answered first. The failure to address (3) at all, coupled with the lack of a clear account of (2), has made the proposed accounts of (1) difficult to assess. This has made the issue of 'when' a subject ripe for classification as a 'dispute with no possibility of resolution'. My intention here is to show that, as the dispute presently stands, this is so; to shed some light on questions (2) and (3); to make a proposal for (1); and, finally, to make a contribution to this debate over 'when' and 'what'.

1 Five interpretations

The chief participants in the discussion are in order of appearance: Williams, Agassi, Berkson and Gooding.[1] Let me begin by arranging them according to their answers on when Faraday had his field concept and what they take it to be. In fairness to the protagonists I should say at the outset that there are significant differences between them in philosophical perspective and in their historical and philosophical method. A complete discussion of their views would have to take these differences into account. However, it is not necessary to do so here because my point is so fundamental that it applies to all of them irrespective of their philosophical and methodological differences. Also I want to make it clear that I am not a 'neutral commentator' (if there can be such a person!). I, myself, have made a contribution to the discussion. My works have appeared too recently to have been considered by others, and also I had not worked out what I am going to say here.[2]

As to *when* Faraday had his field concept, the positions divide into two camps: (a) somewhere between 1821 and 1832 and (b) around 1845–50. Agassi and Berkson fall into camp (a) and Gooding into camp (b). Williams is a bit more difficult to place and should be split into Williams 1 (1965) and Williams 2 (1975).[3] Williams 2 falls into camp (b). Williams 1 is not clear: his discussion of Faraday's interpretation of electromagnetic induction places him in camp (a), but his discussion of magnetic induction places him in (b). The difficulty arises because only Williams 2 is explicit about what he takes a 'field concept' to be.

I claimed earlier that 'what' comes before 'when', so let me now arrange the protagonists according to what they think Faraday's field concept was. This proves more difficult to do because only Agassi and Berkson are explicit about it. According to Agassi, Faraday's field concept was that of 'vibrations without a vibrating matter, . . . a property without a substance and a motion without a substance to have the property to move around'.[4] Berkson claims that for Faraday, 'forces themselves are the sole physical substances' and the physical world was a 'continuous sea of force-substances, each point of which interacts with its neighbours only'.[5] It seems that Gooding believes that only Faraday's later views of magnetism contain a field concept. For Faraday, the magnetic field was '*points* or places characterised only by a certain strength of action'; while magnetism was an 'interaction of matter with a *property* in its immediate vicinity'.[6] Finally, Williams 2 intimates that Faraday's field concept was the 'idea that space, alone, can transmit force', and that he arrived at this 'leap of abstract thought' only after 1845 in connection with magnetic induction since there Faraday held that 'space itself carried the magnetic strain'.[7] What makes Williams 1 difficult to interpret is that early on he claims that Faraday interpretated electromagnetic induction as taking place through the action of lines of force and treated a line of force as an 'actual entity, somehow associated with matter, but independent of it'. He also holds that Faraday 'introduced a new concept' at this time (1832): 'the idea of the field of force generated in time and extending progressively through space'. However he claims in his later discussion of magnetic induction, that the 'foundations' for field theory are to be found in Faraday's conception of magnetism as a 'strain in space, produced by ponderable matter in one way or another'.[8] The variety of answers to the question 'what was Faraday's field concept?' makes it difficult to provide a useful classification of the protagonists simply on the basis of that question. Rather this must be combined with question (2) raised at the outset. That is, to classify the positions taken about what Faraday's field concept was we need first to distinguish them on the basis of the prior question óf what they take a 'field concept' to be. This proves quite interesting.

Question (2) is a prior question. If someone calls a particular notion a 'field concept' and attempts to say when it appeared in Faraday's work, it is reasonable to assume that they have a criterion of a 'field concept'. This cannot be the use of the term 'field'. Having a concept does not require use of the customary expression for that concept. It does require having a certain type of representation. Just which type of representation will be the subject of my discussion of question (3), but I should note here that 'having' a concept does not require that we believe that representation to be true of anything. For the moment I will just try to determine which criteria for 'field' have been used by the protagonists.

It is surprising that despite the prior nature of a response to this question, it is difficult to ascertain their answers. Berkson is the only one who is explicit. He says that a 'field theory' is one which maintains that 'all action of one body on a distant body be carried by an intervening medium'.[9] A 'field concept' is one which contains this notion of continuous transmission of action from one body to another through an intervening medium. What they say about the nature of Faraday's field concept and when he had it implies that Agassi, Gooding, and both Williams 1 and 2 hold that a 'field concept' involves the notion of 'properties existing in space'. How were these respective criteria selected? Only Agassi and Berkson tell us explicitly where theirs came from.

Berkson arrived at his criterion by focusing on the nature of the problem for which field theory was supposed to provide a solution: how action is transmitted to a distance. The field conception of forces developed as an alternative to the action-at-a-distance conception. It was distinguished by the idea of continuous transmission of action through an intervening medium. The central problems of this approach were to specify the nature of the process of transmission and to determine the nature of the medium.[10] By concentrating on the metaphysical problem situation, Berkson selected his criterion to capture the key difference between field and action-at-a-distance metaphysics. This way of selecting the criterion allowed it to be formulated very broadly which in turn allowed for the possibility of different field concepts in different theories. In particular, both Faraday and Einstein could 'have' field concepts which nevertheless made quite different assumptions about the nature of the processes used in transmission of actions and about the nature of the medium of transmission. Use of this criterion, coupled with his analysis of Faraday's problem situation, required Berkson to be more specific about the *unique* features of Faraday's field concept. The lines of force are the medium and the means of transmission of force. Berkson thus makes his claims for the early appearance of this conception in Faraday's work on the grounds that Faraday made use of the lines as though they were real entities from the early period onwards.

Agassi selected his field-criterion from the 'modern', or 'Einsteinian' field concept. A central feature of this is the existence of 'propert[ies] and motion without a substance'. Agassi claims that when Einstein said this 'the public was merely puzzled; when Faraday said so the public was deeply shocked and incredulous'.[11] But the question which needs to be asked is 'Did Faraday and Einstein really "say", i.e., "mean" the same thing by their field concepts?' Does Faraday's concept really need to be the same as that of Einstein's in order to be a field concept? Gooding and Williams appear to have selected their criterion from the 'modern' concept as well. Williams is the least clear about what he considers a 'field concept' to be, but the 'properties of space' criterion is implicit in his characterisation of Faraday's contribution to field theory. Use of this criterion creates the ambiguity in Williams 1 because he wants to attribute a significantly new concept to Faraday at the time of his analysis of electromagnetic induction. As he claims, 'It is not an exaggeration to say that a fundamentally new way of looking at physical reality was introduced into science in the second series of the *Experimental Researches*'.[12] But neither Williams 1 nor Williams 2 can call this new way of conceptualising electric and magnetic actions 'field' since 'action through lines of force' does not fit his implicitly modern criterion for 'field'. Only with respect to Faraday's late work on magnetism can a case be made for interpreting Faraday as having a concept which could fit this modern 'properties of space' criterion. In fact this is the crux of the dispute between Agassi and Williams over when Faraday had his field concept. This can be stated as follows: to make his point that Faraday had a field concept in his earliest researches into electricity and magnetism, Agassi's use of this criterion requires him to attribute more to Faraday than the evidence can support. The 'lines of force' were there at the beginning, but not as 'states of space'. This same criterion makes Williams withhold the attribution of 'field' from Faraday's early speculations, even though he wants to argue, along with Agassi, that a significantly new conception was introduced quite early in Faraday's work. We can now see, too, that the dispute between Berkson and Williams has been wrongly characterised as being about 'when' Faraday had a field concept; it is over 'what' Faraday's field concept was and what counts as a 'field concept'.

Finally, implicit reliance on the 'modern' criterion is also responsible for the difficulties I encountered in trying to provide a coherent interpretation of Gooding's position. For example, he analyses quite convincingly how Faraday used lines of force in his attempt to present a unified conception of all forces. Gooding even says that the lines of force were 'a physical theory of the field'. But he does not attribute a 'field' concept to Faraday until his work on magnetism; specifically, until Faraday was able to combine the 'lines or force' representation with the ideas of 'properties' or 'intensities' of 'points of action in space'.[13] He, like Williams, is obliged to wait because these notions fit the 'modern' criterion in a way the 'lines' do not. Use of the 'modern' criterion seems to have allowed Williams and Gooding to avoid being specific about the features of Faraday's concept of field.

2 What is a field concept?

I may be guilty of some simplification in my reconstruction of these positions, but my assessment of the situation is fair enough to show that something is amiss. In the first place most of the discussion about Faraday's field concept has taken place without the benefit of a prior analysis of what criteria are to be used in calling something a 'field concept'. This is often the case in such historical and philosophical analyses. Faraday's case is just a particularly good example. But something further is needed, something to which historians and philosophers of science have given little thought in their analyses of the formation and development of scientific concepts. They have failed to address the question: 'What is a "concept"?' This is question (3). An answer to this question is crucial in that not only do we have to know what the criteria are for a 'field concept' before we can attribute it, but we must also know what count as criteria. To ask 'at what point did X have concept Y' assumes not only that we have criteria for 'Y', but also that we have criteria for what it means to 'have a concept' at all. Such criteria specify what form the representation a concept takes.

Having a concept: the classical view

It is customarily assumed that a concept is represented by a 'definition', i.e. by a set of conditions each of which is necessary and all of which are jointly sufficient to define it. This 'classical' view goes back to Plato and Aristotle. It has influenced contemporary analyses of meaning through the work of Frege and Russell. It is so deeply engrained in our intellectual tradition that it has been acting as a tacitly assumed metatheoretical prescription for what scientific concepts should be like. There have been a few challenges to this conception. These have come mostly from those working in sciences concerned with classification, where classification by 'definition' has proved to be an obstacle.[14] Also, within philosophy the later Wittgenstein criticised the notion of 'analysis by definition' so prevalent in analytic philosophy. But the import of his criticisms has only recently been appreciated.[15] For the most part philosophers and historians have accepted uncritically the thesis that to have a concept is to have a particular set of necessary and sufficient conditions, and that when and only when these conditions are present are we truly entitled to call something a 'Y'. Having a concept is thus an all or nothing affair: if the conditions are not clearly present, as they are, for example, in Faraday's 1832 discussions of electromagnetic induction, then the most we can say is that he had a 'kind of' field concept or that he 'laid the foundations' for such a concept. Or, if we want to say that he really 'had it' earlier, then we must attribute the whole set of necessary and sufficient conditions to him at the outset.

  This notion of a 'concept' underlies the customary view that concept-formation in science is an act of 'discovering', 'grasping' or 'acquiring' concepts. This view makes it seem that concepts are sitting in a Platonic heaven, complete with their necessary and sufficient conditions, waiting for us to 'find' them. This view of 'concepts' is partly responsible for the famous problem of incommensurability of meaning between scientific theories,[16] for if we ascribe different sets of necessary and sufficient conditions to 'Y' in a theory and to 'Y' in a later version of that theory, how can the 'Y's' really be the same thing? Finally, there is the problem of how to select criteria that define a concept. Do we select them to match our modern concepts? If so, then we have to say not only that Faraday did not have a field concept, but that no one else did before Einstein, because no one used all of the modern criteria before Einstein. The alternative is to make Faraday's concept seem identical with Einstein's. If we say, on the other hand, that we choose our criteria from an examination of the problems the concept was designed to solve in the particular period, this would at least allow us to attribute concepts uniquely to individual scientists. However, we run the risk of having many different 'field' concepts throughout the history of science without being able to say how they are related because the use of the term alone is not sufficient to provide the historical connection.[17]

All this, of course, assumes that it is possible to state a set of necessary and sufficient conditions for a concept which will take in all historical uses of that concept. Yet it must be conceded that this is notoriously difficult, if not impossible, to do except in cases where scientists have explicitly defined their concepts. Central among the difficulties are: How do we distinguish between an 'essential property' and an 'accidental' one; i.e. between one which *all* instances must have and which *most* instances would have? And how do we account for the fact that in science, as in ordinary life, we often make use of 'nonessential' features in categorising something as 'Y'. To take a simple example, a flying creature is usually categorised as a 'bird', but 'flies' is only an accidental or non-essential property since not all birds fly. In the case under consideration, these difficulties are apparent when trying to decide, for example, whether 'is a state of space' is essential to the concept of 'field' or not.

The prototype view of concepts

The question of whether such definitions are possible or even necessary, is a subject much disputed in contemporary congitive psychology and in the new discipline of 'cognitive science' now forming at the interface of philosophy, cognitive psychology and artificial intelligence. Fodor, for example, argues quite convincingly against the possibility of definitions. His own claim that even such concepts as 'electrons' are innate, unstructured and 'triggered' by experience, is not useful in trying to understand scientific concept formation.[18] However, it is possible to represent concepts in such a way that while undefinable, they are complex. One form of such a position has been called the 'probabilistic' or 'prototype' view. Although this is far from being a unitary position, the general claim of the view is that the representation of a concept is some sort of measure of a 'central tendency' of the properties of its instances. The representation of a concept is a set of 'family resemblances'. Particular instances vary in the degree to which they share these properties. Thus, 'being' a particular concept or 'having' a particular concept is a matter of degree. This is related to the position Wittgenstein argued for in his critique of philosophical analysis.[19] It has been made more explicit and been given wider scope by the work of Rosch, Mervis and others.[20] On the probabilistic view 'resemblance' means that each feature of a concept is assigned a weight based on the total number of subject instances for which it is listed. The weight reflects the probability of the feature occurring in an instance. The more 'highly weighted' features present in an instance, the more 'resemblance' it has to other instances of the concept. For example, 'flies' would be a highly weighted feature of the concept 'bird', but since it is not an essential feature, its weight would be less than 1.0; while, 'feathered' would carry the weight 1.0, since all birds have feathers. Thus, the features chosen to represent the concept are those which have a substantial probability of occurring rather than those deemed 'necessary' or 'essential'. Also, the possibility is open that the representation can change over time, i.e., that the weights can change or that new features can be added. This is necessary for examinations of the history of scientific concepts. The overlapping set of 'similarities' or 'resemblances' makes a concept into a unit, entitles us to call it *the* 'Y', and enables us to write its history.

The 'probabilistic' view of concepts is still a developing conception and is not without its problems. Yet when we examine how concepts arise, develop, and are used in scientific practice, we find that the 'probabilistic' view suits the scientific case better than the 'classical' view, which is customarily assumed. This new metatheoretical conception of concept fits well with analyses of the historical or 'developmental' dimension of meaning in scientific theories. It can allow for development, change and continuity in a way the 'classical' conception cannot. With it we can grant that there are a number of different concepts of electrical and magnetic action, each of which is a 'field' concept.[21]

3 When did Faraday have his field concept?

We are now in a position to return to Faraday. In this final section I shall outline a reconstruction of the nature of his 'field' concept and when he had it. I hope to make a plausible case for my interpretation. However, the philosophical 'housecleaning' was a necessary prerequisite to clear away confusions in the existing debate and to make it clear that my own interpretation of Faraday embodies a fundamentally different starting point as to what a concept is. In line with the notion of a concept that I propose to adopt, when we examine the features of what we take to be unquestionable instances of 'field' concepts, we see that certain features express 'central tendencies' of these concepts. These include the notions that there are processes taking place in the region surrounding things such as magnets, conductors and charges and that the action of one body on another is through the continuous transmission of such processes from one to the other. What is it possible to say about Faraday with these salient features of the concept of 'field'? At the latest he had a 'field' concept when, in January 1832, he speculated that electromagnetic induction might take place through the 'cutting' of the lines of force.[22] Two months later he speculated in a sealed note that

> when a magnet acts upon a distant magnet or piece or iron, the influencing cause . . . proceeds gradually from magnetic bodies, and requires time for its transmission which will probably be found to be very sensible.
>   I think also, that I see reason for supposing that electric induction (of tension) is also performed in a similar progressive way.[23]

He could not have made such a speculation without 'having' some features of a field concept. However, he did not have a fully articulated field concept at this point. The more specific features of his concept were still to be forged. This he did through further experimentation, analogical reasoning and speculation.

Saying that Faraday had a field concept at this point does not require us to suppose that he could substantiate, or even thought he could substantiate, the claim that electric and magnetic actions are actually field actions. One can 'have' the concept of a 'unicorn' without believing there are any. What he supposed in conjunction with his initial field concept was:

1. Electromagnetic induction is not an action-at-a-distance, but a new action.
2. This new action requires further study, which should provide a new understanding of electric and magnetic forces in general.
3. The lines of force would probably be shown to be essential to the description of the transmission of these actions.

'Having' a field concept at this point meant only that this was a possible way of conceiving the physical phenomena — one which might provide a better interpretation than the action-at-a-distance conception of forces, one which might turn out to be true and which would be fruitful to direct his research.

Essential features of Faraday's field concept

The major ingredients that went into creating his initial conceptions have been discussed by many philosophers and historians. These include his religious beliefs; his critical reflections on the nature of matter and of force (in which such notions as the interconversion of forces and the unity of all force are present as early as 1816–19);[24] his familiarity with the views of Davy and Boscovich concerning matter; his familiarity with iron-filing experiments and with the notion of 'magnetic curves' to represent magnetism by Barlow and

Sturgeon;[25] his belief in the primacy of experimentation and the importance of trying to 'read' what is in 'the book of nature';[26] the problem of how to interpret the Oersted discovery and his own discovery of electromagnetic 'rotations';[27] and, finally, his early belief that the action-at-a-distance conception of forces is a 'speculation' and not a 'certainty'.[28] These formed a network of beliefs and problems: theoretical, methodological, metaphysical, experimental and commonsense, which guided his experimentation and reasoning. In particular they led him to ask the question whether electromagnetic induction was due to the 'cutting' of lines of force.

As I said earlier the specific form of Faraday's field concept had still to be worked out. Just 'what' it was presents a problem because what Faraday said is ambiguous. He was hesitant about stating his views and he never completely articulated all the features of his field concept.[29] The conception I have been able to reconstruct is basically similar to Berkson's. The specific features of Faraday's field concept, in its 'favourite' and most complete form, are that force is a substance, that it is the only substance and that all forces are interconvertible through various motions of the lines of force. These features of Faraday's 'favourite notion' were not carried on. Maxwell, in his approach to the problem of finding a mathematical representation for the continuous transmission of electric and magnetic forces, considered these to be states of stress and strain in a mechanical aether. This was part of the quite different network of beliefs and problems with which Maxwell was working.

The primary concept in Faraday's work is that of 'lines of force'. One aspect of this is a *vectorial* notion which he called 'representative lines of force'. The other aspect is a *field* notion which he called 'physical lines of force'.[30] Both aspects are present from the time of his introduction of the cutting of the 'magnetic curves', which he quickly changed to 'curved lines of force', to his later explanation of how electromagnetic induction could take place (Table 9.1). Faraday did not make this distinction explicit until the twenty-eighth series of the *Researches*. In the vectorial notion, the lines represent the intensity and direction of the force in space. This notion is neutral between the field conception and the action-at-a-distance and even other possible conceptions of the nature of the actions. As Gooding has pointed out, this 'neutral' aspect was important to Faraday. It provided him means of representing the phenomena and of communicating his discoveries to others without implying a commitment to the physical existence of the lines.[31] The field aspect of the lines of force concept contains the suggestion that the lines

Table 9.1 Aspects of Faraday's lines-of-force concept

LINES OF FORCE		
Neutral: 'representative'	Field: 'physical'	
vectorial	paths of transmission	vehicles of transmission

represent the actual 'physical mode' of the transmission of action. It was through the 'physical lines' that he hoped to construct a unified conception of all forces. This aspect of the lines was to provide him with the means for saying *how* force could be transmitted continuously through space. The tension between these two aspects or uses of lines (as representative and as real) is present from the beginning of his research. This is what makes him so difficult to interpret.[32] He was hesitant to be more explicit about the 'physical lines' until his experiments on magnetic induction provided evidence strong enough to support their existence.

My case for this view of the essential features of Faraday's field concept depends primarily upon:

1. His use of experimentation in attempting to demonstrate the existence of the lines of force and the interconversion of forces via their actions.
2. The terms he used when discussing the lines (such as: 'moving out', 'expanding', 'collapsing', 'bending', 'straining', 'vibrating', 'being cut', 'turning corners') which was not simply metaphorical language.
3. The strong effect of the *image* of the lines on the reasoning and experimentation of one who believed one should read 'the book of nature' so literally.[33]

I think that the influence of the visual image of the lines of force on Faraday has been underestimated. It played a crucial role in the construction of his field concept, in its initial formulation, in its development, and in its final form. The visual image provided Faraday with a means of exploring, both in thought and in experimentation, the possibility of action in and through space. He attempted to demonstrate that electrostatic and magnetic inductions took place along or through *curved* lines of force. Their curvature provided an essential ingredient in his argument against their being actions-at-a-distance. At various times he tried to formulate a coherent conception of how the motions of the lines could account for all the forces of nature. The relationship between static and dynamic electricity might be found in the expansion and collapse of the lines of force while magnetism might consist in a 'vibration' of the lines[34] and might be connected with a 'lateral repulsion' between them. Electrostatic induction might take place through the action of 'contiguous particles' along curved lines of force and magnetic induction by means of 'conduction' of the lines with varying degrees of ease in different media. Light and gravitation could be the result of a 'shaking' or 'vibration' of the lines. Even matter itself might be nothing more than point centres of lines of force. This view was similar to, though hardly identical with that of Boscovich.[35]

The image of the lines makes them discrete. The influence of discreteness is apparent in his formulation of a quantitative relationship between the 'number of lines' cut and the intensity of the induced force in electromagnetic induction. 'Number of' is an integer, while 'field' intensity would be represented by a continuous function. We see the influence of the image also in the analogies he selected to express what he meant, in particular, his choice of other 'line-like' phenomena such as rays of light and heat, rings in water and conduction through wires.

Some problems of interpretation

With the 'field' aspect of the lines of force there is an unresolved tension between the physical lines as the *paths* of transmission of the action through space and the physical lines as the *vehicles* which transmits the actions. This ambiguity is responsible for some of the confusion surrounding Faraday's position on the aether. If the lines simply mark out the geometrical path of the motion, then we need to ask what they are paths in. They could represent states or processes in an 'aether', which Faraday does allow, although he emphasised that such an aether would be quite unlike 'ordinary' matter. Or, they could just as well be paths in 'mere space'. The conception of lines as 'vehicles' transmitting the action does nor foreclose the possibility of an aether but really makes it unnecessary. The lines themselves transmit all the forces of nature and connect every 'particle' with every other so that its sphere of influence is 'the whole of the solar system'. There is no need for an additional aether. Whether we choose to call this field of force 'aether' was, he thought, more a matter of semantics than of physics. The unresolved ambiguity between 'paths' and 'vehicles' stemmed from the fact that, his experiments on unipolar induction and with the search coil notwithstanding, Faraday was never able to demonstrate conclusively the independent existence of the lines themselves.[36]

A further issue, related to this last point, needs discusson. This is the distinction Faraday made between electrostatic lines of force and magnetic lines. He claimed that the electrostatic lines exist 'by a succession of particles', while the magnetic lines exist by a 'condition of space free from matter'.[37] This distinction should be considered as a distinction *in evidence*, rather than *in kind*. Faraday felt that he had some convincing evidence that magnetic lines of force existed in space independently of matter. But he had no comparable evidence that electrostatic lines existed independently of the particles of a dielectric medium. He had no observational evidence for his lines of force conception of particles. Here his argument lay in his demonstration of the 'essentially' dipolar nature of magnetism. Wherever a magnet exists, there must be lines, since they are what connects the poles of the magnet. In fact he thought that the polarities of a magnetic system reside in the lines themselves. Further, since magnetic induction does not involve polarisation of a medium he could make a more convincing case for the magnetic lines of force being the 'vehicles' of transmission than for electrostatic induction, which does involve polarisation. So, in the case of electrostatic induction he felt able to argue only for action in curved lines (i.e., curved paths) by means of 'contiguous particles'. To do full justice to this conception, we must interpret 'particles', even in the electrostatic researches, in terms of a lines of force conception of them.

Faraday did not formulate the views expressed in his 1844 'Speculation' simply in response to Hare's criticism.[38] As he maintained, there was no inconsistency in his notion of action through 'contiguous particles'. Hare failed to grasp the meaning Faraday attached to the 'words of the language of electrical science'.[39] The roots of this 'speculation' lay in his earlier work on electrochemistry and electrical conduction. This substantiates my claim that the electrostatic lines of force were not different *in kind* from magnetic. All that existed for Faraday were lines of force, the variety of forces of nature being nothing more than their possible motions. However, a clear formulation of this position appeared in Faraday's 1846 'Thoughts on Ray-Vibrations'.[40]

4 Conclusion

I have argued first that the question of 'when' Faraday had his field concept requires that we say 'what' it is. This involves three questions: What is a 'concept'?; What is a 'field' concept?; and What was Faraday's 'field' concept? I also argued that the metaquestion 'What is a "concept"?' is of considerable importance not only here, but to historical and philosophical analyses of the history of scientific concepts generally. I have argued that a 'probabilistic' view of a concept fits scientific situations and historical developments far better than the generally assumed 'classical' view. Finally, I have attempted to supply answers for 'when' Faraday had his field concept and 'what' it was. This was not done solely on the basis of the new conception of 'concepts'. However, that conception does allow us more flexibility in interpreting the historical data. With it we can attribute a 'field' concept to Faraday quite early, without having to attribute to him, either all the essential features of his mature concept or those of the modern conception. We can show that its specific features developed over time and that it had features quite unlike other field concepts, yet still maintain that it is connected with other field concepts; in particular with the modern one.

Notes

The research for portions of this articles was done while I was a Fellow of the Netherlands Institute for Advanced Study in the Social Sciences and the Humanities. I am grateful for the support of the Institute and its staff in carrying out this research. I thank the British Academy for support that enabled me to present an earlier version of this paper to the 'Faraday Rediscovered' symposium. I thank the Institution of Electrical Engineers for permission to work on manuscripts in their possession.

1. Williams, L.P. (1965, 1975), Agassi (1971), Berkson (1974), and Gooding (1978, 1980b, 1981).
2. Nersessian (1984a, 1984b).
3. Williams, L.P. (1965, 1975).
4. Agassi (1971), 5.

5. Berkson (1974), 50; (1978), 244.
6. Gooding (1981), 242; (1980b), 112.
7. Williams, L.P. (1975), 250, 252.
8. Williams, L.P. (1965), 204, 458.
9. Berkson (1974), 3.
10. Aether and field approaches are discussed in Hesse (1961), McGuire (1974), Heilbron (1981), Laudan (1981), Nersessian (1984b).
11. Agassi (1971), 5.
12. Williams, L.P. (1965), 204.
13. Gooding (1980b), 112; (1981), especially 242–3 and 253–5.
14. See for example Whewell (1847), 1: 66–91.
15. Wittgenstein (1953), especially sections 65–88.
16. Nersessian (1982).
17. Faraday did not even use the word 'field' until 7 November 1845, *Diary*, 4, 7979; Faraday (1846b), 2247. In Faraday (1851), 2806, he defined 'field' in terms of 'lines of force'. See Gooding (1981), 239 especially note 35.
18. See Fodor *et al.* (1980) and Fodor (1981), 257–316.
19. Wittgenstein (1953), sections 65–88.
20. Rosch and Mervis (1975). For an excellent analysis of the present state of the controversy in cognitive psychology see Smith and Median (1981).
21. Nersessian (1984b).
22. Faraday (1832b), 217ff.
23. Sealed note to the Royal Society, 13 March 1832, *Correspondence*, 1: 130, Williams, L.P. (1965), 181. Faraday (1832b), 217.
24. M. Faraday, 'Chemistry lectures' IEE MS SC 2.
25. Gooding (1985b).
26. Cantor (this volume).
27. Williams (this volume) and Gooding (this volume).
28. Nersessian (1984b), Chapter 3.
29. Gooding (1982b).
30. Faraday (1852a), 3075, 3175 Nersessian (1984b), Chapter 3.
31. Gooding (1980b), 108–11.
32. Other reasons are discussed in Gooding (1975, 1978) and Cantor (this volume).
33. Nersessian (1984b).
34. Faraday (1852b), 3264–9 and Faraday (1855), 3338. Gooding (1980a), 20–5.
35. Williams, L.P. (1965). For detailed analyses of how Faraday's conception of particles differs from Boscovich's see Spencer (1967). See also Berkson (1974), 50–3 and James (this volume).
36. He did not take his experiments on unipolar induction and with the search coil as providing conclusive demonstrations of the independent existence of the lines. Faraday (1832b), 220 and Faraday (1852a), 3070ff.
37. Faraday (1838a), 1164–5 and Faraday (1852b), 3258.
38. This is argued in Gooding (1978). Hare (1840). Faraday (1844).
39. Faraday (1840), *ERE*, 2: 262.
40. Faraday (1846c).

10

Faraday's Discovery of Induction: A Cognitive Approach

Ryan D. Tweney

History is an effort to reconstruct a plausible account of past events. These cannot be directly examined, but must be inferred from whatever records are available. Those interested in Michael Faraday are, in this respect, in an enviable position. Faraday left massive quantities of material which provide, as for few other scientists, an insight into his thinking processes. In one sense we do not need to engage in scholarship to understand how Faraday discovered induction; we merely need to *read* his papers and *Diary*.[1]

Such readings leave our urge to explain unfulfilled. We seek 'causes' and 'reasons' and 'influences' to supplement what Faraday himself recorded. Seekings of this sort are subject to fashion. In Faraday's case, we have moved from Victorian accounts that emphasised his moral character and his genius as causal agents,[2] to recent internalist accounts that focus on the historical movement of ideas in science[3] and to the most recent externalist accounts that focus on the role of social and cultural factors.[4] Causation is difficult to infer in historical analysis and recent scholarship in the history of science is even more cautious in inferring causation. Historians are more willing to acknowledge that the goal of history is the reconstruction, not of causes but of patterns of events which can be located in expanding networks of similarly constructed, patterns. In this respect, we seem to resemble structuralists for whom the goal is the creation of a 'picture . . . in which all evidence combines across time and space, to give us a history in slow motion from which permanent values can be detected'.[5] Reconstructing structural patterns from historical evidence requires that we adopt a consistent framework to order the available evidence and to select and emphasise evidence. In the case of Faraday the consequences of our choice of framework are momentous, as even a brief comparison of, say, Agassi[6] and Williams[7] makes clear! But the same comparison reveals that there is no easy way to reach agreement on which framework to adopt.

The purpose of this essay is to argue for a new framework for the understanding of Faraday's research programme. I have assembled this framework from concepts discussed in recent cognitive psychology and I believe it is sufficiently powerful and flexible to improve our understanding of how Faraday discovered induction. The framework has the advantages of permitting a better account of the dynamics of his day-to-day thought permitting a better 'history in slow motion', one which integrates much prior scholarship on Faraday into a broad, consistent pattern. This claim calls for an outline of the relevant psychological concepts and a demonstration that they lead to a plausible reconstruction of Faraday's activities.

1 Science and cognitive psychology

Our understanding of the principles of human thinking has made enormous strides in recent years. Knowledge about the basic parameters of human memory, learning, language and problem-solving is now sufficiently thorough to allow discussion of what Anderson calls the 'architecture of cognition'.[8] Our theories now allow us to construct detailed models of 'natural cognition' in very complex domains.[9] However, attempts to use cognitive theory as a basis for the understanding of actual scientific inference are still quite new.[10]

The application of cognitive theory to scientists' thinking is difficult. The reasons are best seen by contrasting science with the game of chess. If we wish to understand how chess masters think, we have several advantages; the game is based on a small set of fixed rules, there are clear criteria for 'good' versus 'poor' moves and the goal of the game is unvarying. Discovering how a master thinks in such a domain requires a variety of approaches, for example, the experimental study of what is remembered during the course of play,[11] simulation of chess masters on a computer[12] and mathematical modelling of the temporal structure of actual games.[13] Science by contrast, is played in an 'open problem space'. The rules of play are not fixed, there are no uncontroversial criteria for the quality of a move and goals are generally not known at the outset of play. Scientist's thinking is much more complex to study than chess thinking.

In recent years, laboratory procedures have been developed that aim to mimic some aspect of science. Hypothesis-testing problems have been created that allow subjects to 'play scientist' for a few hours and interviews and field studies have been conducted. At least one detailed analysis of a great scientist has been completed — Howard Gruber's study of Darwin.[14] But none of this work has sought to generate a plausible reconstruction of the detailed day-by-day operation of scientific thought in a single case. With Faraday I believe we can do just that, because of the completeness of the historical record he left. The present essay reports on the first fruits of the effort.

The methodologies and laboratory simulations of experimental psychology possess inherent weaknesses as tools for exploring the nature of science. Nor do historical analysis or observation of naturally occurring phenomena permit us to isolate causal factors from the tangle of texts and variables. Experimentation overcomes this limit by using manipulative control, but it thereby sacrifices the naturalness of a real-world event for the artificiality of the laboratory. This creates a special problem for the psychology of science, where the phenomena occur in a limited population, under special conditions, and in a spontaneous way which seems incompatible with the artificiality of laboratory simulations. The limits can be overcome by using appropriate constructs to model the more complex real-world events that constitute the focus of historical scholarship. Generalisations derived from laboratory work in cognition, together with the theoretical structure they support, can be used to interpret and reconstruct archival records of historical events in science. The elements of this reconstruction can be anchored in the historical record on one side and in current cognitive theory and experimentation on the other.

The choice of theoretical framework for this reconstruction is critical. For example, Freudian personality theory has been advocated for use in a somewhat similar fashion.[15] However, current cognitive theory is likely to be superior to psychoanalytic theory for two reasons. Unlike Freudian theory, cognitive theory now constitutes a network of testable propositions whose key elements have been validated.[16] Current cognitive theory also provides an explicit account of the content and sequence of human verbalisations during some complex problem-solving episodes.[17] This means that it can articulate the relationship between the historical record and the theoretical terms of the reconstruction at a very fine level of detail. It is not necessary to infer the existence of unobservable systems of thought and feeling which 'must have been present' in the scientist because their existence is demanded by theory. The cognitive reconstruction is preserved from such excesses by its own presuppositions. It is an approach which emerged out of behaviourism, carefully circumscribing the kinds of inferences permitted from a verbal protocol. All that is assumed is that the verbal record reflects the information attended during the course of problem solving. As Simon and his associates have shown, the sequence of attended informations is a rich source of data for the development and validation of cognitive models.[18]

2 Three levels of analysis

My goal is to construct a model of Faraday's experimental and theoretical thinking consistent with recent views on the nature of cognition. To do this requires that three general levels of analysis be specified together with the methodologies to be used at each level. The three levels are:

1. The level of schemata, which are recurring conceptual organisations for describing and interpreting *experiences*.
2. The level of scripts, or recurring patterns of *activities*.
3. The level of heuristics, or strategies for attacking specific theoretical and experimental *problems*.

A fourth level is also possible, one at which long-term goals and presuppositions are described. Description at this level is less readily integrated with current cognitive concepts, but, as we shall see, it constitutes an important level for a full understanding of Faraday's research. Note also that the separation into levels is not absolute — at every stage, the interaction of levels must be considered. The process of constructing this model resembles that of constructing historical narratives, insofar as facts are ordered and arranged within a pre-existing theoretical framework. The difference is that here the guiding framework is derived from cognitive science.

Schemata

The term 'schema' is best understood by contrasting it with the term 'concept'.[19] My concept *bird* specifies that a bird is a warm-blooded, egg-laying animal possessing wings and feathers. What I know about birds is of course much broader than this. I know that birds sing, that they are kept in cages as pets, that some of them swim, and so forth. I also have a good deal of concrete knowledge relating such information to my remembered experiences — the particular goose I heard in Canada last year; the migrating flock of ducks I saw this autumn, and so forth. The entire cluster of my experiential knowledge of birds constitutes a schema; it is clearly much broader than my concept of bird. Because it includes my *particular* experiences as well as shared general knowledge, it is unlike your bird schema. We must have similar concepts for communication to occur, but our schemata are idiosyncratic.

In Faraday's case the concept of magnetic force is one instance of his schema of 'force in general'. Across varying levels of concreteness, the schema incorporates Faraday's thinking from the general (such as his belief in the unity of forces) to the very specific (such as his knowledge of how magnetic fields behave in the laboratory). Faraday's *concepts* of electric force, magnetic force, and gravitational force are each part of a single force-*schema*. Therefore we can incorporate the strong parallels in his way of describing all three, as well as the progression of his ideas about fields into that schema. Early in his career, the 'force' schema was relatively undifferentiated. In other words, Faraday spoke of the relations between forces in loose analogical ways. Later as specific knowledge permitted him to elaborate the schema, he was able to incorporate specific relationships between the separate components. This process culminated in his mature scientific concept of a field. Thus, the schematic description can be assimilated within the framework of the psychological evolution of schemata to provide an account of how Faraday's force schemata changed over time.

Several major schemata can be traced from their earliest manifestation in Faraday's work to their appearance as published scientific concepts. In the case of the relations between electric and magnetic forces, for example, an instance can be seen at least as early as 1816, in Faraday's chemistry lecture notes.[20] Similar concepts can be traced through his 1822 'Chemical notes, hints, suggestions and objects of pursuit'.[21] They reappear in 1831 in his *Diary* record of the famous induction experiments and culminate in the paper read to the Royal Society in November and December 1831.[22]

What we consider to be Faraday's field concept depends on just what we regard a field to be in the first place.[23] However, this issue concerns the scientific and philosophical import of Faraday's research rather than the historical and psychological reconstruction of 'what happened'. Moreover, nearly all of the published discussion of the issue centres on Faraday's published papers, in which he presented his concepts to the scientific community, rather than upon his unpublished notes in which particular field-like schemata used by Faraday are a prominent feature. Gooding has pointed out that, for Faraday, the translation of a vague notion (a 'construal' in his terms) into a precise concept was and is essential to the discovery process.[24] 'Schema' is a broader term than either 'construal' or 'concept', and can include both.

How did Faraday's concept of field emerge from the schemata that underlay it? Faraday's field like schemata derived from his schemata of force in general. Consider the comments he made in 1816:

> three apparently distinct kinds of attraction; the attraction of gravitation, electrical attraction and magnetic attraction . . . appear . . . to be sufficient to account for all the phenomena of spontaneous approach and adherence with which we are acquainted. . . . The Science of Chemistry is founded upon the cohesion of matter and the affinities of bodies and every case either of cohesion or of affinity is also a case of attraction. . . . That the attraction of aggregation and chemical affinity are actually the same as the attraction of gravitation and electrical attraction I will not positively affirm but I believe they are. . . .[25]

These comments reveal a great deal about his force schema. Forces are of three kinds, they are manifested by attraction and repulsion, they are responsible for cohesion and affinity, the same forces account for chemical and physical phenomena and so on. We would not want to consider this to be a field *concept*, but it does contain elements which later were part of his field concept. Earlier parts of the same lecture make it clear that, as of 1816, Faraday conceived all three forces as *properties* of matter. He was certain of this in the cases of gravitational force and electricity, and reasonably sure for the case of magnetism.[26] Fig. 10.1 represents this force schema. The diagram uses nodes (which are boxed) and relations (shown by labelled arrows). Each node represents a sub-part of the cluster of knowledge that constitutes the schema and each relationship ties one node to others via a predicate.

The diagram shows that the notion of force is *distinct* (not all properties of matter are forces) and *unitary* (it possesses a structure which is extended, by analogy, to the relatively new case of magnetic force). The schema must operate at different levels of abstraction: the term 'force' is less concrete and more general than the term 'electric force', which is in turn less concrete and more general than the particular instances of 'electricity' (e.g. the voltaic cell).

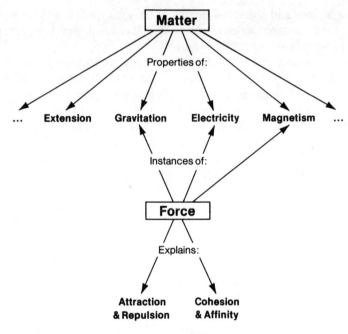

Figure 10.1 Faraday's force schema as of 1816.

The force schema grew and changed in subsequent years. To say that Faraday was a scientist is to acknowledge that it grew in response to new empirical results and the acquisition of new observational techniques. Scripts were used to generate experimental activity whose results were used to modify the schema. His 1822 'Chemical notes, hints, and suggestions of pursuit' allows us to see that Faraday was exploring specific aspects of the 1816 schema. He proposed studies of condensation and the effects of compression on chemical combination of gases. The proposed studies on the nature of heat, light, electricity, magnetism and gravitation fit the framework: there is a schematic unity.[27] Consider page 10 of the notebook, shown in Fig. 10.2. The juxtaposition of topics follows from the unitary nature of the schema in Fig. 10.1: gravity and magnetism are properties of matter, and forces are unitary, so why not seek such direct effects? Compressing gases in an effort to produce chemical combination also makes sense in this context — cohesion and affinity are, after all, explained by the properties of force in general.

As of 1822 Faraday's 1816 schema still predicated force as a property of matter. We can see it at work in Faraday's comments on the electrotonic state.[28] Faraday's failure to obtain empirical evidence for the electrotonic state meant that he ceased to argue in public that electricity was a property of matter. After 1831 Faraday needed a new way to construe electromagnetic induction. He found it in the geometric notion of *lines* of force.[28] This concept was neutral on the relationship between force and matter.

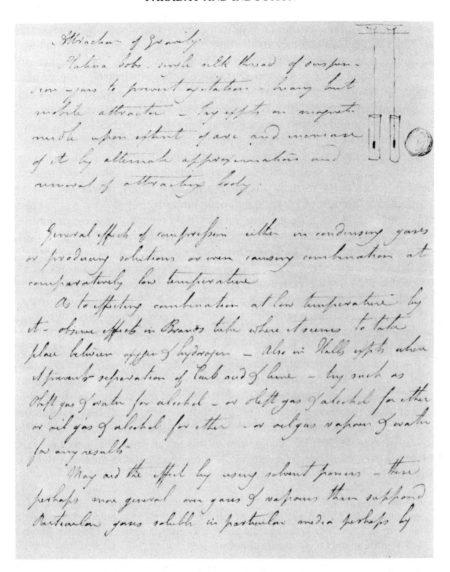

Figure 10.2 Faraday's 1822 notebook, page 10. (From IEE.)

Scripts

Scripts are special sorts of schemata used to represent clusters of actions. For example, I possess a 'library' script which I can use to learn more about birds and a 'walk in the woods' script that could further enlarge my knowledge. My library script consists of a series of actions — checking the card catalogue, locating a book, checking a book out, and so forth. With scripts, as with schemata, it is possible to speak of differing levels of abstraction, concreteness and of change across time. By making a distinction between scripts and schemata, it becomes possible to speak of nearly any cognitively based activity as a conjunction of script and schema. A specific activity, learning more about birds, say, requires retrieval from memory of my existing bird schema and retrieval of appropriate scripts. Once retrieved, I can organise my activity: 'I am going to the library to look up something about birds'.

In Faraday's case the same scripts occur across widely divergent areas of research. For example, one script involved accumulating small effects via the oscillation of a ring or disc until the effects became observable. This script can be seen in an early form in his 1822 notebook where it was used in an unsuccessful attempt to generate magnetic forces from heated wires.[29] It also appeared in a variety of researches in later *Diary* records: on acoustic figures, electromagnetic induction and static electricity.[30] Between 1823 and 1831, other scripts were used, such as a bent tube closed at one or both ends and heated at one end. This is a 'compression' script that was important to his successful 1823 work on the liquefaction of gases.[31] It can be found in earlier records, and its use traced across many problems. In 1828, he attempted to generate motion from magnetism using a suspended copper ring.[32] While the problem of induction was probably still on his mind, the necessary script was not.

For our cognitive model, scripts are to scientific methods as schemata are to scientific concepts. According to most theories of cognitive development, actions play an important role in the emergence of thinking.[33] For the specific case at hand, the point is clear. Faraday's thought was closely tied to his ability to manipulate — to take action with — the entities that he encountered in his investigations. We see his recognition of this in the praise bestowed on Jane Marcet's *Conversations on Chemistry*.[34] Following her death, he wrote to De la Rive that:

> I could trust a fact, — but always cross examined an assertion. So when I questioned Mrs Marcet's book by such little experiments as I could find means to perform, & found it true to the facts as I could understand them, I felt that I had got hold of an anchor in chemical knowledge & clung *fast* to it.[35]

Manipulation was Faraday's anchor. The title page of the first edition of *Chemical Manipulation* bears the motto 'Ce n'est pas assez de savoir les principes, il faut savoir MANIPULER'.[36]

All science is an active pursuit of knowledge. For Faraday, the activity centred on the manipulation of a world of objects, forces and phenomena. Throughout his career, scripts were elaborated as new procedures (and refinements of old procedures) were added. His preference for procedural knowledge was most clearly manifested in the *Chemical Manipulation*, a remarkable book which has been unduly neglected. It was a text for those who needed to learn chemical laboratory practice. The book consists of 1399 numbered paragraphs, a huge collection of specifics. At the end of the book, he provided 'A course of inductive and instructive practices' which lead the student through a sequence of learning activities keyed to the earlier numbered paragraphs. It begins with operations so primitive that they need no explanation, using verbs such as 'put', 'take', 'hold', 'make', etc. These are terms whose meaning is clear to every user of the language. As he proceeds he defines new operations using these primitive terms. For example weighing, with the chemical balance, is defined entirely in terms of putting and taking and observing and so on. Once defined, 'Weigh' was used as a procedure to define still other procedures. For example, 'Determine specific gravity' was defined using 'Weight', 'Measure volume' and the primitive terms. In this fashion, Faraday presented an enormous range of procedures, embedding them within one another, enlarging and differentiating the scripts as he did so. The 'Weighing' script becomes ever richer as it participates in more and more procedures. At the same time, the procedure of weighing remains fixed, an 'anchor' of knowledge. Throughout Faraday's notes, we can find similar progressions. There is, always, the anchor in procedural knowledge.

It is now possible to go beyond the truism that Faraday's thought was closely tied to his laboratory work. One script used frequently by Faraday was 'Accumulate small effects (to make them visible)'. This script is represented in Fig. 10.3. Here each procedure is specified with increasing concreteness by particular activities. If we apply Fig. 10.3 to the 1822 manuscript, we can see that the use of coils was part of his thinking on the problem of inducing electricity from magnetism (see Fig. 10.4, which is page 72 of the notebook). It should be pointed out that the coils may have been wound tightly round the magnet (not free of it as appears from the diagrams). When used on its own in a circuit the coil was generally understood to 'multiply' or 'accumulate' the electromagnetic effect.[37] Even more striking is that on the following page of the same book Faraday assembled the appropriate combination of wires and magnets used on his successful 1831 experiments on induction (Fig. 10.5).

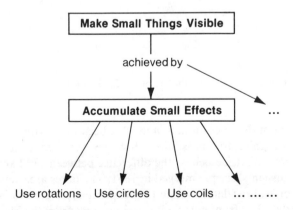

Figure 10.3 Faraday's 'Accumulate small effects' script.

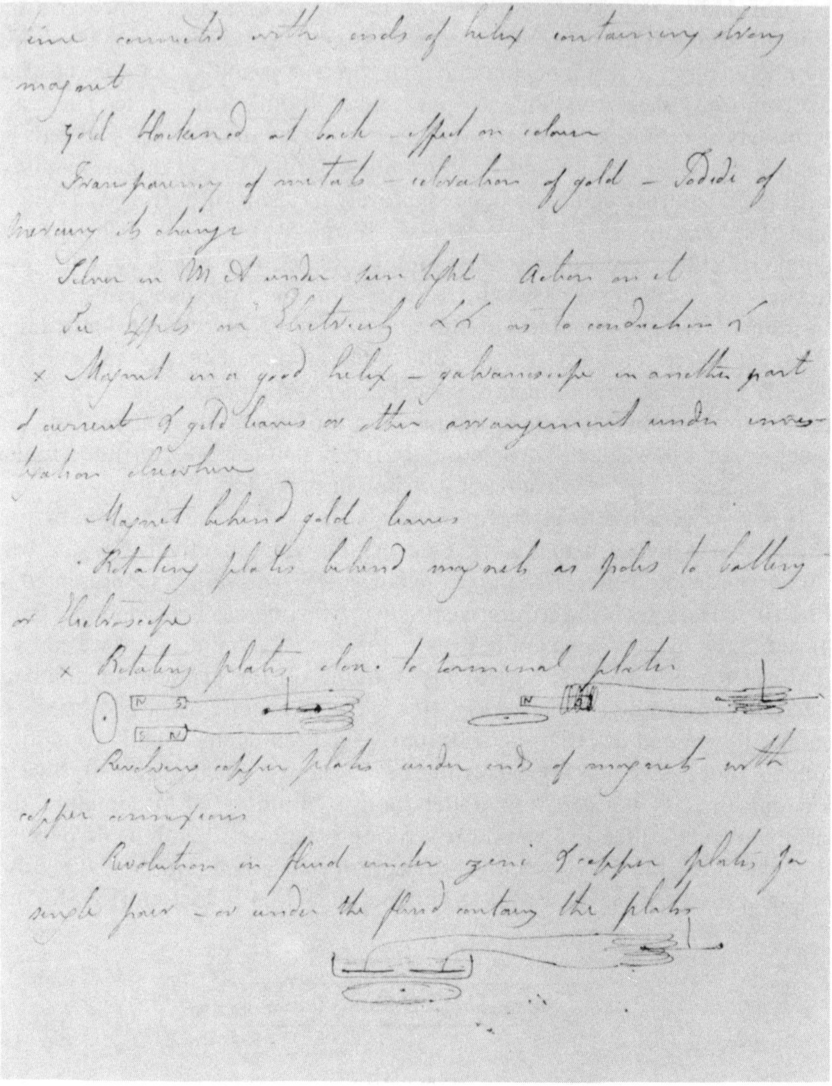
time connected with ends of helix containing strong magnet
gold blackened at back — effect on colour
Transparency of metals — coloration of gold — Iodide of mercury its change
Silver in M. A under sun light Action on it
See effects on Electricity &c as to conduction &c
× Magnet in a good helix — galvanoscope in another part of current & gold leaves or other arrangement under investigation elsewhere
Magnet behind gold leaves
· Rotating plates behind magnets as poles to battery or Electroscope
× Rotating plates close to terminal plates
Revolving copper plates under end of magnet with copper connexions
Revolution in fluid under zinc & copper plates for single poles — or under the fluid containing the plates

Figure 10.4 Faraday's 1822 notebook, page 72. (From IEE.)

Faraday did not discover induction in 1822 because, as others have noted, he did not recognise the possibility that the expected effects could be transient.[38] As I will argue below, the difference between 1822 and 1831 was that a 'seek transients' script emerged in 1831. The notes are sketchy, but we can see that some of the details of the 1831 experiments were available at least nine years earlier. Far from being a mysterious 'bolt from the blue', the 1831 experiments appear to have been a natural extension of Faraday's earlier

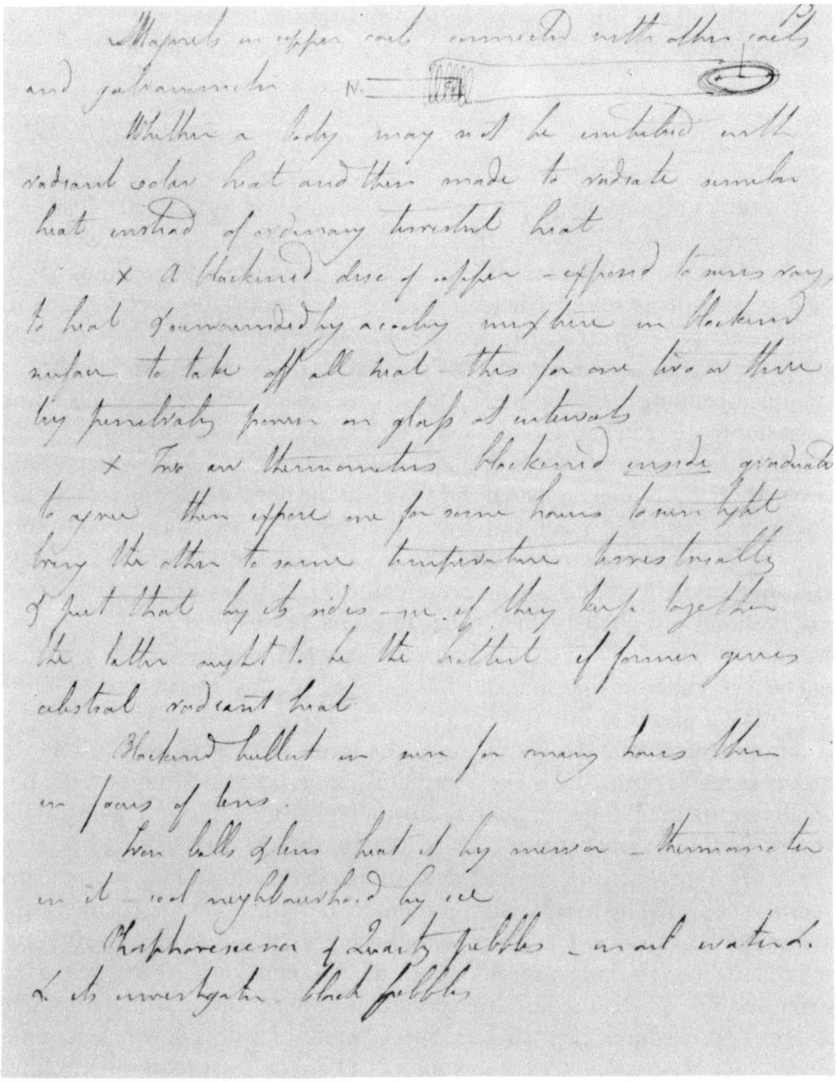

Figure 10.5 Faraday's 1822 notebook, page 73. (From IEE.)

thinking. My account is still incomplete because Faraday was clearly *not* making arbitrary combinations. To understand how he selected his scripts requires that we consider Faraday's thought at two other levels, those of heuristics and of goals.

My proposal is that everything Faraday thought on the induction problem, and everything he did, can be described by classifying specific entries in his *Diary*, notebooks and publications in an appropriate list of schemata and scripts. The distinction between scripts and schemata makes it possible to speak of almost any cognitively-based activity as a conjunction of script and schema.

Heuristic organisation

New results and new concepts can be accounted for by a kind of natural selection from random combinations of ideas. William James advanced such a view, and it is the central concept in Campbell's 'evolutionary epistemology'.[39] Such a position is rejected here in favour of a more purposeful account. Suppose that I wish to learn more about birds. I already possess a richly elaborated schema and several scripts that would further enrich it, for example, spending a week in the woods to observe birds directly, versus going to the library to read about birds. Each such script focuses on the thing I want to learn about. But my choice of one script rather than another will have my own activity as its focus. I may decide to go to the library first and then to the woods, believing that I will not waste time learning what others can more easily teach me. Or I might go to the woods first and then to the library, believing that my reading will reveal more if it takes place after direct observation. Although neither procedure can be justified in a normative fashion, my choice of one over the other will not be blind. Instead my decision will be based upon my notions of what I am best at, how I have learned in the past, what I prefer to do, and so on.

Within recent cognitive psychology, the term heuristic is used to refer to such choices.[40] A heuristic is like a script insofar as it refers to actions, but it is unlike a script in that specific actions are not represented. I have a 'going to the library' script, but my heuristic choice to go to the library is at a higher level. While my library script contains very specific detail concerning actions, my heuristic choice is, by comparison, content free. In this essay we are interested in Faraday's heuristics. These represent *his* choices of how to organise his own activities when attacking a specific problem. We should not expect them to be generalisable. Whereas scripts are special kinds of schemata which represent actions or procedures, heuristics are special kinds of scripts in which action is always that of a particular decision maker. If I go to the woods I might keep a notebook recording whatever observations of birds I happen to make while randomly stolling, but previous experience, which may be peculiar to me, tells me that I will do better if I station myself at a spot where birds frequently gather.

The heuristics surrounding the selection of evidence in hypothesis testing are of particular interest for the understanding of science. Wason first showed that people are likely to use confirmatory heuristics in evaluating the truth or falsity of an hypothesis, even in situations calling for the active pursuit of disconfirmatory evidence.[41] If I hypothesise that all birds chirp I am likely to seek cases of birds that chirp, by listening for chirping creatures and then verifying that they are birds. A disconfirmation heuristic is also possible. I could listen for non-chirping creatures, since a non-chirping creature that *was* a bird would instantly disconfirm my hypothesis.[42] Recent work shows that people use both confirmatory and disconfirmatory heuristics, sometimes to solve the same problem.[43] Such interactions are extremely important in scientific cognition. For example, early in the course of hypothesis testing, a confirmatory heuristic can amass evidence for a vague hypothesis, which can then be subjected to a search for disconfirmation. After successfully identifying ten chirping creatures that turned out to be birds, I might then profitably seek non-chirping birds which, if found, would disconfirm my hypothesis.

Faraday's 1859 research on gravitation displays such a pattern.[44] After a strenuous search for a relation between gravitation and electricity produced confirming evidence, he then sought to disconfirm his own results by seeking artefacts which might be producing the effects. (These turned out to be present.) We will see below that his 1831 research on induction is especially rich in heuristic structure of this sort.

As we saw in the previous section, a wide variety of scripts could be generated with the objects, apparatus and schemata available to Faraday. This raises a different version of the problem of choice. How did Faraday select strategies? Faraday wrote extensively on the advantages and disadvantages of many of the heuristics which he employed. In his 1818 remarks on the 'Inertia of the Mind' Faraday recognised the dangers of becoming prematurely attached to one's own theoretical notions.[45] This is now called 'confirmation bias'. Such views were held by many others including Humphry Davy.[46] But Faraday was unusual in his awareness of the proper use of disconfirmatory evidence. Faraday actively *sought* disconfirmatory evidence, even when things were going well. Few of his contemporaries seem to have been so aware of the day to day need to use disconfirmatory strategies as a guide even in the tiniest details of research — hence the many small errors of detail that have been noted in Davy's papers on potassium, sodium and other metals.[47] Faraday was unusual in appreciating the *positive* benefits of a confirmation heuristic. This point is made forcefully in his 1818 lecture. There he says 'mental inertia' is a blessing as well as a danger because it guarantees that vaguely conceived ideas have advocates who refine the ideas and seek evidence which confirms them. Faraday's view is a balanced one in which it is easy to see the source of the interplay of confirming and disconfirming evidence in his laboratory research.

Faraday's heuristics are further revealed by a detailed account of the 135 experiments on electromagnetic induction he carried out between 29 August 1831 and 4 November 1831. I have discussed his use of confirming and disconfirming evidence elsewhere.[48] There I showed that the research programme changed course on 28 October. On that day Faraday went to Samuel Christie's house in Woolwich to take advantage of the large magnet there.[49] A plot of the proportion of confirming experiments (Fig. 10.6) reveals a striking difference before and after this date. The average number of confirmations per five experiments almost doubled from 2.14 to

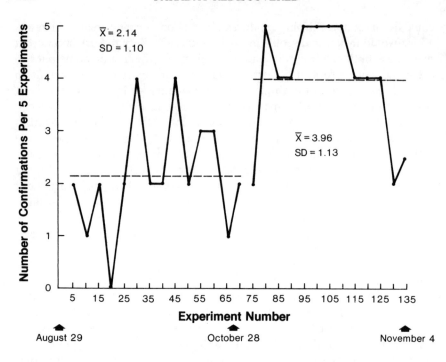

Figure 10.6   Number of confirmations per five experiments, 29 August to 4 November 1831.

3.96. Gooding[50] has characterised the development of Faraday's experimentation in terms of transition from exploratory studies, to 'proving experiments' and to polished demonstrations. Fig. 10.6 confirms this and leads us to ask how Faraday was able to tolerate so much negative evidence. The answer can be found at the heuristic level.

Faraday showed considerable determination during the earlier phase, when three out of every five of his results were negative. Thus, he presented his results to the Royal Society[51] only after the more encouraging series of experiments using Christie's more powerful magnet. But, as we saw earlier, there was more here than confirmation bias. The negative results also had to be explained before Faraday was finished. This sequence needs to be interpreted in terms of Faraday's research strategy.

Fig. 10.7 presents an analytic view of the hypotheses pursued by Faraday during the first, exploratory, phase of his research on induction. Each rounded corner box represents an hypothesis, each square box an observable phenomenon. Each line represents a single experiment, terminating in an arrowhead if the experiment was successful, and in a 'T' if it failed to confirm Faraday's expectation. Note that there are really only two major hypotheses, that electricity can be induced by electromagnets and that electricity can be induced by ordinary magnets. We regard both as the same, but Faraday did

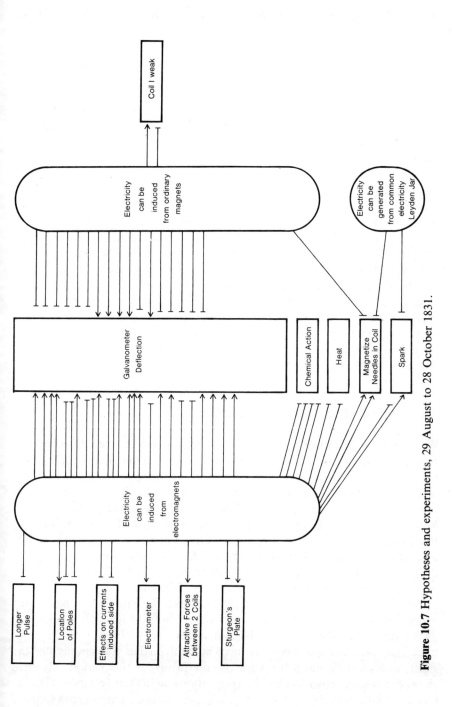

Figure 10.7 Hypotheses and experiments, 29 August to 28 October 1831.

not. In 1831 there was no firm evidence for their identity and the issue was controversial.[52]

It seems likely that Faraday deliberately combined his investigation of the two hypotheses for heuristic reasons. They were closely related in spite of their reference to different magnetisms. Following his successful ring experiment on 29 August, one of the two hypotheses *was* yielding confirming evidence. Faraday seems to have played off an easily verified hypothesis against one that was not so encouraging at the start. So, when things were discouraging on the ordinary magnet side, he switched to electromagnets, to pursue further knowledge about the effect he now knew how to produce. As he gained expertise, he was able to refine his attempts with ordinary magnets until he succeeded.

As with Gooding's reconstruction in Chapter 6 of Davy's and Faraday's earlier experiments on electromagnetism, there is no evidence to prove that Faraday consciously reasoned along the lines sketched. Such reconstructions are plausible and we should not expect to establish that they are certain. However, my reconstruction is plausible from a cognitive standpoint because similar 'dual hypothesis' strategies have been shown to be effective in laboratory studies of problem solving.[53] Working with two closely related hypotheses helps because disconfirming evidence for one leaves the investigator with the other hypothesis as a focus of effort. Platt's advocacy of 'strong inference' is based on the similar point that to pursue several alternative hypotheses is an effective strategy.[54]

3 The origin of the 29 August 1831 experiment

We are now in a position to suggest how Faraday selected the schemata and scripts with which he later successfully produced electromagnetic induction. So far, we have seen that scripts and schemata are integrated within heuristic plans, but to understand the origin of ideas requires more. Unfortunately, at this level we receive less assistance from cognitive psychology than before. Most recent work in the psychology of thinking has ducked such questions by restricting itself to relatively narrow domains in which goals are assumed to be given. For example, analyses of chess performance assume that a desire to play the game and to win are present, and simply do not address the question of why anyone would want to play chess in the first place.[55]

To complete our account, we need to show where the famous 29 August ring experiment come from in the first place. By examining the record leading up to 29 August 1831, it should be possible to discover what had been on Faraday's mind and how that might have influenced his work on that momentous day. In effect, can we delineate a 'network of enterprise' for this period? Gruber showed that such networks played an important role in Darwin's thought, and could be understood as reflections of his deepest values.[56] The interconnectedness of Darwin's thought both 'explains' Darwin's creative achievement and provides the scholar with a basis for its reconstruction. In the present case, we can ask what Faraday had on his mind during 1831, and hope to obtain a clue to the events of August.

Consider what Faraday was investigating in 1831 according to the *Diary*:

2 February to 14 March:	Acoustical figures.[57]
19 April:	An aurora seen at Woolwich.[58]
30 May:	Thermo-electric effect.[59]
17 June to 18 July:	Crispations.[60]
18 July:	Ridges on sand at Hastings.[61]
18 August:	Copper-plate printing.[62]
19 August:	Spontaneous ignition of hot vapours.[63]
29 August to 28 December:	Electromagnetic induction.[64]

Of these eight investigations five have two things in common: they were concerned with *transient* phenomena and with ways to make extremely small effects into larger, visible ones by accumulation. In his work on acoustical figures, for example, he placed fluids of various sorts on vibrating surfaces, and tried to determine how the vibrations affected the motion of the fluid. He studied the development of the nodal resonance patterns when a plate is bowed (Chladni Figures) by using viscous fluids to slow down the development of the patterns. Faraday's observations of the aurora on 19 April involved correlating movements of a compass needle with the development of a streamer in the aurora. The June–July series on crispations continued his explorations of acoustical vibrations. At Hastings on 18 July, he observed sand patterns which at first he related to his experiments of crispations and then verified experimentally. Finally, after two entries in August devoted to industrial safety issues, he was 'ready' for 29 August.

During the first 8 months of 1831, Faraday was much occupied with transient phenomena. This would have made him sensitive to the *momentary* effects of induction, as he had not been in 1822. Can we account for the sudden appearance of the double coil used in the first induction experiment on 29 August? Again, there is a cognitively plausible reason. First, coil scripts are prevalent in the 1822 notebook. We can infer that he was using that notebook in 1831, because the thermo-electric experiment of 30 May is *precisely* the one described in his 1822 notebook. I think this accounts for the sudden appearance of the double coil used in the first induction experiment on 29 August. Second, we know that Faraday was corresponding with Gerrit Moll at Utrecht University between 24 December 1830 and 13 November 1831. Moll's letters to Faraday are of special interest because Moll discussed his experiments with very large horseshoe electromagnets.[65] These were, apparently based on Joseph Henry's work, published in 1831.[66] Williams believes Moll gave Faraday the idea that electromagnets could develop a powerful 'wave of tension' at the poles.[67] Work by Moll, Henry and Sturgeon[68] on electromagnets could have *reminded* Faraday of the coils in the 1822 notebook shown in

Figs 10.4 and 10.5 above. By drawing his attention to certain procedures and arrangements of apparatus, such influences could have narrowed the number of possibilities to be explored. Faraday now had everything he needed to look for *transients* in the generation of *magnetic* effects from *electric* forces whose effects are *accumulated* via *coils*. He had assembled all of these by 29 August.

Faraday, as is well known, observed a brief 'sensible effect'[69] of his galvanometer when he connected the ring to the battery. It is often supposed that this was due to chance or to trial and error. My reconstruction of how he narrowed down the experimental possibilities suggests that this was a deliberate variation of the magnet and coil experiments tried in 1822, arising from the previous 8 months of research.

4 Implications

The reinterpretation of existing historical evidence that I am offering is clearly incomplete, but I believe it opens the way to an integrated picture that captures the richness of Faraday's activity. The approach is founded on very concrete and very specific elements and it places emphasis on Faraday's pursuit of knowledge through the active manipulation of nature. Such a view avoids the disembodied 'ideas' that float through some accounts.[70] Instead, concrete activities and specific elements of knowledge are derived in a direct fashion from the historical record. There are, to be sure, theoretical concepts in my account: facts and procedures are organised into schemata and scripts which are organised by heuristics, which in turn are governed at higher levels by goals and purposes. Except for the last these are concepts which have proven their value as scientific generalisations about human thinking.

I have said the least about Faraday's overall goals. We have seen that his 'network of enterprise' was imbued with transients in 1831, but we cannot say why. That his most general beliefs about the world penetrated his day to day activity seems plausible. Thus, his use of both confirming and disconfirming heuristics is consistent with his belief in a moral responsibility to learn about the world, and his related belief that God would not make the task easy. In one of his personal copies of the Bible, Faraday marked heavily Job 9:20: 'If I justify myself, mine own mouth shall condemn me: If I say, I am perfect, it shall also prove me perverse'. Job, like Faraday, seemed aware of the dangers of exclusive reliance on one's own favourite notions.

Such evidence appears suggestive, but we do not yet know enough about the way values govern thought and are governed by it. We can reconstruct *what* Faraday thought but we cannot use psychology to tell us *why* he thought as he did. I believe that this is an advantage. Some accounts have tried to explain away Faraday the individual as 'nothing but' a social nexus,[71] or 'nothing but' a developer of others' ideas,[72] or 'nothing but' a precursor of Maxwell or Einstein.[73] I think a cognitive account avoids such facile reductionism. What we know of Faraday's larger goals from the work of existing scholars runs 'in slow motion' beneath the dynamic, changing surface of his activity. *He* is still present in our account, a purposeful being and conscious of his purpose. Beneath the complexity of his many activities, there is a pattern. A cognitive approach preserves its complexity and detail while revealing successive layers of structure in Faraday's science. Thus it leads both to understanding and to awe.

Notes

Preparation of this essay was aided by a grant from the Faculty Research Committee of Bowling Green State University. Special thanks are due to Irena McCabe, Librarian of the Royal Institution, and to Lenore Symons, Archivist at the Institution of Electrical Engineers, for assistance with this work. L. Pearce Williams, David Gooding, Howard Gruber and Michael Doherty provided valuable assistance at various stages of the project, but are not responsible for any errors of fact or interpretation which remain. Helpful comments on an earlier draft were provided by J. Baron, K. Danziger, M. Gorman, A. Heim-Calderello, S. Hojnacki, K.G. Hubert, F.A.J.L. James, H.A. Simon and J.F. Voss.

1. An excellent interpretive precis of the available material on electromagnetic induction is given by Martin (1949).
2. For example Tyndall (1894).
3. For example Berkson (1974); Williams, L.P. (1965).
4. For example Cantor (this volume); Berman (1978).
5. Braudel (1972), **1**: 23.
6. Agassi (1971).
7. Williams, L.P. (1965).
8. Anderson (1983).
9. Neisser (1976). For example, eyewitness memory for real-world events, Loftus (1975); medical diagnosis Elstein *et al.* (1978), Fox, J. (1980); chess, Chase and Simon (1973); physics problem solving, Chi *et al.* (1982), Larkin (1980); human computer interaction, Card *et al.* (1983) and scientific inference, Gruber (1974, 1978), Mitroff (1974), Tweney *et al.* (1981).
10. Except for investigations within artificial intelligence and those intended to model human factual knowledge as an 'expert system'. See Barr and Feigenbaum (1981); Langley (1981); Simon (1979).
11. de Groot (1965).
12. Newell and Simon (1972).
13. Chase and Simon (1973).
14. My colleagues and I review these approaches in Tweney *et al.* (1981). Discussions of the limits of generalisability of such work can be found in Tweney and Doherty (1983) and Gorman *et al.* (forthcoming). Gruber's (1974) work on Darwin is a monumental achievement, but was not carried out at as a fine a level of detail as that attempted here. Holmes (1974) used Claude Bernard's notebooks to great effect, but not from a cognitive standpoint.
15. Bushman (1966). Laudan, L. (1983) contains several excellent discussions of the problematic scientific status of psychoanalytic theory.
16. See, for a broad overview, Anderson (1980); Lindsay and Norman (1977). Simon (1979).
17. Ericsson and Simon (1984).

18. As an example of the empirical predictive power of the cognitive theory, see Simon & Reed (1976); and for its power to analyse complex problem solving in natural domains, see Voss *et al.* (1983).

19. Mandler (1984), 55 defines a schema as 'a bounded, distinct, and unitary representation . . . built up in the course of interaction with the environment [and] available at increasing levels of generality and abstraction'. Anderson (1983) has criticised this notion, and favours the computationally more sophisticated concept of production rules (cf. Newell and Simon (1972)), but the differences are only important in the context of computer simulations of cognition. Schema in any case, can be rewritten in the form of production rules should the need arise. On the computational power of a formalised, schematic representation see Barr and Feigenbaum (1981). For the use of schema in psychology see Bartlett (1932, 1958) and Piaget (1970). For its use in computer programs that act intelligently see Schank and Abelson (1977). Danziger (1983) has used the notion within the history of science.

20. M. Faraday, 'Chemistry Lectures', *IEE* MS SC 2.

21. M. Faraday, 'Chemical notes, hints, suggestions and objects of pursuit', *IEE* MS SC 2. Much of this notebook has been ignored by scholars, presumably in consequence of the general neglect of his chemical research. See Porter, G. (1981).

22. Faraday (1832a).

23. See Nersessian (this volume).

24. Gooding (1986 and this volume).

25. Faraday, *op. cit.* (20) Lecture 1, 17 January 1816, 'General properties of matter', 30–1.

26. *Ibid.* Gravitation 5ff, electricity 10ff, magnetism 27ff.

27. Faraday, *op. cit.* (21).

28. Faraday (1832a), 60–77.

29. Faraday, *op. cit.*, (21) 58.

30. Curiously it makes no appearance between 1823 and 1831 (Faraday, *Diary*, 30 May 1831, **1**: 320). That is three months prior to its successful use in the discovery of electromagnetic action.

31. *Ibid.*, 28 March–30 April 1823, **1**: 96–107.

32. *Ibid.*, 22 April 1828, **1**: 310.

33. A point made clearly and forcefully by Piaget (1926), Vygotsky (1962) and Bruner (1967).

34. Marcet (1809).

35. Faraday to De la Rive, 2 October 1858, *Correspondence*, **2**: 691.

36. Faraday (1827).

37. Gooding (1985b), J.O. Marsh, 'Sturgeon and the discovery of electro-magnetic induction' (unpublished), read to the 'Faraday Rediscovered' symposium.

38. For example Ross (1965), Gooding (1980a).

39. James. W. (1880), Campbell (1974).

40. The psychological character of heuristic search has received a great deal of analysis recently, especially in human problem solving derived from Newell and Simon (1972).

41. Wason (1960, 1966, 1968); Wason and Johnson-Laird (1972).

42. I am glossing over a good deal of the complexity of the use of confirmatory and disconfirmatory heuristics. The classical analyses are Popper (1959) and Lakatos (1970). The psychological aspects are discussed in Tweney *et al.* (1981). See also Baron (1985).

43. Doherty *et al.* (1979); Mynatt *et al.* (1978), Tweney *et al.* (1980, 1981).

44. Faraday, *Diary*, 10 February–11 April 1859, **7**, 15785–15917.

45. M. Faraday, 'Observations on the inertia of the mind', in 'Commonplace book 1816–1846' 337–63, *IEE* MS SC 2 published in Bence Jones (1870a), **1**: 261–79.

46. See Thorpe (1896) on Davy's caution in this regard, an apparent result of his early, embarrassing, advocacy of 'phosoxygen'.

47. *Ibid.*

48. Tweney (in press).

49. Faraday *Diary*, 28 October 1831, **1**, 85ff; Faraday (1832a), 44ff.
50. Gooding (this volume).
51. Faraday (1832a).
52. Williams, L.P. (this volume); Ross (1965).
53. Tweney *et al.* (1980).
54. Platt (1964).
55. de Groot (1965), Chase and Simon (1973).
56. Gruber (1974).
57. Faraday, *Diary*, 2 February–14 March 1931, **1**: 329–35.
58. *Ibid.*, 19 April 1831, **1**: 320.
59. *Ibid.*, 30 May 1831, **1**: 320.
60. *Ibid.*, 17 June–18 July 1831, **1**: 336–59.
61. *Ibid.*, 18 July 1831, **1**: 348.
62. *Ibid.*, 18 August 1831, **1**: 320–1.
63. *Ibid.*, 19 August 1831, **1**: 321.
64. *Ibid.*, 29 August to 28 December 1831, **1**, 1–290.
65. Moll to Faraday, 24 December 1830, 11 March 1831, 25 April 1831, 13 November 1831, *Correspondence*, **1**: 105, 108, 111, 120. Snelders (1984).
66. Henry (1831), see also Henry (1832).
67. Williams, L.P. (1965).
68. Marsh, *op. cit.* (37).
69. Faraday, *Diary*, 29 August 1831, **1**: 3.
70. Harman (1982).
71. Berman (1978).
72. Williams, L.P. (1975), Heimann (1971), Heimann & McGuire (1973).
73. Agassi (1971), Heimann (1970a).

11

Learning from Experience

Elspeth Crawford

In creative learning, the kind of learning which is celebrated when Faraday is studied, there is a change in the personal internal world of mind. The evidence of this change is objectively available as the individual's relation to the external world is changed and there is recognition and communication of the ideas which have emerged from the new and more creative point of view. A new vertex for thought creates both growth of ideas and qualitative change in the ways of thinking about them. There is a distinction between this kind of learning, in which the *learner* has changed or grown in the process of getting to know something, and that kind of learning which is simply acquiring knowledge *about* a topic, but which does not involve changes in the individual's states of mind.

When studying Faraday's work, I gradually came to realise that I could either learn much *about* events in his work and life or I could come to know him by empathy in my personal experience. Further, I came to realise that it was only by the latter means that understanding of his creativity could be reached.

In his book *Learning from experience* W.R. Bion[1] focuses upon emotional states and their effects upon learning. The experience referred to in his title and in mine, is emotional experience. Although much of Bion's book refers to the practice of psycho-analysis, he has already said in that context what I want to say about Faraday in this paper. Because I have found his work so helpful in my thinking, I hope that it is not a misrepresentation of his point of view to say that in our different contexts we talk about and are in agreement about the same things. In his introduction Bion explains that his book 'deals with emotional experiences that are directly related both to theories of knowledge and to clinical psycho-analysis . . .'.[2] He goes on to say:

> . . . if it is necessary to change our views about thoughts and the mechanisms of thinking it is likely that the change of views, if it is as significant as I think, will require modification of the way in which we produce 'thoughts' and the methods we employ in using them. . . .[3]

This states the common ground between Bion's work and my aim in this paper: in it I identify in Faraday's creativity a kind of thinking *dependent upon a particular emotional state of mind* which does modify the way in which thoughts are produced and employed. From the description of this thinking, I reach the conclusion that knowledge of personal feelings is necessary to discovery, to creative learning and to understanding of the world.

Two problems of method arise. First, how are we to set about *thinking* about 'thinking', whether the general process of thinking, Faraday's thought, or even our own? When developing a conclusion about the processes of thinking, how can the analysis which precedes the conclusion be constructed without prejudice to the result? Any such analysis is in itself an instance of thinking. Second, is there any reliable way in which we can know Faraday's emotional state of mind? To deal with the first problem, I have made a serious attempt to begin the analysis without using an objective framework. Instead I use a descriptive approach, retracing my own steps in studying Faraday's work, recounting my impressions and discussing evidence from several different levels of observation. Regarding the second problem, I have already said that I came to know Faraday through empathy. I have therefore made the description of my progress a personal account, in order to illustrate how empathy can be brought into play.

My personal experience is not important in itself (except to me). It is worth attention when it illustrates the emotional states of mind which can facilitate or resist learning and when it shows the modification of thought processes which allow insight into Faraday's state of mind. Broadly speaking, there are four viewpoints from which my observations are described:

1. The personal aspect: with the perspective explained above in mind, I shall comment on occasions when my own way of thinking about Faraday and his work changed.
2. Faraday's work: I describe some scientific concepts evident in his *Diary* and other writings and comment on what can be understood of their development.
3. The general problem of thinking: Faraday's achievements are recognised as instances of success in solving the general problem we all face in relation to thinking and learning: that of coping with prejudice.
4. Faraday's views on learning and thinking: his own awareness of the problems of thinking, especially his ideas about prejudice and how to overcome it. I consider these in the light of his own success and offer an analysis of why they distinguish real learning from prejudice.

1 First attempts to understand Faraday's work

I began my earlier study of Faraday[4] because of an interest in understanding the duality of 'particle' and 'field' as we think of them today. I wanted to see how these different forms of construing the physical world had arisen. I thought of them as incompatible notions, so I found my thoughts jolted and stimulated by the fact that they apparently co-existed in Faraday's physics. Even more surprising was that both emerged as precursors to modern theory at about the same time.

'Particle' or 'field'

The concept of an absolute electrical charge, or 'electron', as it is now called, can be traced to its origins in the physical laws of electrochemistry discovered by Faraday in 1833.[5] The concept of the electric field can be said to have begun its scientific development following his discoveries of the phenomena and laws of electromagnetic induction in the autumn of 1831. Both electromagnetic induction and electrochemistry apparently owed much to a seminal idea Faraday called the 'electrotonic state'. The *Diary*[6] and the *Experimental Researches*[7] both show how closely the electrotonic state, electromagnetic induction and electrochemistry were intertwined in Faraday's thoughts, as does a typically enthusiastic letter which he wrote to Richard Phillips in November 1831.[8]

Everyone agrees that Faraday shared in the creation of the theoretical concept of 'field', although, as Nersessian shows in her chapter, the question of when he became a field theorist has many answers.[9] But to state that he gave birth to the idea of 'electrical particle' is a different matter. I do not suggest that he developed it, only that others were later able to do so as a result of his work.[10] In 1834 Faraday presented the newly discovered facts of electrochemistry as well as his conclusion from these facts that electrical forces exist within molecules. Then, in paragraphs which are well known for their thoughtful approach and lack of theoretical dogma, he discussed 'The Absolute Quantity of Electricity associated with the Particles or Atoms of Matter'.[11] Although Faraday himself did not develop a particulate point of view, the possible theoretical development of these paragraphs is clear: if matter is thought of as atomic, then electricity must be 'atomic' also.

From this time the incompatible theoretical ideas of particle and field were available for development from the foundation of the facts supplied by Faraday's quantitative laws. This was a climate for work with these ideas quite distinct from that which existed before 1831, although speculations and hypotheses concerning both particle and field are evident in earlier scientific work.[12] In this climate developments would immediately sharpen an incompatibility. This continued to occur after Faraday's time. It is resolved only by the present acceptance of wave–particle 'duality'.

Some problems in understanding the development of Faraday's thought

Others have offered several kinds of explanation regarding the development of Faraday's thought, particularly with respect to the development of field theory, the 'new thought'.[13]

I was thinking about the occurrence of the origins of 'particle' as well as those of 'field'. My problem changed from considering about the origin and development of ideas to considering in what way Faraday had thought. It seemed that he had pictured the world in some way which allowed him to develop the foundations of opposing points of view. This idea of a 'picture' of the world is described by Holton in terms of 'themata'.[14] Holton's idea is a psychological concept, a supposition that each individual possesses a particular perceptual-mental structure or 'gestalt' determined by the unconscious mind. Both Holton and to some extent Agassi suggest that Faraday's natural outlook was a holistic, dynamic view of the world from which field theory must inevitably emerge.[15] The same idea seems to be expressed in James Clerk Maxwell's comment that: 'the idea of the *all* that is in our consciousness at a given instant is perhaps as primative an idea as that of any individual thing. . . . The method of Faraday seems to be intimately related to [this]'.[16]

Although the notions of 'picture' or 'natural outlook' are persuasive ones, I have never been happy with them. First, they are used in a way that seems to imply that Faraday's genius was an accident, that he was born with the right kind of mentality. Second, there is an implication, which Agassi developed strongly, that the barrier to the 'new' way of thinking is the resistance to it by other individuals, so that the problems faced by the thinker of the new thought are those of communication and conversion. Both these implications negate the effort and involvement which are illustrated in different ways on almost every page of the *Diary*.

Other commentators, for example Heimann and Williams, suggest that there are conceptual, rather than psychological precursors to the field idea in the development of Faraday's thought.[17] They take account of metaphysical ideas, previously suggested theories, or general principles such as Faraday's well-known beliefs in 'unity of force' or the power of revelation. The precursors or traditions contain premises which lead to field theory and suggest physical instances of it to be searched for. This way of thinking about how Faraday's thought developed is flawed because it avoids the problem of creativity, denies the novelty of discovery in phenomena or thought and relocates the problems of originality in metaphysics, religion or elsewhere. It is flawed also because it implies that as the new concept of the field gained in importance, other supposedly 'older' ways of thinking were replaced by it. This is not what happened, as the importance of the 'particle' idea in more recent theories demonstrates. Faraday's work is characterised by an eclectic use of different kinds of concepts at various times during his working life.[18] When describing or explaining phenomena, he used whatever concepts seemed to him to be appropriate or illuminating.

The role of such precursors to 'the field' should be recognised, but these are only one factor in the complex of interactions which combine to produce scientific thought and discovery. In several papers, David Gooding has described Faraday's work as an ordered complex of interactions in which non-scientific precepts of metaphysical or cultural origin are combined with the methodology and practice involved in the experiments which took place.[19]

Empirical facts, theoretical experimental design, technical procedures and the capacity to communicate with known terminology interact to produce a description of the events taking place. Accounts such as Gooding's do give insight into much of Faraday's work because they recognise the importance of both experiment and the experimenter's presuppositions and practice. However, when examining these accounts and when trying to develop my own, I found that their apparently adequate classification of determining factors repeatedly failed to provide a satisfactory description of events at particular stages in the development of Faraday's thought. Moreover, *these failures seemed to occur at precisely those times when an important and creative step forward was being made.*

A typical example of such a failure is found in attempts to describe Faraday's thought about the following thought experiment:

> If all the electricity resides upon the exterior of a globe or mass of conducting matter, then what is the condition of our globe of the earth as a conductor suspended in air? . . .
> If the globe and its surrounding air were actually electrified with a surplus portion of P. or N. Electricity, we should not be able to discover it, moving as we do upon its surface and having no other point of comparison than what it affords.[20]

His conclusion was that there could be no way of measuring absolute charge. This is a statement about the nature of knowledge which does not deny the possible existence of absolute charge. However, Faraday used the conclusion to reach a *decision* that absolute charge was a 'natural impossibility'.[21] I agree with Gooding's interpretation in Chapter six, that this thought experiment provided the rationale behind Faraday's certainty that charges always occurred in pairs and that he developed the theory of induction from this foundation. Yet I find it unsatisfactory because recording this event does not explain why a personal aspect of thought, this decision, should lead to lasting scientific knowledge.

It is of course necessary to make decisions in scientific work: conclusions are drawn with respect to theory so that work can proceed; choices are made concerning areas on which attention is to be focused. These conclusions and choices are often influenced by pressure of time, costs and culture.[22] Such influences do not provide explanations of Faraday's capacity to make good decisions at crucial times. Until this personal aspect of his thought is addressed the problem of creativity is avoided.

I encountered another kind of difficulty when trying to construct an ordered narrative of Faraday's thought. On occasions he seemed to be well aware of ideas which we would consider useful to his objectives, yet he nevertheless failed to use them. For example, it is well documented that he had a preference for the 'states-in-matter' or 'vibrations' type of hypotheses on the nature of electricity and was very suspicious of 'fluid' hypotheses. In 1834, while investigating the phenomenon of self-induction, Faraday at first wondered if the effect might be explained as a consequence of an expected property of fluid, its inertia.[23] From experiments which showed the dependence of self-induction effects upon the geometry of the circuit concerned, he was able to show that this was not the case and also that if electricity was a fluid, it did not possess any discernible inertia at all. This was quite strong evidence against the fluid theories. However, Faraday did not use it. Instead he continued to refer to the 'fluid hypothesis' and continued to use explanations and language depending upon it. In other words, Faraday knew of a sound argument in support of his declared preference, and inexplicably he failed to exploit it.

Faraday knew how to marshal arguments and how to develop new language when it was necessary.[24] These failures to use available evidence and ideas shows that the statement of an idea is not enough to establish it as usable in argument. Such occurrences also show that the development of new thought is a far more complex process than that of replacing concepts which have been shown to be unsatisfactory. To reject revalued concepts is easy; what is difficult and takes time is to maintain varying and doubtful points of view until the meaning and value of a new concept takes its place in relation to previously held concepts. The emergence of a framework of thoughts in which all concepts, old and new, have an understood coherence is a process of evolution, not revolution.

Difficulty leading to understanding

A third kind of difficulty, which at first seemed intractable, provided the key to my understanding of Faraday's way of thinking. This difficulty, familiar to scholars, was that of finding the material confused, and finding that attempts to sort out the confusion led to an escalating complexity of factors to be considered. As well as prior thought, attitudes, techniques and experiment, it seemed necessary to take account of culture, institution, age, religion, illness, health . . . to name only those which came immediately to mind. To describe Faraday's thought by means of interacting determinants became an impossible task and an evolution from it to a new method was needed.[25] In what follows the modification of my own approach to Faraday's work can be observed as an example of an evolutionary process, which helps to explain the process of Faraday's thinking.

In 1838, Faraday paid attention to what he called the 'lateral action' or 'transverse force' of electric current. The phenomena involved are electromagnetic and Faraday had from time to time speculated that their cause was an 'electrotonic state' of matter. The complex details of this speculation are not important here, only its effect upon his thinking.

Faraday argued first that magnetic force was independent of the matter through which it passed because only few materials are magnetic; then he argued that, like electric force, its action did depend on matter.[26] The first line of reasoning led to an hypothesis that magnetic force belonged to a 'higher power'[27] which acted at a distance without effects in intervening matter; the second was based on his belief that the cause of electromagnetic phenomena was the 'electrotonic state' which enabled both electric and magnetic forces to act and be connected by the particles of matter.[28] He designed and performed experiments intended to decide between these alternatives. Blocks of iron, copper or sulphur were placed so that they would 'screen'[29] the lateral effects produced by a conducting circuit on a nearby secondary circuit. Faraday expected that copper and sulphur would show a difference in their screening power and that the kind of difference found would indicate the correct hypothesis. But he found no screening effects of any kind. The *Researches* and the *Diary* of 1838 both show that Faraday could not find a satisfactory way forward from this evidence.

Faraday is often rightly considered to be an admirably clear and concise writer. In relation to these paragraphs, I was relieved to find that in his biography of Faraday, Pearce Williams refers to Faraday's 'obscurity of exposition'.[30] After months of work, at one time I could only agree in a most heartfelt manner. It seemed at first that for once Faraday had become confused between 'fact' and 'fancy' and that his earlier capacity to make good use of speculative thought had deserted him. However, it was quite unsatisfactory to have to dismiss these events as unusual, as a lapse on his part, because his study of lateral action and magnetic force clearly played an important part in the thinking which led to his later discovery of the diamagnetic properties of all matter. Once again a difficulty in understanding Faraday's thinking had occurred at a point linked directly with his creativity.

I now see that this difficulty was caused by my approach. This had produced the appearance of confusion in Faraday's thinking by its attempt to describe logically processes of thought which did not take place via any logical process of reasoning.

2 A change of aim; observations

Darwin commented that it is fatal 'to reason whilst observing, though so necessary beforehand and so useful afterwards'. In my case the inspiration to simply observe and stop trying to reason things out, came from Heinz Post.[31] At his suggestion, I began a chronological list of things which Faraday had actually done from 1838 onwards. From it I select the following observations:

1. In 1839, Faraday collected the first fourteen series of the *Experimental Researches in Electricity* into a single volume. In what was probably an editorial aid to this collection, he bound a personal set of the *Researches* as they had first been printed in the *Philosophical Transactions* of the Royal Society, inserting a blank page of paper between each printed page of the papers. On these blank pages he then wrote comments of his notes, references and thoughts about the paragraphs printed on the opposite pages. This interleaved volume is a treasure store of what Faraday himself thought was relevant and important with respect to the topics in each paragraph.[32]

2. Opposite the 'obscure' paragraphs of the 'higher power' there are unequivocally clear comments and references to other paragraphs of the *Researches*, to paragraphs of the *Diary*, and to papers by Joseph Henry.[33] The latter describes screening experiments similar to Faraday's but which had had positive results, contrary to Faraday's experiments. The breakthrough in understanding offered by the interleaved version of the *Researches* was to show that however problematical the topic of 'lateral action' was, Faraday realised that it was re-opened by Henry's results and was inspired to begin work again.

3. The references given in these annotated notes also stated that understanding of lateral action had been worked through to complete clarification in the unpublished *Diary* passages of August and September 1840.[34] I consulted these paragraphs and found that a set of passages less likely to produce a clarification of anything could hardly be imagined. They are a superb example of a particular kind of *Diary* entry: there are repetitions of ideas apparently realised with a sense of achievement, then jotted down to lie unused until recognised once more; there are sudden jumps from idea to idea; there are references and reminders about possibly connected phenomena; there are strange diagrams and mistakes. The work began with a complex and obsessively detailed system of notation for primary and secondary currents, illustrated by the page reproduced in Fig. 11.1. This was at one point extended, and then abandoned. He introduced new names for proposed new categories of currents, which disagree with his 1832 demonstration of identity between all kinds of electricity. However, these new categories were soon abandoned. Among these confusing speculations, he also made a very odd mistake. 'Tertiary' current was the name given to a current electromagnetically induced by a current which was itself an induced current. Faraday stated categorically that it was different in kind from other currents which had been induced because it flowed continually and was not transient. This statement is wrong and Faraday of all people must have had the experience to know it.[35]

'Negative capability'

Once again I felt confused, but decided to hold on to the knowledge afforded by the interleaved copy of the *Researches*. Whatever the 1840 work looked like, Faraday had thought it an important clarification. Later, I identified this as the most important step in the change in my way of thinking which led to my being able to observe more freely and thoughtfully than before. This led to insight into Faraday's way of thinking. The step taken was to be in a state of mind where I could trust Faraday's judgment and at the same time remain aware of my doubts and difficulties. John Keats, in a letter to his brothers said:

> I had not a dispute but a disquisition with Dilke on various subjects; several things dovetailed in my mind, and it at once struck me what quality went to form a Man of Achievement . . . I mean Negative Capability, that is when a man is capable of

10TH AUG. 1840.

6088. In relation to dynamic induction (see Researches 1660, etc.).

6089. For the present let P——→ or ←——P represent a primary, i.e. a common voltaic or Leyden current; let S——→ or ←——S represent a secondary effect, and let T——→ or ←——T represent a tertiary effect; and let S—⊖— or —⊖—S represent the supposed state of the secondary wire after S——→ or ←——S has occurred. Then are not the following propositions true?

6090. It is clear that whilst a primary current is *rising*, thus P——→, a short current or rather a demi current ←——S is produced – that whilst P——→ continues, S is —⊖—S or apparently nothing, and that when P——→ ceases, —⊖—S passes into S——→.

6091. The cycle of conditions in the primary wire is: the natural state; the rising of the current P——→; the continuance of P——→; the fall of P——→; the natural state, etc. The corresponding cycle of conditions in the secondary wire is: the natural state; ←——S; then —⊖—S; then S——→; then the natural state.

6092. Now is it possible that P wire natural or —P—, and ←——P and also P——→, can be exactly alike in their action on —S—, producing not the least difference of effect on or in it?

6093. P——→ and ←——P are magnetic; —P— is not.

6094. As —S— approaches P——→ or ←——P, it is acted upon by them and becomes more and more ←——S or S——→, and as it receeds and is relieved from this influence, it returns more and more nearly to its natural state —S—.

6095. So it would seem that —⊖—S or S—⊖— is in a peculiar state of tension and not in the natural state; and that these changes with distance are the rising and falling of the state by such alteration of distance.

6096. But then how is this related to the effects with magnetic curves, for when a wire is taken towards a horseshoe magnet so as to pass between its poles, S——→ is produced; but when it has passed through and is receeding to a distance, still S——→ continues? Now the state of that wire at the first and last must be the same surely, and the neutral state; it can hardly be supposed to be —S— at one time and then afterwards S—⊖—.

Figure 11.1 Faraday's *Diary*, 10 August 1840. Volume 4, page 52.

being in uncertainties, mysteries, doubts, without any irritable reaching after fact and reason.[36]

The state of mind to which I refer allows 'negative capability' to operate so that observations are made from a new point of view.

Working from the principle that Faraday had been right, I noticed something outside the context of the material itself. This 1840 work was unpublished, but it was not private, as other parts of the *Diary* were. J.F. Daniell was present during the performance of the experiments described. He and Faraday must also have had the support of nearly every physicist in London, because in order to perform the experiments, they had borrowed practically every coil and magnet in the city.[37] Then I noticed something else which I had always known but not given any significance. Faraday's apparently obscure reasonings in 1838 on the 'higher power' and the 'screening' experiments were published in the *Philosophical Transactions* of the Royal Society.[38] This journal was not noted for condoning obscurity, even from Faraday. Further reading of nineteenth-century commentators soon showed that although Faraday's ideas were considered difficult, they were not thought of as confusing or contradictory. Although Tyndall called them 'dark sayings' and said that Faraday's mind 'habitually dwells in the "boundless contiguity of shade" ',[39] he meant that Faraday's work was difficult because it was profound; Faraday grappled with the boundaries of his knowledge. I found Faraday obscure and confusing because I was trying to relate his ideas to 'the field concept', which was of course a concept not yet available to Faraday. This approach had led to a spurious classification of the material, as that which fitted progression to the field concept and that which did not.

Realisations

Returning to the 1840 work I tried to consider it as Faraday and his contemporaries had considered it; as a useful piece of scientific activity which clarified some previously difficult concepts. I tried to avoid all knowledge of field theory, and searched for what it was that was being clarified on the basis of what prior ideas. However, confusion set in again. Faraday always had been pedantically meticulous in the development of his notation, yet here he seemed to make no attempt to develop a sequential argument. The *Diary* entries have the familiar and irritating form of ideas jotted down, repeated and forgotten. There are only brief episodes of reasoning, and not all of these are in the same line of thought. I realised that this *lack of pattern* was not an irritating failure to be ordered, but *was itself the evidence of how Faraday thought*. In these passages, one does not see 'Faraday's reasoning', one sees what he did.

The prejudice which had prevented my understanding was the idea that Faraday's thinking must have had a single coherent framework. It did not. Faraday thought about and worked at various notions of 'lateral action' without elevating any idea to the status of 'framework'. This clarification took place, *not by rational analysis of any prior thoughts*, but by a quite different mode of thinking, a *selection of thought*. From the morass of articulated and unarticulated principles, concepts, observations and physical facts, Faraday suspended the need to understand and simply acknowledged the thoughts which came into his mind. The coherence of ideas was not imposed by any prior framework, but was allowed to emerge from the chaos of thoughts he experienced.

In 1840, the clarification reached was that all action was *via* the medium. In spite of his earlier preference for this type of hypothesis, he had previously approached the topic from several, sometimes contradictory points of view. This eclectic use of many ideas whose order within a framework is not known, is evident in much of Faraday's work. The difficulties in historical narratives based on reconstruction are created by failure to recognise this fact.

4 'Learning from experience' defined

The recognition that Faraday could think without need for a conceptual framework within which relationships between ideas could be ordered, even tentatively, gave me an insight into the state of mind from which 'negative capability' develops. When consciously reasoned experience of ideas and their relationships escalates in complexity the usual apparatus of thinking, in which concepts can be discerned with our conscious minds, fails to cope. Selective thinking takes place via a process over which we have no control; the thought which emerges is selected from the total flow of experience of the individual concerned. It is important to notice that, (a) while we do not have control over the process, we do have the capacity to choose at least some of our experience; and that (b) this thinking, which I call 'learning from experience', is characterised by negative capability. In learning from experience, there are genuine changes of mind and the possibility of creation or discovery. It is a mode of thinking *different in kind* from modes accessible to conscious processes.[40]

Different kinds of thinking

In trying to describe this difference, I have found the following quotation helpful. Henri Poincaré described the process of creation of a mathematical formulation in this way:

> If a new result is to have any value, it must unite elements long since known, but until then scattered and seemingly foreign to each other, and suddenly introduce order where the appearance of disorder reigned. Then it enables us to see at a glance each of these elements in the place it occupies in the whole. Not only is the new fact valuable on its own account, but it alone gives a value to the old facts it unites.[41]

Why are such ordering results necessary? According to Poincaré:

> Our mind is as frail as our senses are; it would lose itself in the complexity of the world if that complexity were not harmonious; like the short-sighted, it would see only the details, and would be obliged to forget each of these details before examining the next, because it would be incapable of taking in the whole. The only

facts worthy of our attentions are those which introduce order unto this complexity and so make it accessible to us.[42]

Faraday's 'learning from experience' was a kind of thinking which selected facts such as Poincaré described.

However, a point which Poincaré does not make, and may not have noticed, is implicit in the idea of *selection*: before order, there was disorder. Before he found the 'fact which introduced order' Faraday did have to 'lose himself in the complexity of the world', at least for a time. This kind of thinking begins with 'negative capability', a state of mind which implies *strength*, not frailty, in its capacity to *tolerate complexity, disorder and even confusion*.

This state of mind can be compared with ones associated with other kinds of thought, such as one identified by Tyndall. Faraday was heard to agree with this comment on prejudice:

> In our conceptions and reasonings regarding the forces of nature, we perpetually make use of symbols which, when they possess a high representative value, we dignify with the name of theories. Thus, prompted by certain analogies, we ascribe electrical phenomena to the action of a peculiar fluid, sometimes flowing, sometimes at rest. Such conceptions have their advantages and their disadvantages; they afford peaceful lodging to the intellect for a time, but they also circumscribe it, and by-and-by, when the mind has grown too large for its lodging, it often finds difficulty in breaking down the walls of what has become its prison instead of its home.[43]

This is a benevolent, often very useful, form of prejudice. However good the intention or the result, thinking by means of this process can 'bow down the mind' and 'bind it in chains of error' as Faraday put it when writing about Joseph Priestley. He was also aware that escape was not a matter of either hard work or intelligence, saying,

> The more acute a man is, the more strongly he is bound by the chains of error; for he only uses his ingenuity to falsify the truth which lies before him.[44]

Two examples of 'benevolent prejudice' have been given in this essay: Faraday's attempts in 1838 to decide between alternative hypotheses of the nature of magnetic action by comparisons of the evidence favouring each, and my own attempt to reconstruct an historical account of Faraday's thinking by analysing interactions between the various discernible factors. The process involves making use of experience piece by piece. In this kind of thinking, reasoning organises the best possible construction *for the purpose of understanding*. However, as it can only operate on something which is already in mind, there is no new creation, and perception is circumscribed. This happens whether or not understanding is generated. When the circumstances require a new idea which cannot be reached, the result is a 'block' to learning. One can be aware that prejudice is operating, even if one cannot find its source.

In 'learning from experience' the purpose or intention behind the desire to know is *curiosity*, rather than gaining the satisfying feeling of ordered knowledge which understanding brings. Instead of finding Tyndall's 'peaceful lodging to the intellect', curiosity leads to acceptance of the previously unknown perception, however it fits in with previous experience. If perceptions and previous ideas are incompatible within existing ways of organising thoughts in the mind, 'learning' is necessary, although it may not be easy. 'Negative capability' involves the ability to tolerate the threat to one's existing understanding.

A state of mind can be identified which allows and even encourages this toleration. In describing Faraday's thinking, as observed from the record of his work on lateral action of 1840, it could only be recorded that 'learning from experience' was taking place. However, I had another example of both processes of thought available: my own switch from reasoning and feeling blocked, to feeling confused and then becoming able to observe once more. I made use of my recollection to explore the state of mind which had produced toleration, negative capability and genuine unprejudiced curiosity.[45] When I realised that this had been an emotional state of dependence, I realised that Faraday had also been able to identify the personal qualities needed. He had even tried to communicate his understanding of them in a public lecture.

5 The lecture on 'mental education'[46]

It is well known that Faraday was always aware of prejudice and the difficulties to which it led. When he was 62 years old, he gave a lecture which outlined his views on the progress of science and learning, his 'Observations on Mental Education'. One of his remarks shows that he recognised that learning begins in a state of perplexity:

> The very progress which science makes . . . as a body is a continual correction of ignorance, *i.e.* of a state which is ignorance in relation to the future, though wisdom and knowledge in relation to the past.[47]

He also observed that in unfamiliar situations, most people made a 'presumptuous judgment'[48] rather than respond with the appropriate feeling of doubt. He was able to state clearly the human tendencies which lead to prejudice and he listed, with illustrations from his own long career in science, the capacities which scientists and others should develop. Most of these observations are not new: scientists should be prepared to be wrong, they should form clear and precise ideas and communicate them, they should experiment and so on. On the whole, his observations refer to the *criticism* of thought, not to its *creation*.

Faraday did not distinguish criticism from creation, but he did regard as essential a point which does make the distinction. He said:

> Among those points of self-education which take up the form of *mental discipline*, there is one of great importance, and, moreover, difficult to deal with, because it involves an internal conflict, and equally touches our vanity and our ease. It

consists in the *tendency to deceive ourselves* regarding all we wish for, and the necessity of *resistance to these desires*.[49]

Of course we know how important this is. But we often fail to understand that the key is not the self-deception itself. It is the recognition that this is an *emotional* problem. Faraday was saying that *objectivity* was reached by paying conscious attention to *subjective tendencies*, and that this was emotionally difficult. In a concluding paragraph, it becomes clear that he was talking about a difference in the kind of attention paid. He did not mean that one should try harder to be *less* emotional, more objective and more on guard against prejudice.

> This education has for its first and last step *humility*. It can commence only because of a conviction of deficiency; and if we are not disheartened under the growing revelations which it will make, that conviction will become stronger unto the end. But the humility will be founded, not on comparison of ourselves with the imperfect standards around us, but on the increase of that internal knowledge which alone can make us aware of our internal wants.[50]

Faraday is talking about self-knowledge:

> The first step in correction is to learn our deficiencies and having learned them, the next step is almost complete: for no man who has discovered that his judgment is hasty, or illogical, or imperfect, would go on with the same degree of haste, or irrationality, or presumption as before. I do not mean that all would at once be cured of bad mental habits, but I think better of human nature than to believe, that a man in any rank of life, who has arrived at the consciousness of such a condition, would deny his common sense, and still judge and act as before. And though such self-schooling must continue to the end of life to supply an experience of deficiency rather than of attainment, still there is abundant stimulus to excite any man to perseverance. What he has lost are things imaginary, not real; what he gains are riches before unknown to him, yet invaluable; and though he may think more humbly of his own character, he will find himself at every step of his progress more sought for than before, more trusted with responsibility and held in pre-eminence by his equals, and more highly valued by those whom he himself will esteem worthy of approbation.[51]

The value of 'humility' for emotional experience

As Faraday said, the mental discipline of 'humility' touches 'our vanity and our ease'. That is, it is our *feelings* which are involved when our own *judgement* is recognised as deficient. The second point means that 'humility' requires something like *faith*. For Faraday, faith was in God, and he depended on the revelation of God. For me, faith means a willingness to depend upon the reality of an unconscious process. This question remains open: what can be understood is that it involves a state of mind characterised by *dependence*. This exposes us to emotional difficulty but it gives us the capacity to tolerate and accept our experience.

Yet, even if we understand that our feelings are involved, if the *message* is to be communicated, it is our feelings which have to be used as guides to the recognition of its importance in the personal experience of learning. Empathy is the medium for communication of feeling. This is why I have written this essay from a personal point of view. My own understanding began when I suffered feelings of confusion and was willing to depend upon Faraday's assessment of his work. This was a viewpoint quite different from imagining that Faraday's hypotheses and reasonings must be confused. 'Vanity', 'ease', 'disheartened', 'conviction' and 'humility': Faraday's words all describe emotions. He knew how to fight prejudice and make good decisions. His problem in communicating his knowledge of 'how' he thought lay in the nature of the process itself. It could not be demonstrated on a laboratory bench or written down to be critically examined because the very nature of the process is that it abandons conscious assessment and because the feelings to which one is exposed are private. He stated it as clearly as he could: this self-schooling depends upon *humility*.

6 Conclusion

Because humility is a state of mind characterised by dependence or faith, the sequence of mental events which take place is different from those which occur in the mind whose aim is *to know*. The desire to use experience via reasoning to gain knowledge is replaced by a desire to see, accept and appreciate what is actually there. This open-mindedness can be observed. I think that the 'learning from experience' which I have described makes sense of several aspects of Faraday's work: how Faraday's new ideas and discoveries arose directly from his experiments; how his ideas could elicit some of the truth about the real world without need of precursory notions; how he could recognise the importance of a discovery and how often his *Diary* descriptions seem to contain premonitions of future theory. It also gives insight into his deep religious faith. Finally, I think that it helps us understand the most difficult problem of all: how Faraday had the capacity to make unprejudiced judgements. Again and again he made creative, sound decisions and choices.

At the end of the lecture on 'Mental Education' Faraday said:

> The deficiency [of judgement] is known hypothetically, but I doubt if in reality; the individual acknowledges the state in respect of others, but is unconscious of it in regard to himself. As to the world at large, the condition [of ignorance] is accepted as a necessary fact; and so it is left untouched, almost ignored.[52]

I agree with this pessimistic outlook. I think that we have to rediscover and learn for ourselves what Faraday had discovered about prejudice and creativity. It is difficult because 'touching our vanity and ease' is not done lightly, but it is this which gives us access to new experience. The medium by which most of us gain knowledge and try to communicate is language. But its use as an objective medium means we can often keep feelings out, or contain them so that they do not disturb our 'ease'. We do not readily tolerate the disturbance which 'negative capability' brings. However, when we positively accept the feelings associated with dependence, new thoughts are possible. The responsibility for creativity belongs to the individual who accepts his own mental pain. Creativity is not the mechanism of a dummy pushed by society or by mysteriously chosen precepts and principles. By empathy, by using our own feelings, we can come to know Faraday in a way which is distinct from knowing things *about* his life and work. We can know that Faraday reached freedom from prejudice through his emotional courage.

Notes

While studying Faraday's work, I have received help from Irena McCabe at the Royal Institution and Lenore Symons at the Institution of Electrical Engineers and also from the Royal Society, for which I am very grateful. I take this opportunity to thank these institutions and their staff. I would also like to thank the staff of Chelsea College Library, who have willingly supplied me with books and papers. I owe very much to my doctoral supervisor Heinz Post, who did not allow too much 'empathy' and insisted on a great deal more concrete evidence. I am also grateful to David Gooding and Frank James for a lot of time and help. Finally, when I tried to explain my thoughts about what I was finding in Faraday's work to George Crawford, he introduced me to Bion's work. I thank George for understanding what I was trying to say and for a great amount of thoroughness and patience in helping me express it. All these people have helped me with my work on Faraday and with my writing. However, if I have any capacity for empathy and negative capability, I would like to thank Elinor Wedeles for working with me on that.

1. The title of this paper was suggested by that of Bion (1962). I am grateful to Francesca Bion for permitting me to use it.
2. *Ibid.*, [v].
3. *Ibid.*, [viii].
4. Crawford (1985).
5. Faraday (1833a and c).
6. Faraday, *Diary*, 29 August 1831–11 June 1832, **1**, 1–441. See also 27 October 1834, **2**, 2092–2106, 21 October 1837, **3**, 4135, 24 October 1837, **3**, 4209, 14 October 1839, **3**, 5234.
7. Faraday (1832a), in particular 60–84 and Faraday (1838d).
8. Faraday to Phillips, 29 November 1831, *Correspondence*, **1**: 122. In this letter Faraday describes the newly discovered phenomena of induction, suggests the electrotonic state idea and speculates eagerly that the electrotonic state will explain electrochemistry also.
9. Nersessian (this volume).
10. Guralnick (1979).
11. Faraday (1834a), 852–74.
12. Examples which come to mind in relation to 'field' are the dynamic ideas of force in the work of Priestley and of Davy, and 'lines of force' in the work of Barlow; there are 'particle' ideas in plenty, for example in the work of Dalton and of Berzelius. See Levere (1971), Knight (1978), Heimann and McGuire (1971), Heilbron (1981) and Gooding (1985b).
13. I mention only those few whose work has been instrumental in forcing me to think and focus my own ideas, although the literature is much more extensive.
14. Holton (1978).
15. *Ibid.*, Agassi (1971).
16. Maxwell (1892), **2**: 176–7.

17. Heimann (1971), Williams, L.P. (1965).
18. Crawford (1985). See Gooding (1980b), 92–4.
19. Gooding (1982a, 1986) and this volume.
20. Faraday, *Diary*, 3 November 1835, **2**, 2542 and 2549 respectively. This also appeared in another version in Faraday, *Diary*, 15 January 1836, **2**, 2842, quoted by Gooding (this volume), 128.
21. Faraday (1838a), 1177.
22. Knorr-Cetina (1981).
23. Faraday (1835), in particular 1077.
24. This is clearly shown by his introduction of the terms of electrochemistry in 1834. See Faraday (1834a), Faraday to Whewell, 24 April 1834, *Correspondence*, **1**: 160, Whewell to Faraday, 25 April 1834, *ibid.*, 161, Faraday to Lemen, 25 April 1834, *ibid.*, 162, Faraday to Whewell, 3 May 1834, *ibid.*, 163, Whewell to Faraday, 5 May 1834, *ibid.*, 164, Faraday to Whewell, 5 May 1834, *ibid.*, 165, Whewell to Faraday, 6 May 1834, *ibid.*, 166, Faraday to Whewell, 15 May 1834, *ibid.*, 167. See Ross (1961).
25. I think that Cantor in his chapter has been successful in doing this.
26. Faraday (1838c), 1653–1665 and Faraday (1838d), 1709–1730.
27. Faraday's concepts of 'force' and 'power' are discussed in Crawford (1985). A 'higher power' was independent of relationships with other powers or matter, and was thus capable of action at a distance.
28. The 'electrotonic state' indicated an internal arrangement of forces in matter. It was supposed to be a state of strain which would be seen as electric or magnetic force when released. See Crawford (1985).
29. Faraday did not initially use the word 'screen' in describing his experiments, but after its use by Henry (1839) he referred to 'screening' in his interleaved copy of *Experimental Researches* (RI MS F3 B) and in the *Diary* in 1840.
30. Williams, L.P. (1965), 250.
31. Darwin (1958), 159. I am very grateful to Prof Post who suggested that in this instance it might not be Faraday who was confused, but myself. If I have any claim to be a good historian, I feel that I owe it to his capacity to continually make me think more carefully.
32. RI MS F3 B.
33. Joseph Henry (1797–1878), Professor of Natural Philosophy in the College of New Jersey, Princeton. Henry and Faraday conducted their screening experiments independently of each other at about the same time. Henry (1839) reached Faraday in the following year.
34. Faraday, *Diary*, 10 August to 1 September 1840, **4**, 6088–6187.
35. *Ibid.*, 10 August 1840, **4**, 6100.
36. J. Keats to G. and T. Keats, 21 December 1817, in Keats (1952).
37. This was suggested by Frank James. See Faraday, *Diary*, 10 August to 1 September 1840, **4**, 6088–6187, especially the diagrams on 31 August 1840, *ibid.*, 6155–6159.
38. Faraday (1838c and d).
39. Tyndall (1884), 85.
40. Compare Tweney (this volume).
41. Poincaré (1914), 30.
42. *Ibid.*
43. Tyndall (1884), 63 and note.
44. Faraday (1833b).
45. This was with the help of Elinor Wedeles.
46. Faraday (1854).
47. *Ibid.*, *ERCP*, 487–8.
48. *Ibid.*, 468.
49. *Ibid.*, 475. Faraday's emphasis.
50. *Ibid.*, 485. Faraday's emphasis.
51. *Ibid.*
52. *Ibid.*, 489–90.

Bibliographical Notes

Printed sources

With the exception of Faraday sources, *DNB*, *DSB* and anonymous articles all the notes and references following each chapter normally refer to this bibliography by author and year of publication. Volume numbers of both journals and multi-volume works always appear in bold. Numbers following the date in the notes and references or in the bibliographical entries refer to pagination unless specifically stated otherwise (for example art). The exceptions are as follows.

Faraday sources

1. L.P. Williams, R. FitzGerald and O. Stallybrass (eds) *The selected correspondence of Michael Faraday* (2 volumes, Cambridge, 1971). This is cited in the notes and references as *Correspondence* followed by volume and letter number.
2. *Faraday's Diary. Being the various philosophical notes of experimental investigation made by Michael Faraday, DCL, FRS, during the years 1820–1862 and bequeathed by him to the Royal Institution of Great Britain. Now, by order of the Managers, printed and published for the first time, under the editorial supervision of Thomas Martin* (7 volumes and index, London, 1932–6), is cited in the notes and references as 'Faraday, *Diary*'. From p. 367 of volume one this is followed by entry date, volume number and entry number. (NB. Entry numbers begin twice on 29 August 1831 and again on 25 August 1832.) Entries in volume one (until p. 366) have entry date, '1:', followed by pagination. (NB. In the printed diary entries do not always follow chronologically in order.)
3. Faraday's *Experimental Researches in Electricity* covers two sets of papers. The first is his sequentially numbered series of papers that appeared in the *Philosophical Transactions* and in the *Philosophical Magazine* from 1832

onwards. In the bibliography the *Philosophical Transactions* papers are listed in the normal way followed by *ERE*, the series number and the paragraph numbers; the *Philosophical Magazine* papers which did not have series numbers are followed by the paragraph numbers. In the notes and references these papers are cited by Faraday and year followed by the paragraph number. In *Experimental Researches in Electricity. Reprinted from the Philosophical Transactions of 1831–1852. With other electrical papers from the Quarterly Journal of Science, Philosophical Magazine, the Proceedings of the Royal Institution* (3 volumes, London, 1839–55) Faraday included, in volumes two and three, a number of papers which were not part of either the *Philosophical Transactions* or *Philosophical Magazine* series. In the bibliography the original place of publication and the *ERE* volume and page number is given. In the notes and references these papers are cited as normal; if an author refers to a paper from these volumes then this is signified by *ERE* followed by the volume and page number.

4. The identical procedure is adopted for his *Experimental Researches in Chemistry and Physics. Reprinted from the Philosophical Transactions of 1821–1857; the Journal of the Royal Institution; the Philosophical Magazine, and other publications* (London, 1859). This is cited as *ERCP*.

Other sources

Collected papers of other scientists and theologians are referred to in the normal way; if an author refers to a paper via a collected work this is referred to as 'in', followed by pagination (e.g. 'Glas (1741) in Glas (1782), **2**: 1–42').

Collections of original papers are cited in the bibliography under the editor(s) and the author(s) of individual contributions. This latter is cited in the notes and references. Translations of non-English material are listed individually in the bibliography.

Anonymous articles are cited only in the notes'and references. These for the most part form newspaper reports of lectures, meetings and the like.

Encyclopedia entries are cited under the author of the article. Entries from the *Dictionary of National Biography* (*DNB*) and the *Dictionary of Scientific Biography* (*DSB*) are only cited in the notes and references followed by volume and page number.

Manuscripts

All manuscripts are cited only in the notes and references; these include unpublished historical papers.

The only exception here is F. Greenaway, M. Berman, S. Forgan and D. Chilton (eds), *Archives of the Royal Institution, Minutes of the Managers' meetings, 1799–1903* (15 volumes, bound in 7, London, 1971–6), which is a photographic reproduction of the minute books kept in the Royal Institution archive, is cited in the notes and references as 'RI MM' followed by date of meeting, volume and page number.

The following abbreviations are used:

IEE   Institution of Electrical Engineers.
LA   National Trust at Lacock Abbey.
RI   Royal Institution.
F   Faraday papers.
GM   Minutes of general meetings.
HD   Humphry Davy papers.
T   Tyndall papers.
RS   Royal Society.
PT   Manuscripts of *Philosophical Transactions* papers.
UCL University College London.
ULC University Library Cambridge.

Collected Bibliography

Abelson, R.P. *see* Schank, R.C.

Agassi, J. (1971): *Faraday as a Natural Philosopher*, Chicago.

Airy, G.B. (1833): 'Remarks on Sir David Brewster's paper 'On the absorption of specific rays &c'' *Phil. Mag.*, **2**: 419–24.

——(1846): 'remarks on Dr Faraday's paper on Ray vibrations', *Phil. Mag.*, **28**: 532–7.

Ampère, A.-M. (1820): 'Conclusions d'un Mémoire sur l'action mutuelle de deux courans électriques, sur celle qui existe entre un courant électrique et un aimant, et celle de deux aimans l'un sur l'autre; lu a l'Académie royale des Sciences, le 25 septembre 1820', *J. Phys.*, **91**: 76–8.

——(1820–1): 'Description and use of the apparatus employed by M. Ampere in his electro-magnetic researches', *Edinb. Phil. J.*, **4**: 406–16.

——(1821a): 'Réponse de M. Ampère a la lettre de M. Van Beck, sur une nouvelle Expérience électro-magnétique', *J. Phys.*, **93**: 447–67.

——(1821b): 'Notes relatives au Mémoire de M. Faraday', *Ann. Chim. Phys.*, **18**: 370–9.

——(1827): 'Mémoire sur la théorie mathématique des phénomènes électrodynamiques uniquement déduite de l'expérience, dans lequel se trouvent réunis les Mémoires que M. Ampère a communiqués a l'Académie royal des Sciences, dans les séances des 4 et 26 décembre, 1820, 10 juin 1822, 22 décembre 1823, 12 septembre et 21 novembre 1825', *Mém. Acad. Sci. Inst. France*, **6**: 175–387. (This is the volume of *Memoires* dated 1823 which appeared in 1827, some months after the 1826 appearance of the published separate edition which differs from this version.)

——(1831): 'Expériences sur les courans électriques produits par l'influence d'un autre courant', *Ann. Chim. Phys.*, **48**: 405–12.

Anderson, J.R. (1980): *Cognitive Psychology and its Implications*, San Francisco.

——(1983): *The Architecture of Cognition*, Cambridge, Ma.

Ångström, A.J. (1854) 'Optiska Undersökningar', *Kongl. Veten. Akad. Handl.*, 335–60.

——(1855): 'Optical Researches', *Phil. Mag.*, **9**: 327–42.

Appleyard, R. (1931): *A tribute to Michael Faraday*, London.

Arago, D.F.J. (1819): 'Rapport fait par M. Arago à l'Académie des Sciences, au nom de la Commission qui avait été chargée d'examiner les Mémoirs envoyés au concours pour le prix de la diffraction', *Ann. Chim. Phys.*, **11**: 5–30.

Arkkelin, D. *see* Tweney, R.D.

Avogadro, A. (1844): 'Saggio di teoria matematica della distribuzione della elettricità sulla superficie dei corpi conduttori nell'ipotesi della azione induttiva escercitata dalla medesima sui corpi circostanti, per mezzo delle particelle dell'aria frapposta', *Mem. Mat. Fis.*, **23**: 156–184.

Bain, A. (1904). *Autobiography*, London.

Barlow, P. (1820): *An Essay on Magnetic Attractions*, London.

——(1822): 'Notice respecting Mr. Barlow's discovery of the mathematical laws of electro-magnetism', *Edinb. Phil. J.*, **7**: 281–3.

Barnard, G. (1885): *The Theory and Practice of Landscape Painting in Water-colours*, new edition, London.

Barnes, B. (1983): 'Social life as bootstrapped induction', *Sociology*, **17**: 524–45.

Baron, J. (1985): *Rationality and Intelligence*, Cambridge.

Barr, A. and Feigenbaum, E.A. eds (1981): *The Handbook of Artificial Intelligence*, **1**, Los Altos.

Bartlett, F.C. (1932): *Remembering: A study in Experimental and Social Psychology*, Cambridge.

——(1958): *Thinking: An Experimental and Social Study*, London.

Bate, J. (1740): *Experimental Philosophy Asserted and Defended, Against Some Late Attempts to Undermine It*, London.

Bence Jones, H. (1862): *Report on the Past, Present and Future of the Royal Institution, Chiefly in Regard to its Encouragement of Scientific Research*, London.

——(1870a): *The Life and Letters of Faraday*, 1st edition, London.

——(1870b): *The Life and Letters of Faraday*, 2nd edition, London.

——(1871): *The Royal Institution: Its Founders and Its First Professors*, London.

Bénézit, E. (1976): *Dictionnaire critique et documentaire des peintres, sculpteurs, dessinateurs et graveurs*, 10 volumes, Paris.

Benjamin, W. (1970): *Illuminations*, London.

Bennett, J. *see* Bogue, D.

Berkson, W. (1974): *Fields of Force: The Development of a World view from Faraday to Einstein*, New York.

——(1978): 'Reply to Pearce Williams (1975)', *Br. J. Phil. Sci.*, **29**: 243–8.

Berman, M. (1978): *Social Change and Scientific Organization: The Royal Institution, 1799–1844*, London.

Bern, S. *see* Rappard, H.

Bion, W.R. (1962): *Learning from Experience*, London.

Biot, J.-B. (1805a): 'Sur le formation de l'eau par le seule compression, et sur le nature de l'étincelle électrique', *Ann. Chim. Phys.*, **53**: 321–7.

——(1805b): 'Note on the formation of water by mere compression; with reflections on the nature of the electric spark', *J. Nat. Phil.*, **12**: 212–5.

——(1816): *Traité de Physique*, 3 volumes, Paris.

Blondel, C. (1982): *A.-M. Ampère et la Creation de l'électrodynamique (1820–1827)*, Paris.

Bogue, D. and Bennett, J. (1808–12): *History of Dissenters, from the Revolution in 1688, to the Year 1808*, 4 volumes, London.

[Bollaert, W.] (1867): 'Personal recollections', *Laboratory*, **1**: 388–90.

Boscovich, R.J. (1763): *Theoria Philosophiae Naturalis*, 2nd edition, Venice.

——(1922): *A Theory of Natural Philosophy*, London.

Bowers, B.P. (1975a): *The Life and Work of Sir Charles Wheatstone (1802–1875) with Particular Reference to his Contributions to Electrical Science*, University of London (external) PhD thesis.

——(1975b): *Sir Charles Wheatstone FRS 1802–1875*, London.

——(1982): *A History of Electric Light and Power*, Stevenage.

Brande, W.T. (1820): 'On the connexion of electric and magnetic phenomena', *Quart. J. Sci.*, **10**: 361–4.

Braudel, F. (1972): *The Mediterranean and the Mediterranean world in the Age of Philip II*, 2 volumes, New York.

Brewster, D. (1820–1): 'Account of the discoveries of M. Oersted, respecting the connection between magnetism and galvanism and the subsequent researches of Sir Humphry Davy, Bart., M. Ampere, and M. Biot', *Edinb. Phil. J.*, **4**: 167–75.

——(1832): 'Report on the recent progress of optics', *Rep. Brit. Ass.*, 308–22.

——(1833): 'Observations on the absorption of specific rays, in reference to the undulatory theory of light', *Phil. Mag.*, **2**: 360–3.

Brock, W.H. (1968): 'William Bollaert, Faraday and the Royal Institution', *Proc. Roy. Inst.*, **42**: 75–86.

——(1969): 'Lockyer and the chemists: The first dissociation hypothesis', *Ambix*, **16**: 81–99.

[Brougham, H.] (1804): 'The Bakerian Lecture. Experiments and Calculations relative to Physical Optics', *Edinb. Rev.*, **5**: 97–103.

Bruner, J.S. (1967): 'The ontogenesis of symbols' in [Jakobson] (1967), **1**: 427–46.

Brush, S.G. (1970): 'The wave theory of heat: A forgotten stage in the transition from caloric theory to thermodynamics', *Br. J. Hist. Sci.*, **5**: 145–67.

Bryan, M. (1927): *Dictionary of Painters and Engravers*, 5 volumes, London.

Buchwald, J. (1977): 'William Thomson and the mathematization of Faraday's electrostatics', *Hist. Stud. Phys. Sci.*, **8**: 101–36.

Buckland, G. (1980): *Fox Talbot and the Invention of Photography*, London.

Burgess, R. (1973): *Portraits of Doctors and Scientists in the Wellcome Institute for the History of Medicine*, London.

Bushman, R.L. (1966): 'On the uses of psychology: Conflict and conciliation in Benjamin Franklin', *Hist. Theory*, **5**: 225–40.

Caley, G. (1967): *Reflections on the Colony of New South Wales*. (Edited by J.E.B. Currey), London.

Campbell, D.T. (1974): 'Evolutionary epistemology' in Schilpp (1974), **1**: 413–63.

Caneva, K.L. (1978): 'From galvanism to electrodynamics', *Hist. Stud. Phys. Sci.*, **9**: 63–159.

——(1980): 'Ampère, the etherians, and the Oersted connexion', *Br. J. Hist. Sci.*, **13**: 121–38

——(1981): 'What should we do with the monster?' in Mendelsohn & Elkana (1981), 101–31.

Cannon, S.F. (1978): *Science in Culture: The Early Victorian Period*, New York.

Cantor, G.N. (1970): 'The Changing Role of Young's Ether', *Br. J. Hist. Sci.*, **5**: 44–62.

——(1971): 'Henry Brougham and the Scottish methodological tradition', *Stud. Hist. Phil. Sci.*, **2**: 69–89.

——(1975): 'The Reception of the Wave Theory of Light in Britain: A Case Study Illustrating the Role of Methodology in Scientific Debate', *Hist. Stud. Phys. Sci.*, **56**, 109–132.

——(1979): 'Revelation and the cyclical cosmos of John Hutchinson' in Jordanova & Porter (1979), 3–22.

——(1983): *Optics after Newton: Theories of Light in Britain and Ireland, 1704–1840*, Manchester.

Cantor, G.N. and Hodge, M.J.S. eds. (1981): *Conceptions of ether: Studies in the History of Ether Theories, 1740–1900*, Cambridge.

Card, S.K., Moran, T.P. and Newell, A. (1983): *The Psychology of Human–computer interaction*, Hillsdale.

Carnall, G. (1953–4): 'The Surrey Institute and its successor', *Adult Ed.*, **26**: 197–208.

Chilton, D. and Coley, N.G. (1980): 'The laboratories of the Royal Institution in the nineteenth century', *Ambix*, **27**: 173–203.

Challis, J. (1845a): 'On the aberration of light', *Rep. Brit. Ass.*, part 2, 9.

——(1845b): 'A theoretical explanation of the aberration of light', *Phil. Mag.*, **27**: 321–7.

——(1846a): 'On the aberration of light, in reply to Mr. Stokes', *Phil. Mag.*, **28**: 90–3.

——(1846b): 'On the principles to be applied in explaining the aberration of light', *Phil. Mag.*, **28**: 176–7.

Chase, W.G. ed. (1973): *Visual Information Processing*, New York.

Chase, W.G. and Simon, H.A. (1973): 'The mind's eye in chess', in Chase (1973), 215–81.

Chi, M.T.H., Glaser, R. and Rees, E. (1982): 'Expertise in problem solving' in Sternberg (1982), 7–75.

Christie, J.R.R. *see* Morrison-Low, A.D.

Clark, R.E.D. (1967): 'Michael Faraday on science & religion', *Hibbert J.*, **65**: 144–7.

——(1974): 'Faraday, Michael' in *New International Dictionary of the Christian Church*, Exeter, p. 369.

Clarke, E.M. (1836): 'Description of E.M. Clarke's magnetic electrical machine', *Phil. Mag.*, **9**: 262–6.

——(1837): 'Reply of Mr E.M. Clarke to Mr J. Saxton', *Phil. Mag.*, **10**: 455–9.

Cohen, R.S. and Wartofsky, M.W. eds. (1974): *Methodological and Historical Essays in the Natural and Social Sciences*, Dordrecht.

Coley, N.G. *see* Chilton, D.

Collier, K.B. (1934): *The Cosmogonies of our Fathers*, New York.

Collingwood, S.D. (1961): *The Unknown Lewis Carroll*, New York.

Collins, H.M. (1974): 'The TEA set: Tacit knowledge and scientific networks', *Sci. Stud.*, **4**: 165–85.

——(1975): 'The seven sexes: A study in the sociology of a phenomenon, or the replication of experiments in physics', *Sociology*, **9**: 205–24.

——(1981): 'The place of the "core-set" in modern science: Social contingency with methodological propriety in science', *Hist. Sci.*, **19**: 6–19.

——(1985): *Replication and Induction in Scientific Practice*, London.

Cooke, W.F. (1895): *Extracts from the Private Letters of the Late Sir William Fothergill Cooke, 1836–39, Relating to the Invention and Development of the Electric Telegraph*, (edited by F.H. Webb), London.

Copleston, W.J. (1851): *Memoir of Edward Copleston DD, Bishop of Llandaff*, London.

Crawford, E. (1985): *The Ideas of Particle and Field in Michael Faraday's Work, 1831–1845*, University of London (Chelsea College) PhD thesis.

Crosland, M. (1978): *Gay-Lussac, Scientist and Bourgeois*, Cambridge.

——(1980): 'Davy and Gay-Lussac: Competition and contrast' in Forgan (1980), 95–120.

——(1983): 'Explicit qualifications as a criterion for membership of the Royal Society: A historical review', *Notes Records Roy. Soc. Lond.*, **37**: 167–87.

Crosland, M. and Smith, C. (1978): 'The transmission of physics from France to Britain: 1800–1840', *Hist. Stud. Phys. Sci.*, **9**: 1–61.

Crosse, C. (1891): 'Science and society in the fifties', *Temple Bar*, **93**: 33–51.

Cumming, J. (1822): 'On the application of magnetism as a measure of electricity', *Trans. Camb. Phil. Soc.*, **1**: 281–6.

——(1827): *A Manual of Electro-dynamics, Chiefly Translated from the Manuel d'électricité dynamique, or Treatise on the Mutual Action of Electric Conductors and Magnets of J.F. Demonferrand with Notes and Additions*, Cambridge.

Cutler, J.C. (1976): *The London Institution, 1805–1933*, University of Leicester PhD thesis.

Daniell, J.F. (1843): *An Introduction to the Study of Chemical Philosophy*, 2nd edition, London.

Danziger, K. (1983): 'Origins of the schema of stimulated motion: Towards a pre-history of psychology', *Hist. Sci.*, **21**: 183–210.

Darwin, C. (1958): *The Autobiography of Charles Darwin, 1809–1882*, edited by N. Barlow, London.

Davidoff, L. and Hall, C. (1983): 'The architecture of public and private life: English middle-class society in a provincial town, 1780–1850' in Fraser & Sutcliffe (1983), 327–45.

Davies, G.E. (1961): *The Democratic Intellect: Scotland and her Universities in the Nineteenth Century*, Edinburgh.

Davy, H. (1812): *Elements of Chemical Philosophy*, London.

——(1813): *Elements of Agricultural Chemistry*, London.

——(1816): 'On the fire-damp of coal mines, and on methods of lighting the mines so as to prevent its explosion', *Phil. Trans.*, **106**: 1–22.

——(1817): 'Some researches on flame', *Phil. Trans.*, **107**: 45–76.

——(1818a): 'On the fallacy of the experiments in which water is said to have been formed by the decomposition of chlorine', *Phil. Trans.*, **108**: 169–71.

——(1818b): 'New experiments on some of the combinations of phosphorus', *Phil. Trans.*, **108**: 316–37,.

——(1821a): 'On the magnetic phenomena produced by electricity', *Phil. Trans.* **111**: 7–19.

——(1821b): 'Farther researches on the magnetic phenomena produced by electricity with some new experiments on the properties of electrified bodies in their relations to conducting powers and temperature', *Phil. Trans.*, **111**: 425–39.

——(1822): 'On the electrical phenomena exhibited in vacuo', *Phil. Trans.*, **112**: 64–74.

——(1823): 'On a new phenomenon of electro-magnetism', *Phil. Trans.*, **113**: 153–9.

Davy, J. (1836): *Memoirs of the Life of Sir Humphry Davy*, 2 volumes, London.

Dawkins, R. (1976): *The Selfish Gene*, Oxford.

deGroot, A. (1965): *Thought and Choice in Chess*, The Hague.

De la Rive, A. (1822): 'Mémoire sur l'action qu'exerce le globe terreste sur une portion mobile du circuit voltaïque', *Ann. Chim. Phys.*, **21**: 24–48.

De Launay *see* Launay.

Doherty, M.E., Mynatt, C.R., Tweney, R.D. and Schiavo, M.D. (1979): 'Pseudodiagnosticity', *Acta Psy.*, **43**: 111–21.

Doherty, M.E. *see also* Mynatt, C.R.; Tweney, R.D.

Doran, B.G. (1975): 'Origins and consolidation of field theory in nineteenth century Britain: From the mechanical to the electromagnetic view of nature', *Hist. Stud. Phys. Sci.*, **6**: 132–260.

Dumas, J.B.A. (1868): 'Michael Faraday, Éloge prononcé dans la séance publique annuelle de l'Académie de Sciences le 18 Mai 1868', in *Discours et éloges académiques*, 2 volumes, Paris, 1885, **1**: 49–124.

Einstein, A. (1905): 'Zur Elektrodynamik bewegter Körper', *Ann. Phys.*, **17**: 891–921.
    See also Lorentz, H.A.

Elkana, Y. *see* Mendelsohn, K.

Elstein, A.S., Shulman, L.S. and Sprafka, S.A. (1978): *Medical Problem Solving: An Analysis of Clinical Reasoning*, Cambridge, Ma.

Engen, R.K. (1979): *Dictionary of Victorian Engravers, Print Publishers and their Works*, Cambridge.

Ericsson, K.A. and Simon, H.A. (1984): *Protocol Analysis: Verbal Reports as Data*, Cambridge, Ma.

Escott, H. (1960): *A History of Scottish Congregationalism*, Glasgow.

Fahie, J.J. (1884): *A History of Electric Telegraphy to the Year 1837*, London.

Faraday, M. (1816): 'Analysis of the native caustic lime', *Quart. J. Sci.*, **1**: 261–2: *ERCP*, 1–5.

——(1819): 'Some experimental observations on the passage of gases through tubes', *Quart. J. Sci.*, **7**: 106–10.

——(1821a): 'On two new compounds of chlorine and carbon, and on a new compound of iodine, carbon and hydrogen', *Phil. Trans.*, **111**: 47–74.

——(1821b): 'On some new Electro-Magnetical Motions, and on the Theory of Magnetism', *Quart. J. Sci.*, **12**: 74–96; *ERE*, **2**: 127–47.

——(1821c): 'Sur les Mouvemens électro-magnétiques et la théorie du magnétisme', *Ann. Chim. Phys.*, **18**: 337–70.

——(1821–2): 'Historical Sketch of Electro-magnetism', *Ann. Phil.*, **18**: 195–200, 274–90; **19**, 107–21.

——(1822): 'Note on new electro-magnetical motions', *Quart. J. Sci.*, **12**: 416–21; *ERE*, **2**: 151–8.

——(1823a): 'On fluid chlorine', *Phil. Trans.*, **113**: 160–4.

——(1823b): 'Historical statement regarding electro-magnetic rotation', *Quart. J. Sci.*, **15**: 288–92: *ERE*, **2**: 159–62.

——(1827): *Chemical Manipulation: Being Instructions to Students in Chemistry*, London.

——(1832a): 'On the induction of electric currents. On the evolution of electricity from magnetism. On a new electrical condition of matter. On Arago's magnetic phenomena', *Phil. Trans.*, **122**: 125–62; *ERE*, 1, 1–139.

——(1832b): 'Terrestrial magneto-electric induction. Force and direction of magneto-electric induction generally', *Phil. Trans.*, **122**: 163–94; *ERE*, 2, 140–264.

——(1833a): 'Identity of electricities derived from different sources. Relation by measure of common and voltaic electricity' *Phil. Trans.*, **123**: 23–54; *ERE*, 3, 265–379.

——(1833b): 'Address delivered at the commemoration of the centenary of the birth of Rev Joseph Priestley', *Phil. Mag.*, **2**: 390–1.

——(1833c): 'On a new law of electric conduction. On conducting power generally', *Phil. Trans.*, **123**: 507–22: *ERE*, 4, 380–449.

——(1834a): 'On electro-chemical Decomposition. On the absolute quantity of electricity associated with the particles or atoms of matter', *Phil. Trans.*, **124**: 77–122; *ERE*, 7, 661–874.

——(1834b): 'On the Electricity of the Voltaic Pile; its sources, quantity, intensity and general character', *Phil. Trans.*, **124**: 425–70: *ERE*, 8, 875–1047.

——(1835): 'On the influence by induction of an electric current on itself: – and on the inductive action of electric currents generally, *Phil. Trans.*, **125**: 41–56; *ERE*, 9, 1048–1118.

——(1836): 'On the general magnetic relations and characters of the metals', *Phil. Mag.*, **8**: 177–181.

——(1838a): 'On Induction' *Phil. Trans.*, **128**: 1–40, 79–81; *ERE*, 11, 1161–1317.

——(1838b): 'On Induction', *Phil. Trans.*, **128**: 83–123; *ERE*, 12, 1318–1479.

——(1838c): 'On Induction. Nature of the electric current', *Phil. Trans.*, **128**: 125–68; *ERE*, 13, 1480–1666.

——(1838d): 'Nature of the electric force or forces. Relation of the electric and magnetic forces. Note on electrical excitation', *Phil. Trans.*, **128**: 265–82, *ERE*, 14, 1667–1748.

——(1840): 'An answer to Dr. Hare's letter to certain theoretical opinions', *Phil. Mag.*, **17**: 54–65; *ERE*, **2**: 262–74.

——(1843): 'On static electrical inductive action', *Phil. Mag.*, **22**: 200–4; *ERE*, **2**: 279–84.

——(1844): 'A Speculation touching Electric Conduction and the Nature of Matter', *Phil. Mag.*, **24**: 136–44; *ERE*, **2**: 284–93.

——(1845): 'On the magnetic relations and characters of the metals', *Phil. Mag.*, **27**: 1–3.

——(1846a): 'On the magnetization of light and the illumination of magnetic lines of force', *Phil. Trans.*, **136**: 1–20; *ERE*, 19, 2146–2242.

——(1846b): 'On new magnetic actions, and on the magnetic condition of all matter', *Phil. Trans.*, **136**: 21–40; *ERE*, 20, 2243–2342.

——(1846c): 'Thoughts on Ray-vibrations', *Phil. Mag.*, **28**: 345–50.

——(1850): 'On the polar or other condition of diamagnetic bodies', *Phil. Trans.*, **140**: 171–88; *ERE*, 23, 2640–2701.

——(1851): 'Magnetic conducting power. Atmospheric Magnetism', *Phil. Trans.*, **141**: 29–84; *ERE*, 26, 2797–2968.

——(1852a): 'On lines of magnetic force; their definite character; and their distribution within a magnet and through space', *Phil. Trans.*, **142**: 25–56, *ERE*, 28, 3070–3176.

——(1852b): 'On the physical character of the lines of magnetic force', *Phil. Mag.*, **3**: 401–28; *ERE*, 3243–3299.

——(1853a): 'On table-turning', *Times* (30 June 1853), 8; *ERCP*, 382–5.

——(1853b): 'Experimental investigation of table moving', *Athenaeum* (2 July 1853), 801–3; *ERCP*, 385–91.

——(1854): 'Observations on Mental Education', in *Lectures on Education Delivered at the Royal Institution of Great Britain*, London, 39–88; *ERCP*, 463–91.

——(1855): 'On some points of magnetic philosophy', *Phil. Mag.*, **9**: 81–113; *ERE*, 3300–3362.

——(1856): 'On M. Petitjean's process for silvering glass: Some observations on divided gold', *Proc. Roy. Inst.*, **2**: 308–12.

——(1857a): 'Experimental relations of gold (and other metals) to light', *Phil. Trans.*, **147**: 145–81.

——(1857b): 'On the conservation of force', *Phil. Mag.*, 1857, **13**: 225–39, *ERCP*, 443–63. (This has an additional note that was reprinted in *Phil. Mag.* 1859, **17**: 166–9.)

See also Stodart, J.

Feigenbaum, E.A. *see* Barr, A.

Fish, S.E., ed. (1971): *Seventeenth Century Prose*, Oxford.

Fisher, H.J. (1979): 'The great electrical philosopher', *The College*, 1–13.

Fodor, J.A., Garrett, M.F., Walker, E.C.T., and Parkes, C.H. (1980): 'Against definition', *Cognition*, **8**: 263–367.

Forgan, S. (1977): *The Royal Institution of Great Britain 1840–1873*, University of London (Westfield College) PhD thesis.

——ed. (1980): *Science and the Sons of Genius: Studies on Humphry Davy*, London.

Foss, B.M. ed. (1966): *New Horizons in Psychology*, **1**, Harmondsworth.

Foucault, M. (1970): *The Order of Things: An Archaeology of the Human Sciences*, London.

Fox, J. (1980): 'Making decisions under the influence of memory', *Psy. Rev.*, **87**: 190–211.

Fox, R. (1974): 'The rise and fall of Laplacian Physics', *Hist. Stud. Phys. Sci.*, **4**: 89–136.

Frankel, E. (1976): 'Corpuscular Optics and the Wave Theory of Light: The Science and Politics of a Revolution in Physics', *Soc. Stud. Sci.*, **6**, 141–84.

Fraser, D. and Sutcliffe, A. (1983): *The Pursuit of Urban History*, London.

Fresnel, A.J. (1820): 'Note sur des essais ayant pour but de décomposer l'eau avec un aimant', *Ann. Chim. Phys.*, **15**: 219–22.

——(1821–2): 'Mémoire sur la Diffraction de la Lumière', *Mém. Acad. Sci.*, [published 1826], **5**: 339–475.

——(1822): 'De la Lumière' in supplement to Thomson, T. (1818–22).

——(1827): 'Second Mémoire sur la Double Réfraction' (written 1822), *Mém. Acad. Sci.*, **7**: 45–176.

——(1827–9): 'Elementary view of the Undulatory Theory of Light', *Quart. J. Sci.*, **23**: 127–41, 441–54; **24**: 113–35, 431–48; **25**: 198–215; **26**: 168–91, 389–407; **27**: 159–65.

——(1852): 'Memoir on Double Refraction', *Taylor's Sci. Mem.*, **5**: 238–333.

——(1866–70): *Oeuvres Complètes D'Augustin Fresnel*, 3 volumes (edited by H. de Senarmont, E. Verdet and L. Fresnel). Paris (Reprinted New York, 1965.)

Friday, J. *see* Porter, G.

Fullmer, J.Z. (1969): *Sir Humphry Davy's published works*, Cambridge, Ma.

——(1980) 'Humphry Davy, Reformer' in Forgan (1980), 59–94.

Fusinieri, A. (1827): 'Sopra il trasporto di materia ponderabile nelle folgori', *Gior. Fis. Chim.*, **10**: 353–69.

——(1844): 'On the transport of ponderable matter which occurs during electrical discharges', *Elec. Mag.*, **1**: 235–47.

Galilei, G. (1967): *Dialogue Concerning the Two Chief World Systems — Ptolemaic & Copernican*, Berkeley.

Garrett, M.F. *see* Fodor, J.A. *et al.*

Gernsheim, H. and A. (1955); *The History of Photography from the Camera Obscura to the Beginning of the Modern Era*, London.

Gill, A.T. (1967): 'Faraday and Photography', *Proc. Roy. Inst.*, **42**: 54–67.

Gladstone, J.H. (1872): *Michael Faraday*, London.

Glas, J. (1733): *On the Right of the Christian People, and the Power of their Pastors, in the Ordination of Ministers of the Gospel Asserted. With some Directions for Reformation*, Edinburgh.

——(1739a): 'A discourse on predestination, which is still professedly maintained by several of our dissenters, and likely to spread at present amongst the ignorant people of the church of England by the means of some enthusiasts lately risen up in this kingdom', *Scots Mag.*, **1**: 159–64.

——(1739b): 'To the author of the discourse on predestination', *Scots Mag.*, **1**: 560–4.
——(1740): *A Letter to a Minister of the Established Church, in Answer to one from Him on Forbearance*, n.p.
——(1741): *A Plea of Pure and Undefiled Religion*, Edinburgh.
——(1759): 'Of Mr. Hutchinson's philosophy and divinity', *Edinb. Mag.*, **3**: 110–3.
——(1782): *The Works of Mr John Glas*, 2nd edition, 5 volumes, Perth.
Glaser, R. *see* Chi, M.T.H.
Glymour, (1980): *Theory and Evidence*, Princeton.
Godfrey, R.T. (1978): *Printmaking in Britain: A General History from its Beginnings to the Present Day*, Oxford.
Goldman, M. (1983): *The Demon in the Aether: The story of James Clerk Maxwell*, Edinburgh.
Goldman, P. (1981): *Looking at Prints: A Guide to Technical Terms*, London.
Gooding, D. (1975): *Faraday and the Powers of Matter. The Role of Principles, Hypotheses, and the Interpretation of Experiment in the Development of Faraday's Field Theory, as Presented in his Experimental Researches in Electricity, 1830–1855*, University of Oxford DPhil thesis.
——(1978): 'Conceptual and experimental bases of Faraday's denial of electrostatic action at a distance', *Stud. Hist. Phil. Sci.*, **9**: 117–49.
——(1980a): 'Metaphysics versus measurement: The conversion and conservation of force in Faraday's physics', *Ann. Sci.*, **37**: 1–29.
——(1980b): 'Faraday, Thomson, and the concept of the magnetic field', *Br. J. Hist. Sci.*, **13**: 91–120.
——(1981): 'Final steps to the field theory: Faraday's study of magnetic phenomena, 1845–1850, *Hist. Stud. Phys. Sci.*, **11**: 231–75.
——(1982a): 'Empiricism in practice: Teleology, Economy, and Observation in Faraday's Physics', *ISIS*, **73**: 46–67.
——(1982b): 'A convergence of opinion on the divergence of lines: Faraday and Thomson's discussion of diamagnetism', *Notes Records Roy. Soc. Lond.*, 1982, **36**: 243–59.
——(1985a): ' "He who proves, discovers": John Herschel, William Pepys and the Faraday Effect', *Notes Records Roy. Soc. Lond.*, **39**: 229–44.
——(1985b): 'Experiment and concept-formation in electromagnetic science and technology in England, 1820–1830', *Hist. and Tech.*, **2**: 151–76.
——(1986): 'How do scientists reach agreement about novel observations', *Stud. Hist. Phil. Sci.*, **17**: 205–30.
Goodman, D.C. *see* Russell, C.A.
Gorman, M.E., Tweney, R.D. and Siegel, H. (in press), *Toward a Psychology of Discovery and Justification*.
Gosse, E. (1907): *Father and son*, London.
Grabham, M.C. (1931): *Recollections of Faraday*, n.p.
Graves, R.P. (1882–9): *Life of Sir William Rowan Hamilton*, 3 volumes, Dublin.
Greene, T.R. *see* Voss, J.F.
Greville, C.C.F. (1885): *A journal of the reign of Queen Victoria from 1837–1852*, 3 volumes, London.
Griffiths, A. (1980): *Prints and printmaking: An introduction to the history and techniques*, London.
Gross, K. *see* Tweney, R.D.
Gruber, H.E. (1974): *Darwin on man: A psychological study of scientific creativity*, New York.
——(1978): 'Darwin's "Tree of nature" and other images of wide scope', in Wechsler (1978), 121–40.
Guralnick, S.M. (1979): 'The contexts of Faraday's electrochemical laws', *ISIS*, **70**: 59–75.
Hachette, J.N.P. (1832a): 'Nouvelle construction d'une machine électro-magnétique', *Ann. Chim. Phys.*, **50**: 322–4.

——(1832b): 'De l'action chimique produite par l'induction électrique; décomposition de l'eau', *Ann. Chim. Phys.*, **51**: 72–4.

Hacking, I. (1983): *Representing and intervening: Introductory topics in the philosophy of natural science*, Cambridge.

Hall, C. *see* Davidoff, L.

Hall, M.B. (1984): *All Scientists Now: The Royal Society in the Nineteenth Century*, Cambridge.

Hall, S.C. (1871): *A Book of Memories of Great Men and Women of the Age, from Personal Acquaintance*, London.

Hankins, T.L. (1980): *Sir William Rowan Hamilton*, Baltimore.

Hannaway, O. (1975): *The Chemists and the Word*, Baltimore and London.

Harding, S.G. ed. (1976): *Can Theories be Refuted? Essays on the Duhem-Quine Thesis*, Dordrecht.

Hare, R. (1840): 'A letter to Prof. Faraday on certain theoretical opinions', *Am. J. Sci.*, **38**: 1–11; *Phil. Mag.*, **17**: 44–54; *ERE*, **2**: 251–61.

Harman, P.M. (1982): *Metaphysics and Natural Philosophy: The Problem of Substance in Classical Physics*, Brighton.

Harrison, A. (1978): *Making and Thinking: A Study of Intelligent Activities*, Brighton.

Hartley, H. (1965): 'A letter from Richard Phillips FRS (1778–1857) to Michael Faraday (1791–1867), *Notes Records Roy. Soc. Lond.*, **20**: 220–3.

Hatchett, C. (1821): 'On the electro-magnetic experiments of MM. Oersted and Ampere', *Phil. Mag.*, **57**: 40–9.

Haydn, J. (1855): *Dictionary of Dates*, 7th edition, London.

Hays, J.N. (1974): 'Science in the City: The London Institution, 1819–40', *Br. J. Hist. Sci.*, **7**: 146–62.

——(1983): 'The London lecturing empire, 1800–50' in Inkster & Morrell (1983), 91–119.

Heilbron, J.L. (1981): 'The electrical field before Faraday' in Cantor & Hodge (1981), 187–213.

——(1982): *Elements of Early Modern Physics*, Berkeley.

Heimann, P.M. (1970a): *James Clerk Maxwell, His Sources and Influence*, University of Leeds PhD thesis.

——(1970b): 'Maxwell and the modes of consistent representation', *Arch. Hist. Exact Sci.*, **6**: 171–213.

——(1971): 'Faraday's theories of matter and electricity', *Br. J. Hist. Sci.*, **5**: 235–57.

——(1974): 'Conservation of forces and the conservation of energy', *Centaurus*, **18**: 147–61.

Heimann, P.M. and McGuire, J.E. (1971): 'Newtonian forces and Lockean powers: Concepts of matter in eighteenth-century thought', *Hist. Stud. Phys. Sci.*, **3**: 233–306.

Henry, J. (1831): 'On the application of the principle of the galvanic multiplier to electro-magnetic apparatus, and also to the development of great magnetic power in soft iron, with small galvanic elements', *Am. J. Sci.*, **19**: 400–8.

——(1832): 'On the production of currents and sparks of electricity from magnetism', *Am. J. Sci.*, **22**: 403–8.

——(1835): 'Facts in reference to the sparks, &c. from a long conductor uniting the poles of a galvanic battery', *Am. J. Sci.*, **28**: 327–31.

——(1839): 'Contributions to electricity and magnetism, number 3: On electro-dynamic induction', *Trans. Am. Phil. Soc.*, **6**: 303–38.

——(1972–9): *The Papers of Joseph Henry*, 3 volumes (edited by N. Reingold *et al.*), Washington.

Herapath, J. (1821): 'A mathematical inquiry into the causes, laws, and principal phaenomena of heat, gases, gravitation, &c.'. *Ann. Phil.*, **17**: 273–93, 340–51, 401–16.

Herschel, J.F.W. (1831): *Preliminary Discourse on the Study of Natural Philosophy*, London.

——(1833): 'On the absorption of light by coloured media, viewed in connexion with the Undulatory theory', *Phil. Mag.*, **3**: 401–12.

Hesse, M. (1961): *Forces and Fields: The Concept of Action at a Distance in the History of Physics*, London.

Hodge, M.J.S. *see* Cantor, G.N.

Hodkinson (1979): *William Sturgeon (1780–1850): His Life and Work to 1840*, UMIST MSc dissertation.

Holloway, J. (1965): *The Victorian Sage: Studies on Argument*, London.

Holmes, F.L. (1974): *Claude Bernard and Animal Chemistry: The Emergence of a Scientist*, Cambridge, Ma.

Holton, G. (1978): *The Scientific Imagination, Case Studies*, Cambridge.

Hornsby, J.T. (1936): *John Glas (1695–1773)*, University of Edinburgh PhD thesis.

Hubbard, G. (1965): *Cooke and Wheatstone and the Invention of the Electric Telegraph*, London.

Hutchinson, J. (1732): *A Treatise of Power, Essential and Mechanical*, London.

——(1748–9): *The Philosophical and Theological Works of the Late Truly Learned John Hutchinson, Esq.*, 12 volumes, London. (Edited by R. Spearman and J. Bate.)

Huxley, I. (1900): *Life and letters of Thomas Henry Huxley*, 2 volumes, London.

Inkster, I. (1977): 'Science and society in the metropolis: A preliminary examination of the social and institutional context of the Askesian Society of London, 1796–1807', *Ann. Sci.* **34**: 1–32.

——(1981): 'Seditious science: A reply to Paul Weindling', *Br. J. Hist. Sci.*, **14**: 181–7.

Inkster, I. and Morrell, J. eds (1983): *Metropolis and Province: Science in British Culture 1780–1850*, London.

Ireland, J. (1791–8): *Hogarth Illustrated*, 3 volumes, London.

Ireland, S. (1794–9): *Graphic Illustrations of Hogarth from Pictures, Drawings, and . . . Prints in the Possession of S. Ireland*, 2 volumes, London.

[Jakobson, R.] (1967): *To Honor Roman Jakobson: Essays on the Occasion of his Seventieth Birthday*, 3 volumes, The Hague.

James, F.A.J.L. (1983a): 'The conservation of energy, theories of absorption and resonating molecules, 1851–1854: G.G. Stokes, A.J. Ångström and W. Thomson', *Notes Records Roy. Soc. Lond.*, **38**: 79–107.

——(1983b): 'The Study of Spark Spectra, 1835–1859', *Ambix*, **30**: 137–62.

——(1983c): 'The debate on the nature of the absorption of light, 1830–1835: A core-set analysis', *Hist. Sci.*, **21**: 335–68.

——(1984): 'The physical interpretation of the wave theory of light', *Br. J. Hist. Sci.*, **17**: 47–60.

——(1985): 'The creation of a Victorian myth: The historiography of spectroscopy', *Hist. Sci.*, **23**: 1–24.

James, W. (1880): 'Great men, great thoughts, and the environment', *Atlantic Monthly*, **46**: 441–59.

Jeffreys, A.E. (1960): *Michael Faraday: A List of his Lectures and Published Writings*, London.

Jerrold, W. (1892): *Michael Faraday: Man of Science*, London.

Johnson-Laird, P.N. *see* Wason, P.C.

Jones, W. (1781): *Physiological Disquistions; or Discourses on the Natural Philosophy of the Elements*, London.

——(1801): *The Theological, Philosophical and Miscellaneous Works*, 12 volumes, London.

Jordanova, L.J. and Porter, R.S., eds. (1979): *Images of the Earth: Essays in the History of the Environmental Sciences*, Chalfont St Giles.

Joubert, J. ed. (1885–7): *Mémoires sur l'Électrodynamique*, (volumes 2 and 3 of the 5 volume *Collection de Mémoires Relatifs a la Physique Publiés par la Société Française de Physique*), Paris.

Keats, J. (1952): *Letters* (edited by H.B. Forman), 4th edition, London.

Kendall, J. (1954): *Michael Faraday, Man of Simplicity*, London.

Knight, D.M. (1978): *The Transcendental Part of Chemistry*, Folkestone.

——(1980): 'Davy's Salmonia' in Forgan (1980), 201–30.

Knorr-Cetina, K.D. (1981): *The Manufacture of Knowledge: An Essay on the Constructivist and Contextual Nature of Science*, Oxford.

Knorr-Cetina, K.D. and Mulkay, M. eds. (1983): *Science Observed*, London.

Knudsen, O. (1976): 'The Faraday effect and physical theory 1845–1873', *Arch. Hist. Exact. Sci.*, **15**: 235–81.

Kuhn, T.S. (1962): *The Structure of Scientific Revolutions*, 1st edition, Chicago.

——(1970): *The Structure of Scientific Revolutions*, 2nd edition, Chicago.

——(1974): 'Second thoughts on paradigms' in Suppe (1974), 459–82.

Lakatos, I. (1970): 'Falsification and the methodology of scientific research programmes' in Lakatos & Musgrave (1970), 91–196.

——(1976): *Proofs and Refutations: The Logic of Mathematical Discovery* (edited by J. Worrall and E. Zahar), Cambridge.

Lakatos, I. and Musgrave, A. eds. (1970): *Criticism and the Growth of Knowledge*, London.

Langley, P. (1981): 'Data-driven discovery of physical laws', *Cog. Sci.*, **5**: 31–54.

Larkin, J.H. (1980): 'Teaching problem solving in physics: The psychological laboratory and practical classroom' in Tuma & Reif (1980), 111–25.

Larmor, J. (1907): *Memoir and Scientific Correspondence of the Late Sir George Gabriel Stokes*, 2 volumes, Cambridge.

Latchford, K.A. (1974): *Thomas Young and the Evolution of the Interference Principle*, University of London (Imperial College) PhD thesis.

Latour, B. (1983): 'Give me a laboratory and I will raise the world' in Knorr-Cetina & Mulkay (1983), 141–70.

Laudan, L. (1981): 'The medium and its message: A study of some philosophical controversies about ether', in Cantor and Hodge (1981), 157–85.

Laudan, L., ed. (1983): *Mind and Medicine: Problems of Explanation and Evaluation in Psychiatry and the Biomedical Sciences*, Berkeley.

Launay, L. de (1924): *Le Grand Ampère*, Paris.

——(1936–43): *Correspondence du Grand Ampère*, 3 volumes, Paris.

Lenoir, T. (1982): *The Strategy of Life*, Dordrecht.

Levere, T.H. (1968): 'Faraday, Matter and Natural Theology — Reflections on an Unpublished Manuscript', *Br. J. Hist.Sci.*, **4**: 95–107.

——(1971): *Affinity and Matter: Elements of Chemical Philosophy 1800–1865*, Oxford.

——(1984): 'Dr. Thomas Beddoes (1750–1808): Science and medicine in politics and society', *Br. J. Hist. Sci.*, **17**: 187–204.

Lindsay, P.H. and Norman, D.A. (1977): *Human Information Processing*, 2nd edition, New York.

Lloyd, H. (1833): 'On the Phenomena presented by Light in its passage along the Axes of Biaxial Crystals', *Phil. Mag.*, **2**: 112–20, 207–10.

Locke, J. (1707): *A Paraphrase and Notes on the Epistle of St. Paul to the Romans*, London.

——(1824): *The Works of John Locke*, 10 volumes, 12th edition, London.

Loftus, E.F. (1975): 'Leading questions and the eyewitness report', *Cog. Psy.*, **7**: 560–72.

Lorentz, H.A., Einstein, A., Minkowski, H. and Weyl, H. (1923): *The Principle of Relativity*, London.

Lyons, H. (1944): *The Royal Society, 1660–1940*, Cambridge.

McCosh, F.W.J. (1984): *Boussingault: Chemist and Agriculturist*, Dordrecht.

McGuire, J.E. (1974): 'Forces, powers, aethers, & fields', in Cohen & Wartofsky (1974). *See also* Heimann, P.M.

McLuhan, M. (1964): *Understanding Media: The Extensions of Man*, London.

Malton, T. (1778): *A Complete Treatise on Perspective, in Theory and Practice, on the True Principles of Dr. Brook Taylor*, 2nd edition, London.

Mandler, G. (1984): *Mind and Body: Psychology of Emotion and Stress*, New York.

Marcet, J. (1809): *Conversations on Chemistry*, 3rd edition, 2 volumes, London.

Mariani, P. (1981): *William Carlos Williams: A New World Naked*, New York.

Martin, T. (1934): *Faraday*, London.

——(1949): *Faraday's Discovery of Electro-magnetic Induction*, London.

Masson, A.-P. (1851): 'Études de photométrie Électrique', *Ann. Chim. Phys.*, **31**: 295–326.

Maull and Polybank (1856–9): *Photographic Portraits of Living Celebrities*, London.

Maxwell, J.C. (1855–6): 'On Faraday's lines of force', *Trans. Camb. Phil. Soc.*, **10**: 27–83.

——(1890): *The Scientific Papers of James Clerk Maxwell* (edited by W.D. Niven), 2 volumes, Cambridge.

——(1892): *A Treatise on Electricity and Magnetism*, 3rd edition, 2 volumes, Oxford.

Mayer, A.M. (1880): 'Henry as a discoverer' in *A Memorial of Joseph Henry*, Washington, 475–508.

Median, D. *see* Smith, E.

Mendelsohn, K. and Elkana, Y. eds (1981): *Science and Cultures*, Dordrecht.

Mendoza, E. (1985). 'Ampère's experimental proof of his law of induction: $i_2 \propto i_1$', *Eur. J. Phys.*, **6**: 281–6.

Mervis, C. *see* Rosch, E.

Miller, D.P. (1983): 'Between hostile camps: Sir Humphry Davy's Presidency of the Royal Society of London, 1820–1827', *Br. J. Hist. Sci.*, **16**: 1–47.

Miller, P. (1971): 'The plain style' in Fish (1971), 147–86.

Minkowski, H. *see* Lorentz, H.A.

Mitroff, I. (1974): *The Subjective Side of Science*, Amsterdam.

Moll, G. (1821): 'Account of the electro-magnetic apparatus of Lieut. Col. Offerhaus', *Edinb. Phil. J.*, **5**: 352–5.

——(1821–2): 'Account of electro-magnetic experiments made by M.M. van Beek, Professor van Rees of Liege, and Professor Moll of Utrecht'. *Edinb. Phil. J.*, **6**: 83–5, 220–4.

Moran, T.P. *see* Card, S.K.

Morrell, J.B. (1972): 'The chemist breeders: The research schools of Liebig and Thomas Thomson', *Ambix*, **19**: 1–46.

See also Inkster, I.

Morrell, J.B. and Thackray, A. (1981): *Gentlemen of Science: Early Years of the British Association for the Advancement of Science*, Oxford.

Morrison-Low, A.D. and Christie, J.R.R. (1984): *'Martyr of Science': Sir David Brewster 1781–1868*, Edinburgh.

Morse, E.W. (1972): *Natural Philosophy, Hypotheses and Impiety: Sir David Brewster Confronts the Undulatory Theory of Light*, University of California (Berkeley) PhD thesis.

Mulkay, M. *see* Knorr-Cetina, K.D.

Murray, D.B. (1976): *The social and religious origins of Scottish non-Presbyterian Protestant Dissent from 1730–1800*, University of St Andrews PhD thesis.

Musgrave, A. *see* Lakatos, I.

Mynatt, C.R., Doherty, M.E. and Tweney, R.D. (1978): 'Consequences of confirmation and disconfirmation in a simulated research environment', *Quart. J. Exp. Psy.*, **30**: 395–406.

Mynatt, C.R. *see also* Chi, M.T.H.; Tweney, R.D.

Neisser, U. (1976): *Cognition and reality: Principles and implications of cognitive psychology*, San Francisco.

Nersessian, N.J. (1982): 'Why is "incommensurability" a problem?' *Acta Biothereotica*, **31**: 205–18.

——(1984a): 'Aether/or: The creation of scientific concepts', *Stud. Hist. Phil. Sci.*, **15**: 175–212.

——(1984b): *Faraday to Einstein: Constructing Meaning in Scientific Theories*, Dordrecht.

Newell, A. and Simon, H.A. (1972): *Human Problem Solving*, Englewood Cliffs.

Newell, A. *see also* Card, S.K.

Newton, I. (1730): *Opticks*, 4th edition, London, Reprinted London, 1952.

Nickles, T. (1983): 'Justification as discoverability', *Proc. 7th Int. Cong. Log. Meth. Phil. Sci.*, **6**: 157–60.

——(1985): 'Beyond divorce: The current status of the discovery debate', *Phil. Sci.*, **52**: 177–207.

Norman, D.A. *see* Lindsay, P.H.

Oersted, H.C. (1820a): 'Experimenta circa effectum conflictus electrici in acum magneticam', *Schweigger J.*, **19**: 275–81.

——(1820b): 'Experiments on the effect of a current of electricity on the magnetic needle', *Ann. Phil.*, **16**: 273–6.

——(1820c): 'Experimenta circa effectum, etc. Expériences sur l'effect du conflict électrique sur l'aiguille aimantée', *Ann. Chim. Phys.*, **14**: 417–25.

——(1820d): 'Versuche über die Wirkung des electrischen Conflicts auf die Magnetnadel', *Gilbert Ann.*, **66**: 295–304.

Ohm, G.S. (1827): *Die Galvanische Kette mathematisch bearbeitet*, Berlin.

——(1841): 'The galvanic circuit investigated mathematically', *Taylor's Sci. Mem.*, **2**: 401–506.

Olson, R. (1975): *Scottish Philosophy and British Physics 1750–1880*, Princeton.

Ormond, R. (1973): *Early Victorian Portraits*, London.

Paris, J.A. (1831): *The Life of Sir Humphry Davy*, London.

Parkes, C.H. *see* Fodor, J.A.

Peacock, G. (1855): *Life of Thomas Young*, London.

Penner, B.C. *see* Voss, J.F.

Perrolle, L. (1799): 'Des expériences relatives à la propagation du son dans diverses substances, tant solides que fluides; Un essai d'expériences qui tendent à deteminer la cause de la réssonnance des corps', *J. Phys.*, **49**: 382–90.

Piaget, J. (1926): *The Language and Thought of the Child*, New York.

——(1970): *Genetic Epistemology*, New York.

Pinch, T. (1985a): 'Towards an analysis of scientific observation: The externality and evidential significance of observation reports in physics', *Soc. Stud. Sci.*, **15**: 3–36.

——(1985b): 'Theory testing in science: The case of solar neutrinos', *Phil. Soc. Sci.*

Platt, J.R. (1964): 'Strong inference', *Science*, **146**: 347–53.

Pliske, D.B. *see* Tweney, R.D.

Poincaré, J.H. (1914): *Science and Method*, London.

Polanyi, M. (1964): *Personal Knowledge*, New York.

[Pollock, J.] (1870): 'Michael Faraday', *St Paul's Mag.*, **6**: 293–303.

[Pollock, J. & W.F.] (1867): 'Michael Faraday', *Ill. Lond. News*, **51**: 280–2.

Pollock, W.F. (1887): *Personal Remembrances of Sir Frederick Pollock, Second Baronet, sometimes Queen's Remembrancer*, 2 volumes, London.

Polybank *see* Maull.

Popper, K.R. (1959): *The Logic of Scientific Discovery*, London.

Porter, G. (1981): 'Michael Faraday — Chemist', *Proc. Roy. Inst.*, **53**: 90–9.

Porter, G. and Friday, J. (1974): *Advice to Lecturers: An Anthology Taken from the Writings of Michael Faraday and Lawrence Bragg*, London.

Porter, R.S. (1977): *The Making of Geology: Earth Science in Britain, 1660–1815*, Cambridge.

See also Jordanova, L.J.

Post, T.A. *see* Voss, J.F.

Price, D.J. de S. (1980): 'Philosophical mechanism and mechanical philosophy: Some notes towards a philosophy of scientific instruments', *Ann. Inst. Mus. Stor. Sci. Firen.*, **5**: 75–85.

Priestley, J. (1767): *The History and Present State of Electricity with Original Experiments*, London.

——(1777): *Disquisitions Relating to Matter and Spirit*, London.

Rappard, H., van Hoorn, W. and Bern, S. eds. (1984): *Studies in the History of Psychology and the Social Sciences*.

Redgrave, S. (1874): *A Dictionary of Artists of the English Schools*, London.

Reed, S.K. *see* Simon, H.A.

Rees, E. *see* Chi, M.T.H.

Reif, F. *see* Tuma, D.T.

Rescher, N. (1980): 'Scientific truth and the arbitrament of praxis', *Nôus*, **14**, 59–73.

Riley, J.F. (1954): *The Hammer and the Anvil: A Background to Michael Faraday*, Clapham.

Roget, P.M. (1826): 'Galvanism' in *Encyclopaedia Metropolitana*, **2**: 173–224.

——(1827): *Treatise on Electro-magnetism*, London.

R[orie], J., ed. (1910): *Selected Exhortations Delivered to Various Churches of Christ by the Late Michael Faraday, Wm. Buchanan, John M. Baxter, and Alex Moir*, Dundee.

Rosch, E. and Mervis, C. (1975): 'Family resemblance studies in the internal structure of categories', *Cog. Psy.*, **7**: 573–605.

Roscoe, H.E. (1864): 'On the metal indium and recent discoveries on spectrum analysis', *Proc. Roy. Inst.*, **4**: 284–90.

Ross, S. (1961): 'Faraday consults the scholars: The origins of the terms of electrochemistry', *Notes Records Roy. Soc. Lond.*, **16**: 187–220.

——(1965): 'The search for electromagnetic induction, 1820–1831', *Notes Records Roy. Soc. Lond.*, **20**: 184–219.

Rudwick. M. (1982): 'Charles Darwin in London: The Integration of Public and Private Science', *ISIS*, **73**: 186–206.

Russell, C.A. and Goodman, D.C. (1972): *Science and the Rise of Technology Since 1800*, Bristol.

Sandeman, R. (1757): *Letters on Theron and Aspasia. Addressed to the Author*, Edinburgh.

——(1760): *The Law of Nature defended by Scripture*, Edinburgh.

[——?] (1835): *The Philosophy of the Creation, as Narrated in Moses' Principia, Gen. Chap. I. v. 1 to 18*, Edinburgh.

——(1857): *Discourses on Passages of Scripture: with Essays and Letters*, Dundee (edited by D. M[ackintosh]).

Saxton, J. (1836): 'On his magneto-electrical machine; with remarks on Mr E.M. Clarke's paper in the preceding number', *Phil. Mag.*, **9**: 360–5.

Schank, R.C. and Abelson, R.P. (1977): *Scripts, Plans, Goals, and Understanding*, Hillsdale.

Schiavo, M.D. *see* Doherty, M.E.

Schilpp, P.A. ed. (1974): *The Philosophy of Karl Popper*, 2 volumes, La Salle.

Sennet, R. (1977): *The Fall of Public Man*, Cambridge.

Shurman, L.S. *see* Elstein, A.S.

Siegel, H. *see* Gorman, M.E.

Siemens, C.W. (1867): 'On the conversion of dynamical into electrical force without the aid of permanent magnetism', *Proc. Roy. Soc.*, **18**: 373–9.

Silliman, R.H. (1974): 'Fresnel and the Emergence of Physics as a Discipline', *Hist. Stud. Phys. Sci.*, **4**: 137–62.

Simon, H.A. (1979): *The Sciences of the Artificial*, Cambridge, Ma.

Simon, H.A. and Reed, S.K. (1976): 'Modelling strategy in a problem-solving task', *Cog. Psy.*, **8**: 86–107.

Simon, H.A. *see also* Chase, W.G.; Ericsson, K.A.; Newell, A.

Smith, C. *see* Crosland, M.

Smith, E. and Median, D. (1981): *Concepts and Categories*, Cambridge, Ma.

Smith, F.M. (1871): *Handbook of the Manufacture and Proof of Gunpowder, as Carried Out at the Royal Gunpowder Factory, Waltham Abbey*, London.

Snelders, H.A.M. (1984): 'The electromagnetic experiments of the Utrecht physicist Gerrit Moll (1785–1838)', *Ann. Sci.*, **41**: 35–55.

Spencer, J.B. (1967): 'Boscovich's theory and its relation to Faraday's researches: An analytic approach', *Arch. Hist. Exact Sci.*, **4**, 184–202.

——(1970): 'On the varieties of nineteenth-century magneto-optical discovery', *ISIS*, **61**: 34–51.

Sprafka, S.A. *see* Elstein, A.S.

Stansfield, D.A. (1984): *Thomas Beddoes M.D., 1760–1808: Chemist, Physician, Democrat*, Dordrecht.

Sternberg, R. ed. (1982): *Advances in the Psychology of Human Intelligence*, **1**, Hillsdale.

Stodart, J. and Faraday, M. (1820): 'Experiments on the alloys of steel, made with a view to its improvements', *Quart. J. Sci.*, **9**: 319–30.

——(1822): 'On the alloys of steel', *Phil. Trans.*, **112**: 253–70.

Stokes, G.G. (1845a): 'On the aberration of light', *Rep. Brit. Ass.*, part 2, 9.

——(1845b): 'On the aberration of light', *Phil. Mag.*, **27**: 9–15.

——(1846a): 'Remarks on Profesor Challis's theoretical explanation of the aberration of light', *Phil. Mag.*, **28**: 15–17.

——(1846b): 'On Fresnel's theory of the aberration of light', *Phil. Mag.*, **28**: 76–81.

——(1852): 'On the change of refrangibility of light', *Phil. Trans.*, **142**: 463–562.

——(1853): 'On the change of refrangibility of light, and the exhibition thereby of the chemical rays', *Proc. Roy. Inst.*, **1**: 259–264.

——(1862): 'On the long spectrum of electric light', *Phil. Trans.*, **152**: 599–619.

Strutt, R.J. (1924): *John William Strutt, 3rd Baron Rayleigh*, London.

Sturgeon, W. (1850): *Scientific Researches, Experimental and Theoretical in Electricity, Magnetism, Galvanism, Electromagnetism and Electrochemistry*, Bury.

Suppe, F. ed. (1974): *The Structure of Scientific Theory*, Urbana.

Sutcliffe, A. *see* Fraser, D.

Tatlock, R.R. (1886–7): 'James Napier', *Proc. Roy. Soc. Edinb.*, **14**: 105–110.

Thackray, A. *see* Morrell, J.B.

Thompson, S.P. (1895): 'Note on a neglected experiment of Ampère', *Phil. Mag.*, **39**: 534–41.

——(1898): *Michael Faraday, His Life and Work*, 1st edition, London.

Thomson, T. (1817): *A System of Chemistry*, 5th edition, 4 volumes, London.

——(1818–22): *Système de Chimie*, 5 volumes, Paris.

Thomson, W. (1845): 'On the elementary laws of statical electricity', *Rep. Brit. Ass.*, part 2, 11–12.

Thorpe, T.E. (1896): *Humphry Davy: Poet and Philosopher*, London.

Tomlinson, C. (1879): 'Michael Faraday', *The Graphic* (23 August 1879), 183.

Tuma, D.T. and Rief, F. eds (1980): *Problem Solving and Education: Issues in Teaching and Research*, Hillsdale.

Turner, F.M. (1978): 'The Victorian conflict between science and religion: A professional dimension', *ISIS*, **69**: 356–76.

Tweney, R.D. (1984): 'Cognitive psychology and the history of science: A new look at Michael Faraday' in Rappard *et al.*

Tweney, R.D. and Doherty, M.E. (1983): 'Rationality and the psychology of inference' *Synthese*, **57**: 139–61.

Tweney, R.D., Doherty, M.E. and Mynatt, C.R. eds. (1981): *On Scientific Thinking*, New York.

Tweney, R.D., Doherty, M.E., Worner, W.J., Pliske, D.B., Mynatt, C.R., Gross, K. and Arkkelin, D., (1980): 'Strategies of rule discovery in an inference task', *Quart. J. Exp. Psy.*, **12**: 129–40.

Tweney, R.D. *see also* Doherty, M.E.; Gorman, M.E.; Mynatt, C.R.

Twyman, M. (1970): *Lithography 1800–1850: The Techniques of Drawing on Stone in England and France and their Application in Works of Topography*, London.

Tyndall, J. (1884): *Faraday as a Discoverer*, 4th edition, London.

——(1894): *Faraday as a Discoverer*, 5th edition, London.

——(1895): *Six Lectures on Light*, 5th edition, London.

Tytler, J. (1797): 'Electricity', *Encyclopaedia Britannica*, 3rd edition, 18 volumes, Edinburgh, **6**: 440.

Valson, C. (1885): *André-Marie Ampère*, Lyons.

van Hoorn, W. *see* Rappard, H.

Varley, C. (1845): *A Treatise on Optical Drawing Instruments*, London.

Vincent, B. (1877): *A Dictionary of Biography, Past and Present*, London.

Voss, J.F., Greene, T.R., Post, T.A., and Penner, B.C. (1983): 'Problem solving skill in the social sciences', *Psy. Learn. Motiv.*, **17**: 165–213.

Vygotsky, L.A. (1962): [*Thought and language*], Cambridge, Ma. (Edited and translated by E. Hanfmann and G. Vakar; originally published 1934).

Walker, E.C.T. *see* Fodor, J.A. *et al.*

Wartofsky, M.W. *see* Cohen, R.S.

Wason, P.C. (1960): 'On the failure to eliminate hypotheses in a conceptual task', *Quart. J. Exp. Psy.*, **32**: 109–23.

——(1966): 'Reasoning' in Foss (1966), 135–51.

——(1968): '"On the failure to eliminate hypotheses . . ." — A second look' in Wason & Johnson-Laird (1968), 165–74.

Wason, P.C. and Johnson-Laird, P.N. eds. (1968): *Thinking and Reasoning*, Harmonds-worth.

——(1972): *Psychology of Reasoning: Structure and Content*, Cambridge, Ma.

Watkins, F. (1828): *A Popular Sketch of Electromagnetism*, London.

Watts, G.F. (1975): *The Hall of Fame: Portraits of his Famous Contemporaries*, London.

Watts, I. (1809), *The Improvement of the Mind*, London.

Wechsler, J. ed. (1978): *On Aesthetics in Science*, Cambridge, Ma.

Weindling, P. (1980): 'Science and sedition: How effective were the acts licensing lectures and meetings, 1795–1819', *Br. J. Hist. Sci.*, **13**: 139–53.

Weld, C.R. (1848): *A history of the Royal Society*, 2 volumes, London.

Weyl, H. *see* Lorentz, H.A.

Wheatstone, C. (1823a): 'Nouvelles expériences sur le son', *Ann. Chim. Phys.*, **23**: 313–22.

——(1823b): 'New experiments on sound', *Ann. Phil.*, **22**: 81–90.

——(1828): 'On the resonances, or reciprocated vibrations of columns of air', *Quart. J. Sci.*, **3**: 175–83.

——(1831): 'On the transmission of musical sounds through solid linear conductors, and on their subsequent reciprocation', *Quart. J. Sci.*, **2**: 223–38.

——(1834): 'An account of some experiments to measure the velocity of electricity and the duration of electric light', *Phil. Trans.*, **124**: 583–91.

——(1835): 'On the prismatic decomposition of electrical light', *Rep. Brit. Ass*, part 2, 11–12; *Phil. Mag.*, **7**: 299.

——(1837a): 'On the thermo-electric spark', *Phil. Mag.*, **10**: 414–7.

——(1837b): 'Willis on reed organ sound', *Lond. Westmin. Rev.*, **28**: 27–41.

——(1843): 'An account of several new instruments and processes for determining the constants of a voltaic circuit', *Phil. Trans.*, **133**: 303–27.

——(1845): 'Note on the electro-magnetic chronoscope', *Elec. Mag.*, **2**: 86–93.

——(1861a): 'On the prismatic decomposition of electrical light', *Chem. News*, **3**: 185.

——(1861b): 'On the prismatic decomposition of the electric, voltaic, and electro-magnetic sparks', *Chem. News*, **3**: 198–201.

——(1867): 'On the augmentation of the power of a magnet by the reaction thereon of currents induced by the magnet itself', *Proc. Roy. Soc.*, **18**, 369–72.

Whewell, W. (1833): 'Address to the 1833 British Association', *Rep. Brit. Ass.*, xi–xxvi.

——(1837): *History of the Inductive Sciences, from the Earliest to the Present Times*, 3 volumes, London.

——(1847): *Philosophy of the Inductive Sciences Founded Upon their History*, 2 volumes, 2nd edition, London.

White, J. (1857): 'Your life or your likeness', *Household Words*, (25 July 1857), 73–5.

White, W. (1898): *Journals*, London.

Whittaker, E. (1962): *A History of Theories of Aether and Electricity*, Edinburgh.

Wilde, C.J. (1980): 'Hutchinsonianism, natural philosophy and religious controversy in eighteenth century Britain', *Hist. Sci.*, **18**: 1–24.

Williams, A. (1948): *The Common Expositor: An Account of the Commentaries on Genesis, 1527–1633*, Chapel Hill, North Carolina.

Williams, L.P. (1965): *Michael Faraday: A Biography*, London.

——(1967): 'Michael Faraday and the Ether: A study in Heresy', *Proc. Roy. Inst.*, **41**: 666–80.

——(1975): 'Should philosophers be allowed to write history' [Review of Agassi (1971) and Berkson (1974)], *Br. J. Phil. Sci.*, **26**: 241–253.

——(1983): 'What were Ampère's earliest discoveries in electrodynamics?', *ISIS*, **74**: 492–508.

——(1985): 'Why Ampère did not discover electro-magnetic induction in 1822 and how he prevented Faraday from doing so', *Am. J. Phys.*, **54**: 306–11.

Wilson, D.B. (1972): 'George Gabriel Stokes on Stellar Aberration and the Luminiferous Ether', *Br. J. Hist. Sci.*, **6**, 57–72.

——(1974): 'Kelvin's scientific realism: The theological context', *Phil. J.*, **11**: 41–60.

——(1976): *Catalogue of the Manuscript Collections of Sir George Gabriel Stokes and Sir William Thomson, Baron Kelvin of Largs in Cambridge University Library*, Cambridge.

——(1984): 'A physicist's alternative to materialism: The religious thought of George Gabriel Stokes', *Vict. Stud.*, **28**: 69–96.

Wise, M.N. (1979a): 'William Thomson's mathematical route to energy conservation: A case study of the role of mathematics in concept formation', *Hist. Stud. Phys. Sci.*, **10**: 49–83.

——(1979b): 'The mutual embrace of electricity and magnetism', *Science*, **203**: 1310–18.

Wittgenstein, L. (1953): *Philosophical Investigations*, Oxford.

Worner, W.J. *see* Tweney, R.D.

Young, T. (1802): 'An Account of some cases of the Production of Colours not hitherto described', *Phil. Trans.*, **92**: 387–397.

——(1824): 'Theoretical Investigations Intended to Illustrate the Phenomena of Polarisation', *Supplement to the Fourth, Fifth and Sixth Editions of the Encyclopaedia Britannica*, 6 volumes, Edinburgh, **6**: 860–3.

——(1855): *Miscellaneous Works of the Late Thomas Young*, 3 volumes. (Edited by G. Peacock and J. Leitch), London.

Index